MW00653736

Worship the Lord

Hymnal of the Church of God

Warner Press

ANDERSON, INDIANA

Coordinator of Publishing & Creative Services
Church of God Ministries, Inc.
PO Box 2420
Anderson, IN 46018-2420
800-848-2464
www.chog.org

To purchase additional copies of this book, to inquire about distribution, and for all other sales-related matters, please contact:

Warner Press, Inc.
PO Box 2499
Anderson, IN 46018-2499
800-741-7721
www.warnerpress.org

The permissions and acknowledgments on pages 750, 756–758, and 780 constitute extensions of this copyright page.

ISBN-10: 0-87162-506-7
ISBN-13: 978-0-87162-506-9

Printed in the United States of America.

13 14 15 /CH/ 25 24 23

Preface

Historically the Church of God as a movement expressed faith through vibrant singing and meaningful worship. The early hymnals produced by the church were more than song books, they were testimonies of faith, expressing our theology through music.

In the creation of this new hymnal we have retained the treasured heritage hymns of the past, carrying them with us into the twenty-first century. Rightfully they take their place along with the great classic traditional and evangelical hymns of Christendom. To assure that the total church was given opportunity to participate in the development of the hymnal, we invited input from every congregation as they were asked to share their suggestions of hymns to be considered. Truly, this is the hymnal of the Church of God. These are the songs which we sing in celebrative worship.

Courageously the committee has used creative innovations throughout the hymnal. Not only have they included selected praise choruses, they have also published some verses of songs in Spanish. This book is for the present hour. It is prepared for service and presented prayerfully, with the belief that it will equip the Church to worship the Lord in the beauty of holiness.

Each new generation presents us with the opportunity to speak to our culture through improved language and revealed theological insights. You will note that some word changes have been made to reflect the inclusiveness of the household of faith. When an alternative wording is given we recommend that you introduce it in the worship of the congregation.

It is our desire that this book be a worship resource. More than a hymnal, it is produced to enable the individual and the congregation to see God in nature, history, art, and literature, as well as music. God is alive! Revealed in the person of Jesus Christ, we know the power of God's love and the glory of the Resurrection. In our varied forms of worship and our many expressions of praise, this resource can be used in any congregation.

This *Hymnal of the Church of God* is "to the glory of God alone"! Glory which can only be experienced when we participate fully in spiritual worship. Worship, we believe, is a verb. It is not something done for us, or to us, but that in which we participate. For that reason, the hymnal is named appropriately. You are invited to become actively involved as we celebrate scriptural holiness through songs of praise, sermons of power, and the silence of meditation. WORSHIP THE LORD!

CONTENTS

INDEXES

Acknowledgements

EDITORIAL DIRECTORS
Arlo F. Newell and Randall W. Vader

CO-EDITORS OF THE HYMNAL PROJECT
Lloyd A. Larson and Frank K. Poncé

EDITORIAL COMMITTEE

James H. Dodson III	Worship Resources
Lloyd A. Larson	New Texts and Tunes
James R. Martin	Classic Hymnody
Cleo P. Myricks	Heritage Hymnody
Frank K. Poncé	Revivalistic Hymnody
Fredrick H. Shively	Text Revision/Modification
Roger L. Stamper	Contemporary Hymnody

CONSULTANTS

Robert A. Adams	Dennis V. Harasty
John L. Albright	J. Ellsworth Jackson
Grant D. Alford	Dale D. Landis
F. Dale Bengtson	James S. McBride
Rodney G. Campbell	Thomas A. Miller
Richard L. Casey	A.C. Phipps
David L. Coolidge	Dean C. Schield
Mark A. Dennis, Jr.	Steven C. Seaton
Joyce D. Foggs	George R. Skramstad
L. Michael Gilliam	Merle D. Strege
Ernest H. Gross, Jr.	Gilbert W. Stafford
J. Perry Grubbs	John A. Walters
L. Fred Harting	Paul E. Yerden

MUSIC EDITING, ARRANGING, AND PROOFREADING
David N. Culross, Randall W. Vader, Lloyd A. Larson, Frank K. Poncé, Jay R.
Rouse, James H. Dodson III, James R. Martin, Cleo P. Myricks, Fredrick H.
Shively, Roger L. Stamper.

REVIEWERS AND SECRETARIAL ASSISTANTS
Wendy L. Kurttila, Frances L. Hess, Rosemary Williams

COPYRIGHT ADMINISTRATION
Debra S. Mayes, Jo Ellen Cramer, Connie L. Williams

DESIGN AND LAYOUT
Gaither Publishing Group, Alexandria, IN, Randall W. Vader, President
Westcott & Associates, Indianapolis, IN, Scott Winegardner, Richard Westcott

LOGO DESIGN
David Liverett of Warner Press

MUSIC TYPOGRAPHY
Music Engraving Services, Indianapolis, IN, Cliff Lehman

WARNER PRESS, INC., ANDERSON, INDIANA
James L. Edwards, President
Arlo F. Newell, Editor in Chief

"Worship the Lord in the beauty

of holiness."

—I Chronicles 16:29

Worship
the
Lord

Hymnal of the Church of God

1 Praise to the Lord, the Almighty

"You are worthy, our Lord and God, to receive glory and honor and power, for you created all things, and by your will they were created and have their being."
—Revelation 4:11

Joachim Neander
Tr. by Catherine Winkworth

14.14.4.7.8.
LOBE DEN HERREN
"Stralsund Gesangbuch"

1 Praise to the Lord, the Al - might-y, the King of cre - a - tion!
2 Praise to the Lord, who o'er all things so won-drous-ly reign - eth,
3 Praise to the Lord, who doth pros-per thy work and de - fend thee;
4 Praise to the Lord! O let all that is in me a - dore Him!

1 O my soul, praise Him, for He is thy health and sal - va - tion!
2 Shel-ters thee un - der His wings, yes, so gen - tly sus - tain - eth!
3 Sure-ly His good-ness and mer - cy here dai - ly at - tend thee.
4 All that hath life and breath, come now with prais - es be - fore Him.

1 All ye who hear, Now to His tem - ple draw near;
2 Hast thou not seen How all thy long - ings have been
3 Pon - der a - new What the Al - might - y can do,
4 Let the A - men Sound from His peo - ple a - gain:

1 Join me in glad ad - o - ra - tion!
2 Grant-ed in what He or - dain - eth?
3 If with His love doth be - friend thee.
4 Glad - ly for - ev - er a - dore Him. A - men.

PRAISE TO GOD

O Praise the Lord, All Ye Nations!

"Praise the Lord, all you nations; extol him, all you peoples."—Psalm 117:1

Charles W. Naylor
Based on Psalm 117

O PRAISE THE LORD
Barney E. Warren

1 O praise the Lord, all ye na - tions! Praise Him, all ye peo - ple!
2 O praise the Lord, all ye na - tions! Praise Him for His good-ness!
3 O praise the Lord, all ye na - tions! He is strong and might - y:
4 O praise the Lord, all ye na - tions! For His love un - fail - ing!

1 For His mer - ci - ful kind - ness is great toward us, And the
2 For He sav - eth His peo - ple from all their sins, And pre -
3 For He keep - eth our steps, that we shall not fall, And de -
4 He doth ten - der - ly lead in the path of peace, And His

1 truth of the Lord en - dur - eth for - ev - er: Praise ye the Lord!
2 serv - eth the souls of all who will trust Him: Praise ye the Lord!
3 liv - ers His saints from all their temp - ta - tions: Praise ye the Lord!
4 name is a ref - uge from the op - press - or: Praise ye the Lord!

Praise Him, praise Him! Praise ye the Lord!
Praise Him, praise Him, praise, O praise Him! Praise ye the Lord, O praise the Lord!

Praise Him, praise Him! Praise ye the Lord!
Praise Him, praise Him, praise, O praise Him!

PRAISE TO GOD

3

Hallelujah, Praise Jehovah

"Let them praise the name of the Lord, for his name alone is exalted; his
splendor is above the earth and the heavens."—Psalm 148:13

Based on Psalm 148
William J. Kirkpatrick

PRAISE JEHOVAH
William J. Kirkpatrick

1 Hal - le - lu - jah, praise Je - ho - vah, From the heav-ens praise His name;
2 Let them prais-es give Je - ho - vah, They were made at His com - mand:

1 Praise Je - ho - vah in the high - est, All His an - gels praise pro - claim.
2 Them for - ev - er He es - tab-lished; His de - cree shall ev - er stand.

1 All His hosts to - geth - er praise Him, Sun, and moon, and stars on high;
2 Kings of earth, and all ye peo - ple, Rul - ers great, earth's judg-es all;

1 Praise Him, O ye heav'ns of heav - ens, And ye floods a - bove the sky.
2 Praise His name, young men and maid - ens, All ye aged and chil - dren small.

PRAISE TO GOD

Let them prais - es give Je - ho - vah, For His name a - lone is high;
Let them prais - es

And His glo - ry is ex - alt - ed, And His glo - ry is ex - alt - ed,
And His glo-ry   And His glo-ry

And His glo - ry is ex - alt - ed, Far a - bove the earth and sky.
And His glo- ry

Thou Art God 4

Lord, you have been our dwelling place throughout all generations.
Before the mountains were born or you brought forth the earth and the
world, from everlasting to everlasting you are God.

The length of our days is seventy years—or eighty, if we have the
strength; yet their span is but trouble and sorrow, for they quickly pass,
and we fly away. Teach us to number our days aright, that we may gain a
heart of wisdom.

Satisfy us in the morning with your unfailing love, that we may sing for
joy and be glad all our days. May your deeds be shown to your servants,
your splendor to their children.

May the favor of the Lord our God rest upon us; establish the work of
our hands for us—yes, establish the work of our hands.

—Psalm 90:1–2, 10, 12, 14, 16–17 (NIV)

5 Praise the Lord! Ye Heavens Adore Him

"Sing, O Heavens! . . . break out in singing . . . For the Lord has comforted
His people, and will have mercy . . . "—Isaiah 49:13

From Psalm 148
Foundling Hospital Collection, Stanzas 1, 2
Edward Osler, Stanza 3

8.7.8.7.D.
AUSTRIAN HYMN
Franz Joseph Haydn

1 Praise the Lord! ye heavens, a - dore Him, Praise Him, an - gels
2 Praise the Lord! for He is glo - rious, Nev - er shall His
3 Wor - ship, hon - or, glo - ry, bless - ing, Lord, we of - fer

1 in the height; Sun and moon, re - joice be - fore Him,
2 prom - ise fail; God hath made His saints vic - to - rious,
3 un - to Thee; Young and old, Thy praise ex - press - ing,

1 Praise Him, all ye stars of light. Praise the Lord! for
2 Sin and death shall not pre - vail. Praise the God of
3 In glad hom - age bend the knee. All the saints in

1 He hath spo - ken, Worlds His might - y voice o - beyed: Laws which nev - er
2 our sal - va - tion, Hosts on high His power pro - claim; Heav'n and earth and
3 heaven a - dore Thee, We would bow be - fore Thy throne: As Thine an - gels

PRAISE TO GOD

```
1  shall   be bro-ken,   For  their guid-ance   He  hath  made.
2  all     cre-a-tion    Laud and mag-ni  -  fy   His  name.
3  serve   be-fore Thee,  So   on earth Thy  will  be  done.   A - men.
```

How Majestic Is Your Name 6

LEADER: O Lord, our Lord, how majestic is your name in all the earth!

PEOPLE: *You have set your glory above the heavens. From the lips of children and infants you have ordained praise because of your enemies to silence the foe and the avenger.*

LEADER: When I consider your heavens, the work of your fingers, the moon and the stars, which you have set in place, what is man that you are mindful of him, the son of man that you care for him?

PEOPLE: *You have made him a little lower than the heavenly beings and crowned him with glory and honor.*

LEADER: You made him ruler over the works of your hands; you put everything under his feet: all flocks and herds, and the beasts of the field, the birds of the air, and the fish of the sea, all that swim the paths of the seas.

PEOPLE: *O Lord, our Lord, how majestic is your name in all the earth!*

—Psalm 8 (NIV)

7
I Will Enter His Gates

"Enter his gates with thanksgiving and his courts with praise . . . "
—Psalm 100:4a

Psalm 100:4, 118:24

I WILL ENTER HIS GATES
Leona Von Brethorst

I will en-ter His gates with thanks-giv-ing in my heart;

I will en-ter His courts with praise.

I will say this is the day that the Lord hath made;

I will re-joice, for He has made me glad.

PRAISE TO GOD

He has made me glad, He has made me glad;

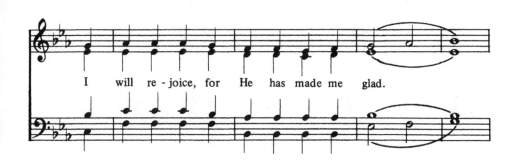

I will re-joice, for He has made me glad.

He has made me glad, He has made me glad;

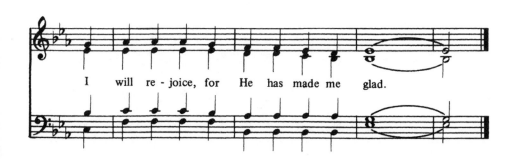

I will re-joice, for He has made me glad.

PRAISE TO GOD

Doxology

"Let everything that has breath praise the Lord."—Psalm 150:6

L.M.

Thomas Ken

DUKE STREET
John Hutton

Praise God from whom all bless - ings flow.

Praise Him, all crea - tures here be - low.

Praise Him a - bove, ye heav'n - ly host.

Praise Fa - ther, Son, and Ho - ly Ghost.

PRAISE TO GOD

This Is the Day

9

"This is the day the Lord has made; let us rejoice and be glad in it."
—Psalm 118:24

Psalm 118:24

THIS IS THE DAY
Les Garrett

This is the day, this is the day that the Lord has made, that the Lord has made. I will re-joice, I will re-joice and be glad in it, and be glad in it. This is the day that the Lord has made, I will re-joice and be glad in it. This is the day, this is the day that the Lord has made.

PRAISE TO GOD

10 Gloria Patri

"Ascribe to the Lord the glory due his name; bring an offering and come into his courts."—Psalm 96:8

Traditional, 2nd century

GLORIA PATRI
Henry W. Greatorex

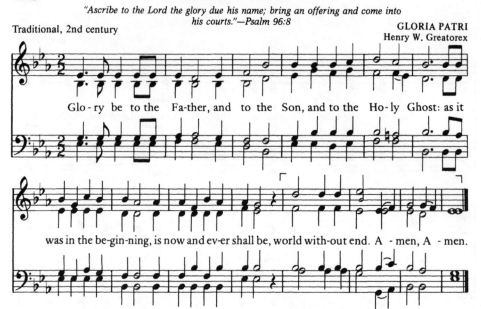

Glo - ry be to the Fa - ther, and to the Son, and to the Ho - ly Ghost: as it

was in the be - gin - ning, is now and ev-er shall be, world with-out end. A - men, A - men.

11 *We Believe in a Triune God*

We believe in God, the Eternal Spirit, Father of our Lord Jesus Christ and our Father, and to His deeds we testify:

He calls the worlds into being,
    creates man in His own image,
    and sets before Him the ways of life and death.
He seeks in holy love to save all people from aimlessness and sin.
He judges men and nations by His righteous will declared through prophets and apostles.
In Jesus Christ, the Man of Nazareth, our crucified and risen Lord,
    He has come to us and shared our common lot,
        conquering sin and death,
        and reconciling the world to Himself.
He bestows upon us His Holy Spirit,
    creating and renewing the Church of Jesus Christ,
    binding in covenant faithful people of all ages, tongues, and races.
He calls us into His Church,
    to accept the cost and joy of discipleship,
    to be His servants in the service of men,
    to proclaim the gospel to all the world,
    to resist the powers of evil,
    to share in Christ's baptism and eat at His table,
    to join Him in His passion and victory.
He promises to all who trust Him:
    forgiveness of sins and fulness of grace,
    courage in the struggle for justice and peace,
    His presence in trial and rejoicing,
    and eternal life in His kingdom which has no end.
Blessing and honor, glory and power be unto Him. Amen.

Holy Is the Lord

12

"Speak to the entire assembly of Israel and say to them: 'Be holy because I, the Lord your God, am holy.'"—Leviticus 19:2

6.5.6.5. D.

Traditional

HOLY IS THE LORD
Franz Schubert

Ho - ly, ho - ly, ho - ly, Ho - ly is the

Lord. Ho - ly, ho - ly, ho - ly,

Ho - ly is the Lord. Ho - ly is the Fa -

ther, Ho - ly is the Son, Ho - ly

is the Spir - it; Bless - ed Three in One.

PRAISE TO GOD

13 Come, O Thou God of Grace

*"Through Jesus, therefore, let us continually offer to God a sacrifice of praise
—the fruit of lips that confess his name."—Hebrews 13:15*

6.6.4.6.6.6.4.
ITALIAN HYMN
Felice de Giardini

William E. Evans

1 Come, O Thou God of grace, Dwell in this ho - ly place, E'en now de - scend. This tem - ple, reared to Thee, O may it ev - er be Filled with Thy maj - es - ty Till time shall end!

2 Be in each song of praise Which here Thy peo - ple raise With hearts a - flame. Let ev - ery an - them rise Like in - cense to the skies, A joy - ful sac - ri - fice To Thy blest name.

3 Speak, O e - ter - nal Lord, Out of Thy liv - ing word; O give suc - cess! Do Thou the truth im - part Un - to each wait - ing heart; Source of all strength Thou art, Thy gos - pel bless.

4 To the great One and Three Glo - ry and prais - es be In love now giv'n! Glad songs to Thee we sing, Glad hearts to Thee we bring, Till we our God and King Shall praise in heaven. A - men.

PRAISE TO GOD

Thou Art Worthy

14

"You are worthy, our Lord and God, to receive glory and honor and power . . ."
—Revelation 4:11a

Based on Revelation 4:11, 5:9
Pauline M. Mills, verse 1
Tom Smail, verse 2

WORTHY LORD
Pauline M. Mills

1 Thou art wor-thy, Thou art wor-thy, Thou art wor-thy, O Lord,
2 Thou art wor-thy, Thou art wor-thy, Thou art wor-thy, O Lamb,

1 To re-ceive glo-ry, glo-ry and hon-or, Glo-ry and
2 To re-ceive bless-ing, glo-ry and hon-or And pow'r at the

1 hon-or and pow'r; For Thou hast cre - at - ed, hast all things cre-
2 Fa-ther's right hand; For Thou hast re-deemed us, hast ran-somed and

1 at - ed, Thou hast cre - at - ed all things, And for Thy
2 cleaned us, By Thy blood set-ting us free, In white robes ar-

1 pleas-ure they are cre - at - ed: Thou art wor-thy, O Lord!
2 rayed us, kings and priests made us: We are reign-ing in Thee!

PRAISE TO GOD

15
Be Exalted, O God

"For great is your love . . . Be exalted, O God, above the heavens; let your
glory be over all the earth."—Psalm 57:10a,11

Based on Psalm 57:9-11
Brent Chambers

BE EXALTED
Brent Chambers

Be ex - alt - ed, O God, a - bove the heav - ens;

Let Thy glo - ry be o - ver all the earth.

Be ex - alt - ed, O God, a - bove the heav - ens;

Let Thy glo - ry be o - ver all the earth.

PRAISE TO GOD

We Have Come into His House 16

"I rejoiced with those who said to me, 'Let us go to the house of the Lord.' "
—Psalm 122:1

Bruce Ballinger

WORSHIP HIM
Bruce Ballinger

1 We have come in-to His house and gath-ered in His name to
2 Let's for - get a-bout our-selves and mag - ni - fy His name and

1 wor - ship Him. We have come in - to His house and
2 wor - ship Him. Let's for - get a - bout our-selves and

1 gath - ered in His name to wor - ship Him. We have
2 mag - ni - fy His name and wor - ship Him. Let's for -

1 come in - to His house and gath-ered in His name to wor - ship Christ the
2 get a - bout our-selves and mag - ni - fy His name and wor - ship Christ the

1 Lord. Wor - ship Him, Christ the Lord.
2 Lord. Wor - ship Him, Christ the Lord.

PRAISE TO GOD

17

To God Be the Glory

"The Lord has done great things for us, and we are filled with joy."
—Psalm 126:3

Fanny J. Crosby

11.11.11.11.wR.
TO GOD BE THE GLORY
William H. Doane

1 To God be the glo - ry—great things He hath done!
2 O per - fect re - demp - tion, the pur - chase of blood,
3 Great things He hath taught us, great things He hath done!

1 So loved He the world that He gave us His Son,
2 To ev - 'ry be - liev - er the prom - ise of God;
3 And great our re - joic - ing through Je - sus the Son;

1 Who yield - ed His life an a - tone - ment for sin,
2 The vil - est of - fen - der who tru - ly be - lieves,
3 But pur - er, and high - er, and great - er will be

1 And o - pened the life - gate that all may go in.
2 That mo - ment from Je - sus a par - don re - ceives.
3 Our won - der, our vic - t'ry, when Je - sus we see.

PRAISE TO GOD

PRAISE TO GOD

18 Come, Thou Fount of Every Blessing

"O my Strength, I sing praise to you; you, O God, are my fortress, my loving God."—Psalm 59:17

8.7.8.7.D.
NETTLETON

Robert Robinson

John Wyeth

1 Come, Thou Fount of ev - ery bless-ing, Tune my heart to sing Thy grace;
2 Here I raise my Eb - e - ne -zer;* Hith-er by Thy help I'm come.
3 O to grace how great a debt - or Dai - ly I'm con-strained to be!

1 Streams of mer - cy, nev - er ceas - ing, Call for songs of loud-est praise.
2 And I hope, by Thy good pleas-ure, Safe-ly to ar - rive at home.
3 Let Thy good-ness, like a fet - ter, Bind my wan-d'ring heart to Thee:

1 Teach me some me - lo - dious son - net, Sung by flam - ing tongues a - bove;
2 Je - sus sought me when a strang-er, Wan-dering from the fold of God.
3 Prone to wan - der, Lord, I feel it, Prone to leave the God I love:

1 Praise the mount! I'm fixed up - on it, Mount of Thy re-deem-ing love.
2 He, to res - cue me from dan-ger, In - ter - posed His pre -cious blood.
3 Here's my heart, O take and seal it, Seal it for Thy courts a - bove.

*Ebenezer – "Stone of help" (I Samuel 7:12)

PRAISE TO GOD

Christians, We Have Met to Worship

" . . . offer your bodies as living sacrifices, holy and pleasing to God . . . "
—Romans 12:1b

8.7.8.7.D.

George Atkins
Alt. Bryan Jeffery Leech

HOLY MANNA
William Moore
in *Columbian Harmony*

1 Christians, we have met to worship To adore the Lord our God;
2 Let us love our God supremely, Let us love each other, too;

1 Will you pray with expectation As we preach the living Word?
2 Let us pray and care for people 'Til God makes their lives anew.

1 All is vain unless the Spirit Of the Holy One comes down;
2 When at last we're called to heaven, In His presence we'll sit down;

1 Let us pray, and God's great blessing Will be showered all around.
2 And the Lord will then reward us Giving us a heavenly crown.

PRAISE TO GOD

20 O How Glorious, Full of Wonder

"O Lord, our Lord, how majestic is your name in all the earth!"—Psalm 8:1

8.7.8.7.D.

Based on Psalm 8
Curtis Beach

HYMN TO JOY
Ludwig van Beethoven
Adapted by Edward Hodges

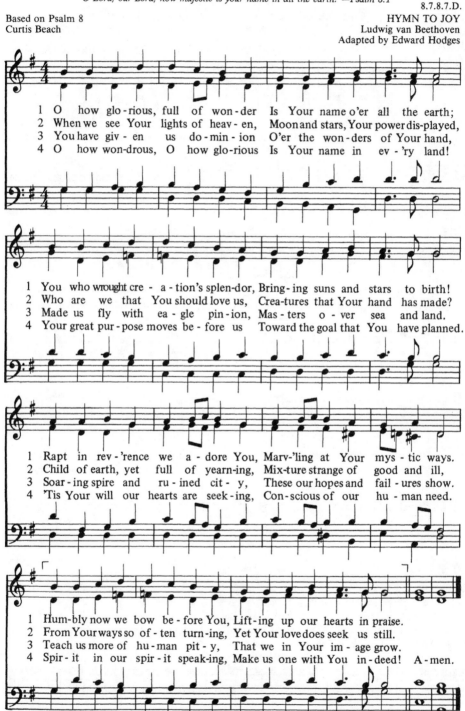

1 O how glo-rious, full of won-der Is Your name o'er all the earth;
2 When we see Your lights of heav-en, Moon and stars, Your power dis-played,
3 You have giv-en us do-min-ion O'er the won-ders of Your hand,
4 O how won-drous, O how glo-rious Is Your name in ev-'ry land!

1 You who wrought cre-a-tion's splen-dor, Bring-ing suns and stars to birth!
2 Who are we that You should love us, Crea-tures that Your hand has made?
3 Made us fly with ea-gle pin-ion, Mas-ters o-ver sea and land.
4 Your great pur-pose moves be-fore us Toward the goal that You have planned.

1 Rapt in rev-'rence we a-dore You, Marv-'ling at Your mys-tic ways.
2 Child of earth, yet full of yearn-ing, Mix-ture strange of good and ill,
3 Soar-ing spire and ru-ined cit-y, These our hopes and fail-ures show.
4 'Tis Your will our hearts are seek-ing, Con-scious of our hu-man need.

1 Hum-bly now we bow be-fore You, Lift-ing up our hearts in praise.
2 From Your ways so of-ten turn-ing, Yet Your love does seek us still.
3 Teach us more of hu-man pit-y, That we in Your im-age grow.
4 Spir-it in our spir-it speak-ing, Make us one with You in-deed! A-men.

PRAISE TO GOD

Doxology
21

"Let everything that has breath praise the Lord."—Psalm 150:6

L.M.
OLD HUNDREDTH
Attributed to Louis Bourgeois
Genevan Psalter

Thomas Ken

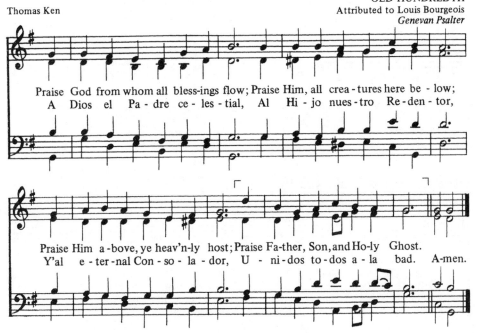

Praise God from whom all bless-ings flow; Praise Him, all crea-tures here be - low;
A Dios el Pa - dre ce - les - tial, Al Hi - jo nues-tro Re - den - tor,

Praise Him a-bove, ye heav'n-ly host; Praise Fa-ther, Son, and Ho-ly Ghost.
Y'al e - ter-nal Con - so - la - dor, U - ni-dos to-dos a - la bad. A-men.

O God, Our Help in Ages Past
22

"Help us, O God of our salvation, for the glory of Your name."—Psalm 79:9

C.M.
ST. ANNE
William Croft

Based on Psalm 90
Isaac Watts

1 O God, our help in a - ges past, Our hope for years to come,
2 Un - der the shad - ow of Thy throne Still may we dwell se - cure;
3 Be - fore the hills in or - der stood, Or earth re - ceived her frame,
4 A thou-sand a - ges in Thy sight Are like an eve - ning gone,
5 O God, our help in a - ges past, Our hope for years to come,

1 Our shel-ter from the storm-y blast, And our e - ter - nal home!
2 Suf - fi - cient is Thine arm a - lone, And our de-fense is sure.
3 From ev - er - last - ing Thou art God, To end-less years the same.
4 Short as the watch that ends the night, Be - fore the ris - ing sun.
5 Be Thou our guide while life shall last, And our e - ter - nal home! A-men.

PRAISE TO GOD

23 God of the Ages, History's Maker

"Before the mountains were born or you brought forth the earth and the world,
from everlasting to everlasting you are God."—Psalm 90:2

Margaret Clarkson

10.9.10.9.
BUNESSAN
Traditional Gaelic Melody

1 God of the a - ges, His - to - ry's Mak - er,
2 God of this morn - ing, Glad - ly Your chil - dren
3 God of to - mor - row, Strong O - ver - com - er,
4 Lord of past a - ges, Lord of this morn - ing,

1 Plan - ning our path - way, Hold - ing us fast,
2 Wor - ship be - fore You, Trust - ing - ly bow:
3 Princ - es of dark - ness Own Your com - mand:
4 Lord of the fu - ture, Help us, we pray:

1 Shap - ing in mer - cy All that con - cerns us:
2 Teach us to know You Al - ways a - mong us,
3 What then can harm us? We are Your peo - ple,
4 Teach us to trust You, Love and o - bey You,

1 Fa - ther, we praise You, Lord of the past.
2 Qui - et - ly sov - 'reign— Lord of our now.
3 Now and for - ev - er Kept by Your hand.
4 Crown you each mo - ment, Lord of to - day.

PRAISE TO GOD

Earth and All Stars

24

"Great is the Lord and most worthy of praise; his greatness no one can fathom."
—Psalm 145:3

9.7.9.7.7.9.
DEXTER
David Johnson
Harmonized by Jan Bender

Herbert Brokering

1 Earth and all stars, loud rush - ing plan - ets, Sing to the
2 Hail, wind and rain, loud blow - ing snow - storm, Sing to the
3 Trum - pet and pipes, loud clash - ing cym - bals, Sing to the
4 Ma - chines and steel, loud pound - ing ham - mers, Sing to the
5 Knowl - edge and truth, loud sound - ing wis - dom, Sing to the

1 Lord a new song! O vic - to - ry, loud shout-ing ar - my,
2 Lord a new song! Flow-ers and trees, loud rus - tling dry leaves,
3 Lord a new song! Harp, lute and lyre, loud hum-ming cel - los,
4 Lord a new song! Lime-stone and beams, loud build-ing work - men,
5 Lord a new song! Daugh-ter and son, loud pray - ing mem - bers,

Sing to the Lord a new song! He has done

mar - vel - ous things; I too will praise Him with a new song!

PRAISE TO GOD

25 God Our Maker, God Most Holy

". . . which is Christ in you, the hope of glory."—Colossians 1:27b

David L. Coolidge

8.7.8.7.D.
BEECHER
John Zundel

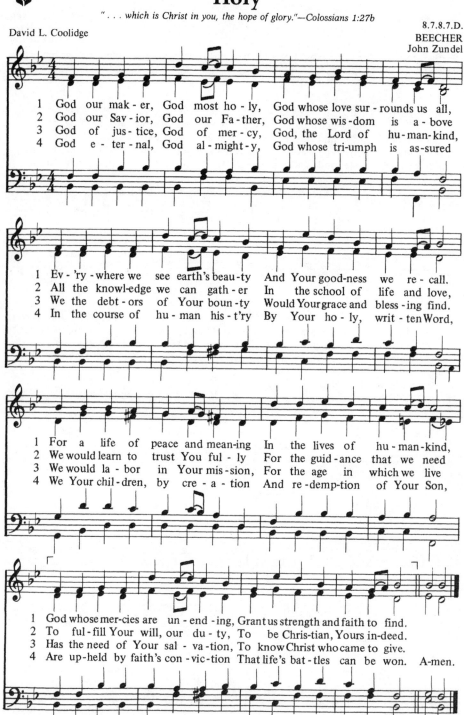

1 God our mak - er, God most ho - ly, God whose love sur - rounds us all,
2 God our Sav - ior, God our Fa - ther, God whose wis - dom is a - bove
3 God of jus - tice, God of mer - cy, God, the Lord of hu - man - kind,
4 God e - ter - nal, God al - might - y, God whose tri - umph is as - sured

1 Ev - 'ry - where we see earth's beau - ty And Your good - ness we re - call.
2 All the knowl - edge we can gath - er In the school of life and love,
3 We the debt - ors of Your boun - ty Would Your grace and bless - ing find.
4 In the course of hu - man his - t'ry By Your ho - ly, writ - ten Word,

1 For a life of peace and mean - ing In the lives of hu - man - kind,
2 We would learn to trust You ful - ly For the guid - ance that we need
3 We would la - bor in Your mis - sion, For the age in which we live
4 We Your chil - dren, by cre - a - tion And re - demp - tion of Your Son,

1 God whose mer - cies are un - end - ing, Grant us strength and faith to find.
2 To ful - fill Your will, our du - ty, To be Chris - tian, Yours in - deed.
3 Has the need of Your sal - va - tion, To know Christ who came to give.
4 Are up - held by faith's con - vic - tion That life's bat - tles can be won. A - men.

PRAISE TO GOD

Glorify Thy Name

26

*"All the nations thou hast made shall come and bow down before thee, O Lord,
and shall glorify thy name."—Psalm 86:9 (RSV)*

Donna Adkins

GLORIFY THY NAME
Donna Adkins

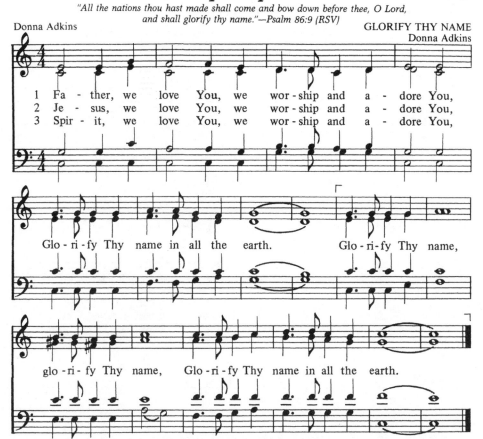

1 Fa - ther, we love You, we wor - ship and a - dore You,
2 Je - sus, we love You, we wor - ship and a - dore You,
3 Spir - it, we love You, we wor - ship and a - dore You,

Glo - ri - fy Thy name in all the earth. Glo - ri - fy Thy name,

glo - ri - fy Thy name, Glo - ri - fy Thy name in all the earth.

An Affirmation

27

WE BELIEVE IN JESUS CHRIST THE LORD,
>Who was promised to the people of Israel,
>Who came in the flesh to dwell among us,
>Who announced the coming of the rule of God,
>Who gathered disciples and taught them,
>Who died on the cross to free us from sin,
>Who rose from the dead to give us life and hope,
>Who reigns in heaven at the right hand of God,
>Who comes to judge and bring justice to victory.

WE BELIEVE IN GOD HIS FATHER,
>Who raised Him from the dead,
>Who created and sustains the universe,
>Who acts to deliver His people in times of need,
>Who desires all men everywhere to be saved.

WE BELIEVE IN THE HOLY SPIRIT,
>Who is the form of God present in the church,
>Who is the guarantee of our deliverance,
>Who leads us to find God's will in the Word,
>Who guides us in discernment,
>Who impels us to act together.

—The Mennonite Hymnal, 1967

PRAISE TO GOD

28 We Praise Thee, O God, Our Redeemer

"Give thanks to the Lord, for he is good; his love endures forever. Let the redeemed of the Lord say this—those he redeemed from the hand of the foe . . . "—Psalm 107:1-2

Julia C. Cory

12.11.12.11.
KREMSER
Netherlands Folk Song
Arranged by Edward Kremser

1 We praise Thee, O God, our Re - deem - er, Cre - a - tor;
2 We wor - ship Thee, God of our fa - thers, we bless Thee;
3 With voic - es u - nit - ed our prais - es we of - fer,

1 In grate - ful de - vo - tion our trib - ute we bring.
2 Through life's storm and tem - pest our guide hast Thou been.
3 And glad - ly our songs of true wor - ship we raise.

1 We lay it be - fore Thee, we kneel and a - dore Thee,
2 When per - ils o'er - take us, Thou wilt not for - sake us,
3 Thy strong arm will guide us, our God is be - side us,

1 We bless Thy ho - ly name, glad prais - es we sing.
2 And with Thy help, O Lord, life's bat - tles we win.
3 To Thee, our great Re - deem - er, for - ev - er be praise. A - men.

PRAISE TO GOD

Joyful, Joyful, We Adore Thee 29

"Shout with joy to God, all the earth! Sing to the glory of his name; offer him glory and praise!"—Psalm 66:1–2

8.7.8.7.D.
HYMN TO JOY
Ludwig van Beethoven
Adapted by Edward Hodges

Henry van Dyke

1 Joy-ful, joy-ful, we a-dore Thee, God of glo-ry, Lord of love;
2 All Thy works with joy sur-round Thee, Earth and heaven re-flect Thy rays,
3 Thou art giv-ing and for-giv-ing, Ev-er bless-ing, ev-er blest,
4 Mor-tals, join the might-y cho-rus Which the morn-ing stars be-gan;

1 Hearts un-fold like flowers be-fore Thee, Open-ing to the sun a-bove.
2 Stars and an-gels sing a-round Thee, Cen-ter of un-bro-ken praise.
3 Well-spring of the joy of liv-ing, O-cean depth of hap-py rest!
4 Fa-ther love is reign-ing o'er us, Bind-ing all with-in its span.

1 Melt the clouds of sin and sad-ness, Drive the dark of doubt a-way;
2 Field and for-est, vale and moun-tain, Flow-ery mead-ow, flash-ing sea,
3 Thou our Fa-ther, Christ, our Broth-er— All who live in love are Thine;
4 Ev-er sing-ing, march we on-ward, Vic-tors in the midst of strife,

1 Giv-er of im-mor-tal glad-ness, Fill us with the light of day.
2 Chant-ing bird and flow-ing foun-tain, Call us to re-joice in Thee.
3 Teach us how to love each oth-er, Lift us to the joy di-vine.
4 Joy-ful mu-sic leads us sun-ward In the tri-umph song of life. A-men.

PRAISE TO GOD

30 God of Grace and God of Glory

" . . . for everyone born of God overcomes the world. This is the victory that has overcome the world, even our faith."—I John 5:4

Harry Emerson Fosdick

8.7.8.7.8.7.7.
CWM RHONDDA
John Hughes

1 God of grace and God of glo - ry, On Thy peo - ple
2 Lo! the hosts of e - vil round us Scorn Thy Christ, as -
3 Cure Thy chil - dren's war - ring mad - ness; Bend our pride to
4 Save us from weak re - sig - na - tion to the e - vils

1 pour Thy power; Crown Thine an - cient church's sto - ry, Bring her bud to
2 sail His ways! From the fears that long have bound us, Free our hearts to
3 Thy con - trol; Shame our wan - ton, self - ish glad - ness, Rich in things and
4 we de - plore; Let the search for Thy sal - va - tion Be our glo - ry

1 glo - rious flower. Grant us wis - dom, Grant us cour - age,
2 faith and praise. Grant us wis - dom, Grant us cour - age,
3 poor in soul. Grant us wis - dom, Grant us cour - age,
4 ev - er - more. Grant us wis - dom, Grant us cour - age,

1 For the fac - ing of this hour, For the fac - ing of this hour.
2 For the liv - ing of these days, For the liv - ing of these days.
3 Lest we miss Thy kingdom's goal, Lest we miss Thy king - dom's goal.
4 Serv - ing Thee whom we a - dore, Serv - ing Thee whom we a - dore. A - men.

Holy, Holy, Holy Is the Lord of Hosts

31

"And they were calling to one another: 'Holy, holy, holy is the Lord Almighty;
the whole earth is full of his . . . glory."—Isaiah 6:3

LORD OF HOSTS
Nolene S. Prince

Isaiah 6:3

Ho - ly, Ho - ly, Ho - ly, is the Lord of Hosts.

Ho - ly, Ho - ly, Ho - ly, is the Lord of Hosts. The

whole earth is full of His glo - ry. The whole earth is full of His glo - ry. The

whole earth is full of His glo - ry. Ho - ly is the Lord.

PRAISE TO GOD

32 Holy, Holy, Holy

"Each of the four living creatures had six wings and was covered with eyes
all around, even under his wings. Day and night they never stop saying:
'Holy, holy, holy is the Lord God Almighty, who was, and is, and is to come.' "
—Revelation 4:8

Reginald Heber

11.12.12.10.
NICAEA
John B. Dykes
Descant by Jay Rouse

1 Ho - ly, ho - ly, ho - ly! Lord God Al - might - y!
2 Ho - ly, ho - ly, ho - ly! all the saints a - dore Thee,
3 Ho - ly, ho - ly, ho - ly! though the dark - ness hide Thee,
4 Ho - ly, ho - ly, ho - ly! Lord God Al - might - y!

1 Ear - ly in the morn - ing our song shall rise to Thee;
2 Cast - ing down their gold - en crowns a - round the glass - y sea;
3 Though the eye of sin - ful flesh Thy glo - ry may not see;
4 All Thy works shall praise Thy name in earth and sky and sea;

Ho - ly Ho - ly, Ho - ly,

1 Ho - ly, ho - ly, ho - ly! mer - ci - ful and might - y!
2 Cher - u - bim and ser - a - phim fall - ing down be - fore Thee,
3 On - ly Thou art ho - ly— there is none be - side Thee
4 Ho - ly, ho - ly, ho - ly! mer - ci - ful and might - y!

God in three per - sons, bless - ed Trin - i - ty! A-men.

1 God in three per - sons, bless - ed Trin - i - ty!
2 Who wert, and art, and ev - er - more shall be.
3 Per - fect in power, in love and pu - ri - ty.
4 God in three per - sons, bless - ed Trin - i - ty! A - men.

PRAISE TO GOD

All Creatures of Our God and King 33

"For God is the King of all the earth; sing to him a psalm of praise."
—Psalm 47:7

8.8.4.4.8.8.wA.

Francis of Assisi
Tr. by William H. Draper

LASST UNS ERFREUEN
Geistliche Kirchengesäng
Harmonization by Ralph Vaughn Williams

1 All crea-tures of our God and King, Lift up your voice and with us
2 Thou rush-ing wind that art so strong, Ye clouds that sail in heaven a-
3 Thou flow-ing wa - ter, pure and clear, Make mu - sic for Thy Lord to
4 Let all things their Cre - a - tor bless, And wor-ship Him in hum-ble-

1 sing, Al - le - lu - ia! Al - le - lu - ia! Thou burn-ing sun with
2 long, O praise Him! Al - le - lu - ia! Thou ris - ing morn, in
3 hear, Al - le - lu - ia! Al - le - lu - ia! Thou fire so mas-ter-
4 ness. O praise Him! Al - le - lu - ia! Praise, praise the Fa - ther,

1 gold-en beam, Thou sil - ver moon with soft-er gleam, O praise Him!
2 praise re - joice, Ye lights of eve-ning, find a voice! O praise Him!
3 ful and bright, pro - vid-ing warmth and giv-ing light, O praise Him!
4 praise the Son, And praise the Spir-it, Three in One! O praise Him!

O praise Him! Al - le - lu - ia! Al - le - lu - ia! Al - le - lu - ia!

PRAISE TO GOD

34 Immortal, Invisible, God Only Wise

"Now to the King eternal, immortal, invisible, the only God, be honor and glory forever and ever. Amen."—I Timothy 1:17

Walter Chalmers Smith

11.11.11.11.
ST. DENIO
Welsh Melody

1 Im - mor - tal, in - vis - i - ble, God on - ly wise,
2 Un - rest - ing, un - hast - ing, and si - lent as light,
3 To all, life Thou giv - est, to both great and small;
4 Great Fa - ther of glo - ry, pure Fa - ther of light,

1 In light in - ac - ces - si - ble hid from our eyes,
2 Nor want - ing, nor wast - ing, Thou rul - est in might;
3 In all life Thou liv - est, the true life of all;
4 Thine an - gels a - dore Thee, all veil - ing their sight;

1 Most bless - ed, most glo - rious, the An - cient of Days,
2 Thy jus - tice like moun - tains high soar - ing a - bove
3 We blos - som and flour - ish as leaves on the tree,
4 All praise we would ren - der: O help us to see

1 Al - might - y, vic - to - rious, Thy great name we praise.
2 Thy clouds, which are foun - tains of good - ness and love.
3 And with - er and per - ish— but naught chang - eth Thee.
4 'Tis on - ly the splen - dor of light hid - eth Thee. A - men.

PRAISE TO GOD

Let Everything That Hath Breath Praise the Lord

"Let everything that has breath praise the Lord."—Psalm 150:6

Bernadette Blount Salley

WHEN YOU PRAISE HIM
Bernadette Blount Salley

When you praise Him, things will hap - pen, When you praise Him, things will change; When you praise Him, joy re - turns, When you praise Him, strength is gained. When you praise Him, heav - en hears, And the Lord is glo - ri - fied; Let ev - 'ry-thing that hath breath praise the Lord!

PRAISE TO GOD

36 Revive Us Again

"Will you not revive us again, that your people may rejoice in you?"
—Psalm 85:6

William P. Mackay

REVIVE US AGAIN
John J. Husband

1 We praise Thee, O God, for the Son of Thy love,
2 We praise Thee, O God, for Thy Spir-it of light,
3 All glo-ry and praise to the Lamb that was slain,
4 Re-vive us a-gain— fill each heart with Thy love;

1 For Je-sus who died and is now gone a-bove.
2 Who has shown us our Sav-ior and ban-ished our night.
3 Who has tak-en our sins and has cleansed ev-ery stain.
4 May each soul be re-kin-dled with fire from a-bove.

Hal-le-lu-jah, Thine the glo-ry! Hal-le-lu-jah, a-men! Hal-le-

lu-jah, Thine the glo-ry! Re-vive us a-gain.

PRAISE TO GOD

My Tribute

37

"To our God and Father be the glory forever and ever . . . "—Philippians 4:20a

Andraé Crouch

MY TRIBUTE
Andraé Crouch

To God be the glo - ry, To God be the glo - ry,

To God be the glo - ry For the things He has done.

With His blood He has saved me; With His power He has raised me;

To God be the glo - ry for the things He has done.

PRAISE TO GOD

38 Praise, My Soul, the King of Heaven

"Sing to the Lord, for he has done glorious things; let this be known to all the world."—Isaiah 12:5

8.7.8.7.8.7.
LAUDA ANIMA
Mark Andrews

Henry Francis Lyte

Unison

1 Praise, my soul, the King of heav-en, To the throne thy
2 Praise the Lord for grace and fa - vor To all peo - ple
3 Frail as sum-mer's flow'r we flour-ish, Blows the wind and
4 An - gels in the height, a - dore Him; Ye be - hold Him

1 trib - ute bring; Ran - somed, healed, re - stored, for - giv-en,
2 in dis - tress; Praise Him, still the same as ev - er,
3 it is gone; But, while mor - tals rise and per-ish,
4 face to face; Saints tri - um - phant, bow be - fore Him,

1 Ev - er - more His prais - es sing; Al - le - lu - ia!
2 Slow to chide and swift to bless; Al - le - lu - ia!
3 God en - dures un - chang-ing on: Al - le - lu - ia!
4 Gath - ered in from ev - ery race; Al - le - lu - ia!

1 Al - le - lu - ia! Praise the ev - er - last - ing King.
2 Al - le - lu - ia! Glo - rious in His faith - ful - ness.
3 Al - le - lu - ia! Praise the high e - ter - nal one.
4 Al - le - lu - ia! Praise with us the God of grace. A-men.

PRAISE TO GOD

Sing Praise to God Who Reigns Above

39

"May the peoples praise you, O God; may all the peoples praise you."
—Psalm 67:3

8.7.8.7.8.8.7.

Johann J. Schütz
Tr. by Frances E. Cox

MIT FREUDEN ZART
Bohemian Brethren's "Kirchengesänge"

1 Sing praise to God who reigns a-bove, The God of all cre-a-tion, The God of pow'r, the God of love, The God of our sal-va-tion; With heal-ing balm my soul He fills, And ev-ery faith-less mur-mur stills: To God all praise and glo-ry.

2 What God's al-might-y power hath made His gra-cious mer-cy keep-eth; By morn-ing glow or eve-ning shade His watch-ful eye ne'er sleep-eth; With-in the king-dom of His might, Lo! all is just and all is right: To God all praise and glo-ry.

3 The Lord is nev-er far a-way, But, through all grief dis-tress-ing, An ev-er-pres-ent help and stay, Our peace, and joy, and bless-ing; As with a moth-er's ten-der hand, He leads His own, His cho-sen band: To God all praise and glo-ry.

4 Thus, all my glad-some way a-long, I sing a-loud His prais-es, That all may hear the grate-ful song My voice un-wea-ried rais-es, Be joy-ful in the Lord, my heart, Both soul and bod-y bear your part: To God all praise and glo-ry. A-men.

PRAISE TO GOD

40 Come, Thou Almighty King

"For where two or three come together in my name, there am I with them."
—Matthew 18:20

6.6.4.6.6.6.4.
ITALIAN HYMN
Felice de Giardini

Anonymous

1 Come, Thou Al-might-y King, Help us Thy name to sing, Help us to praise: Fa-ther, all-glo-ri-ous, O'er all vic-to-ri-ous, Come, and reign o-ver us, An-cient of Days.

2 Come, Thou In-car-nate Word, Gird on Thy might-y sword, Our prayer at-tend: Come, and Thy peo-ple bless, And give Thy word suc-cess; Spir-it of ho-li-ness, On us de-scend.

3 Come, Ho-ly Com-fort-er, Thy sa-cred wit-ness bear In this glad hour: Thou who al-might-y art, Now rule in ev-ery heart, Nev-er from us de-part, Spir-it of power.

4 To Thee, great One in Three, The high-est prais-es be, Hence ev-er-more! Thy sov-ereign maj-es-ty May we in glo-ry see, And to e-ter-ni-ty Love and a-dore. A-men.

PRAISE TO GOD

The Lord Is King!

41

"The Lord reigns, let the earth be glad . . . "—Psalm 97:1a

Josiah Conder
Adapted by Norman Johnson

10.6.10.6.8.8.8.6.
ALL IS WELL
J. T. White's "Sacred Harp"

1 The Lord is King! Lift up, lift up your voice— Sing His praise, sing His praise!
2 The Lord is King! Let all His worth de-clare— Great is He, great is He!
3 The Lord is King! And bow to Him we must— God is great, God is good!
4 The Lord is King! Thro'-out His vast do-main He is all, all in all!

1 All heav'n and earth be-fore Him now re-joice— Sing His praise, sing His praise! From
2 Bow to His will and trust His ten-der care— Great is He, great is He! Nor
3 The Judge of all to all is ev-er just— God is great, God is good! Ho-
4 The Lord Je - ho - vah ev-er-more shall reign— He is all, all in all! Thro'

1 world to world the joy shall ring, For He a-lone is God and King; From
2 mur-mur at His wise de-crees, Nor doubt His stead-fast prom-is-es; In
3 ly and true are all His ways: Let ev - ery crea - ture shout His praise; The
4 earth and heav'n one song shall ring, From grate-ful hearts this an-them spring: A -

1 sky to sky His ban-ners fling— Sing His praise, sing His praise!
2 hum-ble faith fall on your knees— Great is He, great is He!
3 Lord of Hosts, An - cient of Days— God is great, God is good!
4 rise, O saints, sa - lute your King— All your days, sing His praise!

PRAISE TO GOD

42

O Worship the King

"You who fear him, trust in the Lord—he is their help and shield."
—Psalm 115:11

Robert Grant

10.10.11.11.
LYONS
Adapted from Johann Michael Haydn

1 O worship the King all glorious above, And
2 O tell of His might and sing of His grace, Whose
3 Thy bountiful care what tongue can recite? It
4 Frail children of dust, and feeble as frail, In

1 gratefully sing His wonderful love; Our
2 robe is the light, whose canopy space; His
3 breathes in the air, it shines in the light, It
4 Thee do we trust, nor find Thee to fail; Thy

1 Shield and Defender, the Ancient of Days, Pa-
2 chariots of wrath the deep thunderclouds form, And
3 streams from the hills, it descends to the plain, And
4 mercies how tender, how firm to the end, Our

1 vilioned in splendor and girded with praise.
2 dark is His path on the wings of the storm.
3 sweetly distills in the dew and the rain.
4 Maker, Defender, Redeemer and Friend. A-men.

PRAISE TO GOD

Doxology

"Let everything that has breath praise the Lord."—Psalm 150:6

Thomas Ken

L.M.
FAIRHILL
Jimmy Owens

Praise God from whom all bless - ings flow; Praise Him, all

crea - tures here be - low. Praise Him a - bove, ye heav-en-ly host;

Praise Fa - ther, Son and Ho - ly Ghost. A - men.

O Sing to the Lord
44

LEADER: Sing to the Lord a new song; sing to the Lord, all the earth.

PEOPLE: *Sing to the Lord, praise his name; proclaim his salvation day after day.*

LEADER: Declare his glory among the nations, his marvelous deeds among all peoples.

PEOPLE: *For great is the Lord and most worthy of praise; he is to be feared above all gods.*

LEADER: For all the gods of the nations are idols, but the Lord made the heavens.

PEOPLE: *Splendor and majesty are before him; strength and glory are in his sanctuary.*

LEADER: Ascribe to the Lord, O families of nations, ascribe to the Lord glory and strength.

PEOPLE: *Ascribe to the Lord the glory due his name; bring an offering and come into his courts.*

—Psalm 96:1–8 (NIV)

PRAISE TO GOD

45 Holy, Holy

" . . . I will extol the Lord with all my heart in the council of the upright and in the assembly."—Psalm 111:1b

Jimmy Owens

HOLY, HOLY
Jimmy Owens

1 Ho - ly, ho - ly, ho - ly, ho - ly, Ho - ly, ho - ly, Lord God Al - might - y; And we lift our hearts be - fore You as a to - ken of our love, Ho - ly, ho - ly, ho - ly, ho - ly.

2 Gra - cious Fa - ther, gra - cious Fa - ther, We're so blest to be Your chil - dren, gra - cious Fa - ther; And we lift our heads be - fore You as a to - ken of our love, Gra - cious Fa - ther, gra - cious Fa - ther.

3 Pre - cious Je - sus, pre - cious Je - sus, We're so glad that You've re - deemed us, pre - cious Je - sus; And we lift our hands be - fore You as a to - ken of our love, Pre - cious Je - sus, pre - cious Je - sus.

4 Ho - ly Spir - it, Ho - ly Spir - it, Come and fill our hearts a - new, Ho - ly Spir - it; And we lift our voice be - fore You as a to - ken of our love, Ho - ly Spir - it, Ho - ly Spir - it.

5 Ho - ly, ho - ly, ho - ly, ho - ly, Ho - ly, ho - ly, Lord God Al - might - y; And we lift our hearts be - fore You as a to - ken of our love, Ho - ly, ho - ly, ho - ly, ho - ly.

6 Hal - le - lu - jah, hal - le - lu - jah, Hal - le - lu - jah, hal - le - lu - jah; And we lift our hearts be - fore You as a to - ken of our love, Hal - le - lu - jah, hal - le - lu - jah.

PRAISE TO GOD

What A Mighty God We Serve!

46

" . . . the Lord is the everlasting God, the Creator of the ends of the earth."
—Isaiah 40:28b

Clara M. Brooks

8.7.8.7.wR.
MIGHTY GOD
Barney E. Warren

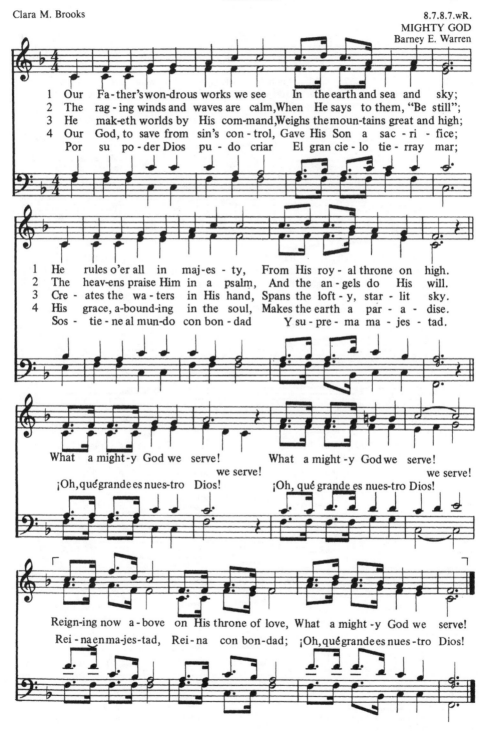

1 Our Fa-ther's won-drous works we see In the earth and sea and sky;
2 The rag-ing winds and waves are calm, When He says to them, "Be still";
3 He mak-eth worlds by His com-mand, Weighs the moun-tains great and high;
4 Our God, to save from sin's con-trol, Gave His Son a sac-ri-fice;
Por su po-der Dios pu-do criar El gran cie-lo tie-rra y mar;

1 He rules o'er all in maj-es-ty, From His roy-al throne on high.
2 The heav-ens praise Him in a psalm, And the an-gels do His will.
3 Cre-ates the wa-ters in His hand, Spans the loft-y, star-lit sky.
4 His grace, a-bound-ing in the soul, Makes the earth a par-a-dise.
Sos-tie-ne al mun-do con bon-dad Y su-pre-ma ma-jes-tad.

What a might-y God we serve! What a might-y God we serve!
we serve! we serve!
¡Oh, qué grande es nues-tro Dios! ¡Oh, qué grande es nues-tro Dios!

Reign-ing now a-bove on His throne of love, What a might-y God we serve!
Rei-na en ma-jes-tad, Rei-na con bon-dad; ¡Oh, qué grande es nues-tro Dios!

PRAISE TO GOD

47 How Great Thou Art

"For you are great and do marvelous deeds; you alone are God."—Psalm 86:10

Stuart K. Hine

11.10.11.10.wR.
O STORE GUD
Stuart K. Hine

1 O Lord my God! when I in awe-some won-der Con-sid-er
2 When through the woods and for-est glades I wan-der And hear the
3 And when I think that God, His Son not spar-ing, Sent Him to
4 When Christ shall come with shout of ac-cla-ma-tion And take me
Se-ñor, mi Dios, al con-tem-plar los cie-los El fir-ma-

1 all the worlds Thy hands have made, I see the stars, I hear the roll-ing
2 birds sing sweet-ly in the trees; When I look down from loft-y moun-tain
3 die, I scarce can take it in; That on the cross, my bur-den glad-ly
4 home, what joy shall fill my heart! Then I shall bow in hum-ble ad-o-
men-to y las es-tre-llas mil Al oif tu voz en los po-ten-tes

1 thun-der, Thy power through-out the u-ni-verse dis-played:
2 gran-deur And hear the brook and feel the gen-tle breeze:
3 bear-ing, He bled and died to take a-way my sin:
4 ra-tion, And there pro-claim, my God, how great Thou art!
true-nos y ver bri-llar al sol en su ce-nit.

Then sings my soul, my Sav-ior God, to Thee: How great Thou
Mi co-ra-zón en-to-na la can-ción: ¡Cuán gran-de es

PRAISE TO GOD

art,   how great Thou art!   Then sings my   soul, my Sav - ior God to
El!   ¡Cuán gran-de es El!   Mi   co - ra - zón en - to - na la   can-

Thee: How great Thou   art,   how great Thou   art!
ción: ¡Cuán gran - de es   El!   ¡Cuan gran - de es   El!

A Prayer for Worship   48

Eternal God, from whom streams every impulse that is beautiful and true,
help us in this hour of worship to take grateful inventory of what sustains us:
    the friendships,
       the shared goals,
          the intimate labors that lace life with meaning.

We thank You for music, and for everything that elevates our spirits above
the smoggy confusions of our time and gives us hope.
Remind us that to every gift there is attached a responsibility,
    to every privilege an obligation.
Therefore, make it our purpose, as it is Yours throughout the universe,
to bring creativity rather than chaos,
    harmony rather than discord,
       talent and appreciation rather than cynicism and apathy.
Arrange our sympathies into your symphony, O Lord, in whom we trust,
    and in whose grace we are never confounded.

Amen.

—Philip Anderson
Used By Permission.

49   Be Still and Know

"Be still, and know that I am God; I will be exalted among the nations, I will be exalted in the earth."—Psalm 46:10

Based on Psalm 46:10, Exodus 15:26

BE STILL AND KNOW
Anonymous

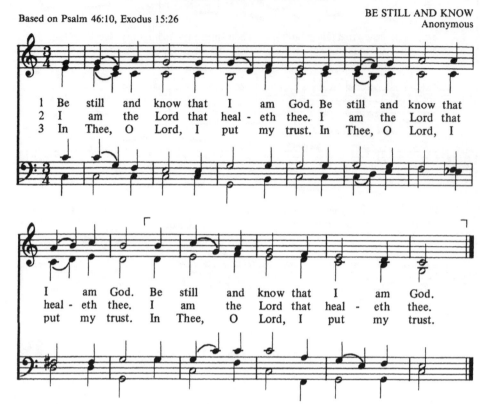

1 Be still and know that I am God. Be still and know that
2 I am the Lord that heal-eth thee. I am the Lord that
3 In Thee, O Lord, I put my trust. In Thee, O Lord, I

I am God. Be still and know that I am God.
heal-eth thee. I am the Lord that heal-eth thee.
put my trust. In Thee, O Lord, I put my trust.

50   In Holy Reverence, Lord

"Let all the earth fear the Lord; let all the people of the world revere him."
—Psalm 33:8

D. Otis Teasley

8.6.8.8.6.
REVERENA
D. Otis Teasley

1 In ho-ly rev-'rence, Lord, we come; Be-fore Your throne this hour,
2 Our lives and all are in Your hands, Our souls, O Lord, re-store;
3 Al-might-y Fa-ther, God of love, Our hopes are clear and bright;

1 To wor - ship at Your hallowed feet, To drink the cup of joy so
2 Your grace has kept us thru the past, Your lov - ing arms have held us
3 We drink of life's e - ter - nal fount And bask on Zi - on's sun-lit

1 sweet, Great God of love and pow'r.
2 fast, And shall for - ev - er - more.
3 mount, Where heav - en seems in sight. A - men.

Father, I Adore You

51

"Dear children, let us not love with words or tongue but with actions and in truth."—1 John 3:18

Terrye Coelho

MARANATHA
Terrye Coelho

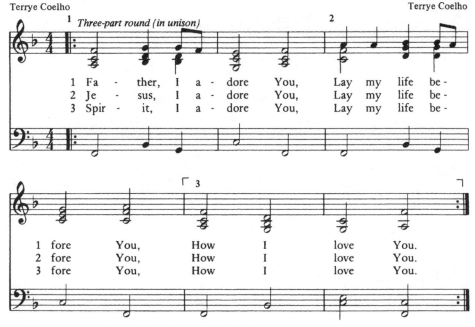

Three-part round (in unison)

1 Fa - ther, I a - dore You, Lay my life be -
2 Je - sus, I a - dore You, Lay my life be -
3 Spir - it, I a - dore You, Lay my life be -

1 fore You, How I love You.
2 fore You, How I love You.
3 fore You, How I love You.

PRAISE TO GOD

52 Ye Servants of God, Your Master Proclaim

"And they cried out in a loud voice: 'Salvation belongs to our God, who sits on the throne, and to the Lamb.'"—Revelation 7:10

10.10.11.11.
LYONS

Charles Wesley

Adapted from Johann Michael Haydn

1 Ye ser-vants of God, your Mas-ter pro-claim,
2 God rul-eth on high, al-might-y to save,
3 "Sal-va-tion to God, who sits on the throne!"
4 Then let us a-dore and give Him His right—

1 And pub-lish a-broad His won-der-ful name;
2 And still He is nigh, His pres-ence we have;
3 Let all cry a-loud and hon-or the Son;
4 All glo-ry and power, all wis-dom and might,

1 The name, all vic-to-rious, of Je-sus ex-tol:
2 The great con-gre-ga-tion His tri-umph shall sing,
3 The prais-es of Je-sus the an-gels pro-claim,
4 All hon-or and bless-ing, with an-gels a-bove,

1 His king-dom is glo-rious, He rules o-ver all.
2 As-crib-ing sal-va-tion to Je-sus, our King.
3 Fall down on their fac-es and wor-ship the Lamb.
4 And thanks nev-er ceas-ing, and in-fi-nite love. A-men.

PRAISE TO CHRIST, THE ETERNAL WORD

Join All the Glorious Names

53

"Therefore God exalted him to the highest place and gave him the name that is above every name."—Philippians 2:9

6.6.6.6.8.8.

DARWALL'S 148TH

Isaac Watts

John Darwall

1. Join all the glo-rious names Of wis-dom, love, and pow'r, That ev-er mor-tals knew, That an-gels ev-er bore: All are too poor to speak His worth, Too poor to set my Sav-ior forth.

2. Great Proph-et of my God, My tongue would bless Thy name: By Thee the joy-ful news Of our sal-va-tion came, The joy-ful news of sins for-giv'n, Of hell sub-dued, and peace with heav'n.

3. Je-sus, my great High Priest, Of-fered His blood and died; My guilt-y con-science seeks No sac-ri-fice be-side: His pow'r-ful blood did once a-tone And now it pleads be-fore the throne.

4. Thou art my Coun-se-lor, My Pat-tern, and my Guide, And Thou my Shep-herd art; O keep me near Thy side, Nor let my feet e'er turn a-stray To wan-der in the crook-ed way.

5. My Sav-ior and my Lord, My Con-qu'ror and my King, Thy scep-ter and Thy sword, Thy reign-ing grace, I sing: Thine is the pow'r; be-hold I sit In will-ing bonds be-neath Thy feet. A-men.

54 How Majestic Is Your Name

"O Lord, our Lord, how majestic is your name in all the earth!"—Psalm 8:1

HOW MAJESTIC
Michael W. Smith

Michael W. Smith

O Lord, our Lord, how ma-jes-tic is Your name in all the earth. O earth. O Lord, we praise Your name. O Lord, we mag-ni-fy Your name: Prince of Peace, Might-y God; O Lord God Al-might - y. O y.

PRAISE TO CHRIST, THE ETERNAL WORD

All Hail the Power of Jesus' Name 55

" . . . and every tongue confess that Jesus Christ is Lord, to the glory of God the Father."—Philippians 2:11

Edward Perronet
John Rippon, alt.

C.M.wR.
CORONATION
Oliver Holden

1 All hail the power of Je - sus' name! Let an - gels pros - trate
2 Ye cho - sen seed of Is - rael's race, Ye ran - somed from the
3 Let ev - ery kin - dred, ev - ery tribe, On this ter - res - trial
4 O that with yon - der sa - cred throng We at His feet may

1 fall; Bring forth the roy - al di - a - dem, And crown Him
2 fall, Hail Him who saves you by His grace, And crown Him
3 ball, To Him all maj - es - ty as - cribe, And crown Him
4 fall! We'll join the ev - er - last - ing song, And crown Him

1 Lord of all; Bring forth the roy - al di - a - dem, And
2 Lord of all; Hail Him who saves you by His grace, And
3 Lord of all; To Him all maj - es - ty as - cribe, And
4 Lord of all; We'll join the ev - er - last - ing song, And

1 crown Him Lord of all!
2 crown Him Lord of all!
3 crown Him Lord of all!
4 crown Him Lord of all! A - men.

PRAISE TO CHRIST, THE ETERNAL WORD

56 Blessed Be the Name

*"Blessed be your glorious name, and may it be exalted above all blessing and
praise."—Nehemiah 9:5c*

C.M.wR.

W. H. Clark
Refrain added by Ralph E. Hudson

BLESSED BE THE NAME
Ralph E. Hudson
Harmonized by William J. Kirkpatrick

1 All praise to Him who reigns a - bove In maj - es - ty su - preme,
2 His name a - bove all names shall stand, Ex - alt - ed more and more,
3 Re - deem - er, Sav - ior, friend of man Once ru - ined by the fall,
4 His name shall be the Coun - sel - or, The might - y Prince of Peace,

1 Who gave His Son from heav'n to die, That He might all re - deem!
2 At God the Fa - ther's own right hand, Where an - gel - hosts a - dore.
3 Thou hast de - vised sal - va - tion's plan, For Thou hast died for all.
4 Of all earth's king-doms con - quer - or, Whose reign shall nev - er cease.

(in a slower tempo)

Bless-ed be the name! Bless-ed be the name! Bless-ed be the name of the Lord!

Bless-ed be the name! Bless-ed be the name! Bless-ed be the name of the Lord!

PRAISE TO CHRIST, THE ETERNAL WORD

Bless the Lord, O My Soul

57

"Praise the Lord, O my soul; all my inmost being, praise his holy name."
—Psalm 103:1

Adapted from Psalm 103:1

HOLY NAME
Traditional

Bless the Lord, O my soul; Bless the Lord, O my soul;

And all that is with - in me, bless His ho - ly name.

PIANO

Bless the Lord, O my soul; Bless the Lord, O my soul;

And all that is with - in me, bless His ho - ly name.

PRAISE TO CHRIST, THE ETERNAL WORD

58 All Hail the Power of Jesus' Name

" . . . and every tongue confess that Jesus Christ is Lord, to the glory of God the Father."—Philippians 2:11

Edward Perronet
John Rippon, alt.

DIADEM
James Ellor

1 All hail the power of Je - sus' name! Let an - gels
2 Ye cho - sen seed of Is - rael's race, Ye ran - somed
3 Let ev - ery kin - dred, ev - ery tribe, On this ter -
4 O that with yon - der sa - cred throng We at His

1 pros - trate fall, Let an - gels pros - trate fall; Bring forth the
2 from the fall, Ye ran - somed from the fall; Hail Him who
3 res - trial ball, On this ter - res - trial ball, To Him all
4 feet may fall, We at His feet may fall! We'll join the

1 roy - al di - a - dem,
2 saves you by His grace, And crown
3 maj - es - ty as - cribe,
4 ev - er - last - ing song, And crown Him, crown Him,

Him, crown Him, crown Him,
crown Him, crown Him, crown Him, crown Him,

crown

PRAISE TO CHRIST, THE ETERNAL WORD

crown Him, And   crown   Him Lord   of   all.   A - men.

Him,

Bless His Holy Name

59

"Praise the Lord, O my soul; all my inmost being, praise his holy name."
—Psalm 103:1

Andraé Crouch

BLESS HIS HOLY NAME
Andraé Crouch

Bless the Lord,   O my soul,   and   all   that is   with - in me, Bless His

Fine

ho - ly   name.   He has done great   things,   He has done great

D.C. al Fine

things,   He has done great   things, Bless His   ho - ly   name.

PRAISE TO CHRIST, THE ETERNAL WORD

60 I Will Bless the Lord

"I will extol the Lord at all times; his praise will be on my lips."—Psalm 34:1b

Shirley M. K. Berkeley

HIS PRAISE
Shirley M. K. Berkeley

I will bless the Lord at all times; His praise shall con-tin-ual-ly be in my mouth. I will bless the Lord at all times; His praise shall con-tin-ual-ly be in my mouth. In my mouth, in my mouth; His praise shall con-tin-ual-ly be in my mouth. In my mouth, in my mouth; His praise shall con-tin-ual-ly be in my mouth.

PRAISE TO CHRIST, THE ETERNAL WORD

Bless the Lord, O my soul; and all that is
within me, bless His holy name!

*Bless the Lord, O my soul, and forget not all
His benefits,*

Who forgives all your iniquity, who heals all
your diseases,

*Who redeems your life from the Pit, who
crowns you with steadfast love and mercy,*

Who satisfies you with good as long as you
live so that your youth is renewed like the
eagle's.

*The Lord works vindication and justice for
all who are oppressed.*

He made known His ways to Moses, His acts
to the people of Israel.

*The Lord is merciful and gracious, slow to
anger and abounding in steadfast love. He
will not always chide, nor will He keep His
anger forever.*

He does not deal with us according to our sins,
nor requite us according to our iniquities.

*For as the heavens are high above the earth,
so great is His steadfast love toward those
who fear Him;*

As far as the east is from the west, so far does
He remove our transgressions from us.

*As a father pities his children, so the Lord
pities those who fear Him. For He knows our
frame; He remembers that we are dust.*

As for man, his days are like grass; he
flourishes like a flower of the field; for the
wind passes over it; and it is gone, and its
place knows it no more.

*But the steadfast love of the Lord is from
everlasting to everlasting upon those who
fear Him, and His righteousness to children's
children.*

—*From Psalm 103*

PRAISE TO CHRIST, THE ETERNAL WORD

62 That Beautiful Name

"She will give birth to a son, and you are to give him the name Jesus, because he will save his people from their sins."—Matthew 1:21

Jean Perry

BEAUTIFUL NAME
Mabel Johnston Camp

1 I know of a name, A beau-ti-ful name, That an-gels brought
2 I know of a name, A beau-ti-ful name, That un-to a
3 The One of that name My Sav-ior be-came, My Sav-ior of
4 I love that blest name, That won-der-ful name, Made high-er than

1 down to earth; They whis-pered it low, One night long a-go,
2 Babe was giv'n; The stars glit-tered bright Through-out that glad night,
3 Cal-va-ry; My sins nailed Him there, My bur-dens to bear,
4 all in heav'n; 'Twas whis-pered, I know, In my heart long a-go

1 To a maid-en of low-ly birth.
2 And an-gels praised God in heav'n. That beau-ti-ful name, That
3 He suf-fered all this for me.
4 To Je-sus my life I've giv'n.

beau-ti-ful name From sin has pow'r to free us! That beau-ti-ful

name, That won-der-ful name, That match-less name is Je-sus!

PRAISE TO CHRIST, THE ETERNAL WORD

Jesus Is the Sweetest Name
I Know

63

"So he became as much superior to the angels as the name he has inherited is superior to theirs."—Hebrews 1:4

Lela Long

Lela Long

1 There have been names that I have loved to hear, But nev-er has there
2 There is no name in earth or heav'n a-bove, That we should give such
3 And some-day I shall see Him face to face To thank and praise Him

1 been a name so dear To this heart of mine, as the name di-vine, The
2 hon-or and such love As the bless-ed name; let us all ac-claim That
3 for His won-drous grace Which He gave to me when He made me free; The

1 pre-cious, pre-cious name of Je-sus.
2 wondrous, glorious name of Je-sus.
3 bless-ed Son of God called Je-sus.

Je-sus is the sweet-est name I

know, And He's just the same as His love-ly name, And that's the rea-son

rall.

why I love Him so; O Je-sus is the sweet-est name I know.

PRAISE TO CHRIST, THE ETERNAL WORD

64 Magnify Him

"My soul praises the Lord and my spirit rejoices in God my Savior . . . "
—Luke 1:46–47

Randy Vader
Kirk Talley

MAGNIFY
Kirk Talley

Mag - ni - fy Him, mag - ni - fy Him. Lift Him up, bless the name of the Lord. Glo - ri - fy Him, Glo - ri - fy Him. Wor - ship Him, praise the name of the Lord.

PRAISE TO CHRIST, THE ETERNAL WORD

There's Something About That Name

65

" . . . and gave Him the name that is above every name . . . "—Philippians 2:9b

Gloria Gaither
William J. Gaither

THAT NAME
William J. Gaither

Je - sus, Je - sus, Je - sus! There's just some-thing a - bout that name! Mas-ter, Sav-ior, Je - sus! Like the fra - grance af - ter the rain; Je - sus, Je - sus, Je - sus! Let all heav-en and earth pro - claim: Kings and king-doms will all pass a - way, But there's some-thing a - bout that name!

PRAISE TO CHRIST, THE ETERNAL WORD

66 His Name Is Wonderful

" . . . and he will be called Wonderful Counselor, Mighty God, Everlasting Father, Prince of Peace."—Isaiah 9:6b

Audrey Mieir

MIEIR
Audrey Mieir

His name is Won-der-ful, His name is Won-der-ful, His name is

Won-der-ful, Je - sus, my Lord; He is the might-y King,

Mas-ter of ev-ery-thing, His name is Won-der-ful, Je-sus, my Lord.

He's the great Shep-herd, the Rock of all a - ges, Al-might-y

God is He; Bow down be - fore Him, Love and a -

PRAISE TO CHRIST, THE ETERNAL WORD

dore Him, His name is Won-der-ful, Je - sus, my Lord.

Jesus, Name Above All Names 67

"So let Your name be magnified forever . . ."—II Samuel 7:26

Naida Hearn

HEARN
Naida Hearn

Unison

Je - sus, name a - bove all names, beau - ti - ful Sav - ior,

glo - ri - ous Lord. Em - man - u - el, God is

with us, bless - ed Re - deem - er, Liv - ing Word.

PRAISE TO CHRIST, THE ETERNAL WORD

68 Jesus! What a Friend for Sinners

*" . . . while we wait for the blessed hope—the glorious appearing of our great
God and Savior, Jesus Christ, who gave himself for us to redeem us from all
wickedness and to purify for himself a people that are his very own, eager to do
what is good."—Titus 2:13-14*

8.7.8.7.D.
HYFRYDOL

J. Wilbur Chapman

Rowland H. Prichard
Arranged by Robert Harkness

1 Je - sus! what a friend for sin - ners! Je - sus! lov - er of my soul!
2 Je - sus! what a strength in weak - ness! Let me hide my - self in Him;
3 Je - sus! what a help in sor - row! While the bil - lows o'er me roll;
4 Je - sus! what a guide and keep - er! While the tem - pest still is high;
5 Je - sus! I do now re - ceive Him, More than all in Him I find;

1 Friends may fail me, foes as - sail me, He, my Sav - ior, makes me whole.
2 Tempt - ed, tried, and some - times fail - ing, He, my strength, my vic - tory wins.
3 E - ven when my heart is break - ing, He, my com - fort, helps my soul.
4 Storms a - bout me, night o'er - takes me, He, my pi - lot, hears my cry.
5 He hath grant - ed me for - give - ness, I am His, and He is mine.

Hal - le - lu - jah! what a Sav - ior! Hal - le - lu - jah! what a friend!

Sav - ing, help - ing, keep - ing, lov - ing, He is with me to the end.

PRAISE TO CHRIST, THE ETERNAL WORD

Lift High the Cross

"But I, when I am lifted up from the earth, will draw all men to myself."
—John 12:32

George Kitchin
Michael Newbolt

10.10.10.10.
CRUCIFER
Sydney H. Nicholson

Lift high the cross, the love of Christ pro - claim, Till
all the world a - dore His sa - cred name.

1 Come, Chris - tians, fol - low where our Sav - ior trod, Our
2 Led on their way by this tri - um - phant sign, The
3 O Lord, once lift - ed on the glo - rious tree, As
4 Set up Thy throne, that earth's de - spair may cease Be -
5 For Thy blest cross which doth for all a - tone, Cre -

1 King vic - to - rious, Christ, the Son of God.
2 hosts of God in u - ni - ty com - bine.
3 Thou hast prom - ised, draw the world to Thee.
4 neath the shad - ow of its heal - ing peace.
5 a - tion's prais - es rise be - fore Thy throne.

PRAISE TO CHRIST, THE ETERNAL WORD

70 Let's Just Praise the Lord

"Lift up your hands in the sanctuary and praise the Lord."—Psalm 134:2

Gloria Gaither
William J. Gaither

LET'S JUST PRAISE THE LORD
William J. Gaither

Let's just praise the Lord! Praise the Lord! Let's just lift our hands* to

heav-en and praise the Lord; Let's just praise the Lord!

Fine

Praise the Lord! Let's just lift our hands* to heav-en and praise the Lord!

1 O we thank You for Your kind-ness, we thank You for Your
2 Just the pre-cious name of Je-sus is worth-y of our

1 love, We have been in heaven-ly plac-es, felt bless-ings from a-
2 praise, Let us bow our knees be-fore Him, our hands to heav-en

*Alternate lyrics, "voices", "hearts"

PRAISE TO CHRIST, THE ETERNAL WORD

1 bove; We've been shar - ing all the good things the fam - ily can af -
2 raise; When He comes in clouds of glo - ry, with Him we'll ev - er

D.C.

1 ford, Let's just turn our praise toward heav - en and praise the Lord.
2 reign, so let's lift our hap - py voic - es, and praise His name.

Trusting in the Lord 71

LEADER: Rejoice! The Lord is here. He loves us, forgives us, and
wants to set us free of care.

PEOPLE: *We come to worship You, Lord, and experience Your peace*
which releases us from the burden of cares so that we can
care profoundly about Your guidance in our lives and
people who need Your love through us.

LEADER: Trust in the Lord with all your heart, and lean not on your
own understanding; in all your ways acknowledge Him, and
He shall direct your paths. (*Proverbs 3:5–6*)

PEOPLE: *Lord, we need that above all else. Here are our minds,*
think Your thoughts through them. Here are our wills ready
to be guided to do Your will. Here are our emotions open
to receive and express Your love. Here are our lives—make
us carefree but not careless, responsive to You so that we
can be responsible in being Your faithful disciples. May this
time of worship heal our worries so that we can be free to
live truly joyful lives. In the power of the indwelling Christ,
Amen.

PRAISE TO CHRIST, THE ETERNAL WORD

72 Jesus Christ Is the Lord

" . . . and every tongue confess that Jesus Christ is Lord, to the glory of God the Father."—Philippians 2:11

C.M.wR.

Frederick G. Shackleton
Based on Philippians 2:9-11

JESUS CHRIST IS THE LORD
Frederick G. Shackleton

1 We sing of Him whose won-drous name Fills all our hearts with
2 Our Lord through all the com-ing years A faith-ful guide will

1 song; Our high - est praise to Him we'll raise Through-out all a - ges long.
2 be, Un - til the day of heav - en's dawn When we His glo - ry see.

Je - sus Christ is the Lord   To the glo - ry of God the   Fa - ther.
Our Lord   to the glo - ry of God;

Je - sus Christ is the Lord,   Let ev - 'ry tongue pro - claim.
Our Lord   pro - claim.

PRAISE TO CHRIST, THE ETERNAL WORD

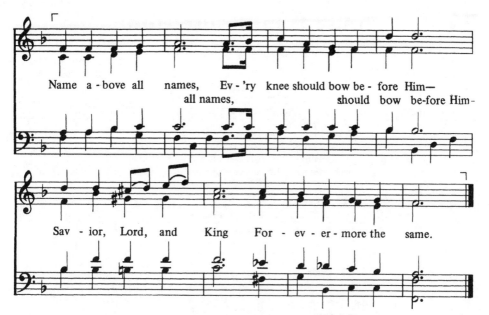

Name a-bove all names, Ev-'ry knee should bow be-fore Him—
all names, should bow be-fore Him—

Sav-ior, Lord, and King For-ev-er-more the same.

Praise the Name of Jesus 73

"You are . . . . His own special people, that you may proclaim the praises of Him who called you out of darkness."—I Peter 2:9

Based on Psalm 18:1
Roy Hicks, Jr.

HICKS
Roy Hicks, Jr.

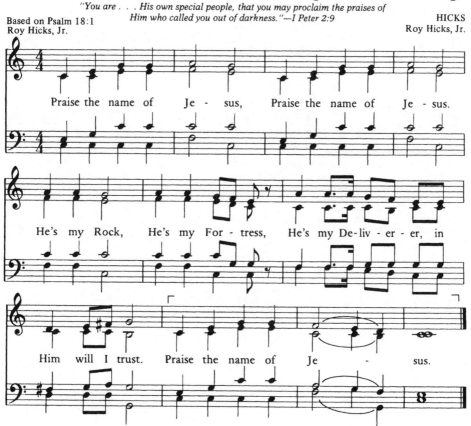

Praise the name of Je - sus, Praise the name of Je - sus.

He's my Rock, He's my For - tress, He's my De - liv - er - er, in

Him will I trust. Praise the name of Je - sus.

PRAISE TO CHRIST, THE ETERNAL WORD

74 Praise Him! Praise Him!

"Then all mankind will know that I, the Lord, am your Savior, your Redeemer, the Mighty One of Jacob."—Isaiah 49:26b

Fanny J. Crosby

JOYFUL SONG
Chester G. Allen

1 Praise Him! praise Him! Je-sus our bless-ed Re-deem-er! Sing, O
2 Praise Him! praise Him! Je-sus our bless-ed Re-deem-er! For our
3 Praise Him! praise Him! Je-sus our bless-ed Re-deem-er! Heav'n-ly

1 earth—His won-der-ful love pro-claim! Hail Him! hail Him!
2 sins He suf-fered and bled and died; He our Rock, our
3 por-tals loud with ho-san-nas ring! Je-sus, Sav-ior,

1 high-est arch-an-gels in glo-ry; Strength and hon-or give to His ho-ly
2 hope of e-ter-nal sal-va-tion, Hail Him! hail Him! Je-sus the Cru-ci-
3 reign-eth for-ev-er and ev-er, Crown Him! crown Him! Prophet and Priest and

1 name! Like a shep-herd Je-sus will guard His chil-dren;
2 fied. Sound His prais-es— Je-sus who bore our sor-rows;
3 King! Christ is com-ing, o-ver the world vic-to-rious;

PRAISE TO CHRIST, THE ETERNAL WORD

1 In His arms He car-ries them all day long.
2 Love, un - bound - ed, won-der-ful, deep and strong!
3 Pow'r and glo - ry un-to the Lord be - long.

Praise Him! praise Him! tell of His ex-cel-lent great-ness!

Praise Him! praise Him! ev-er in joy-ful song!

Praise the Savior, Ye Who Know Him
75

Thomas Kelly
Bryan Jeffery Leech, alt. stanza 4

"Let the redeemed of the Lord say so . . ."—Psalm 107:2a

8.8.8.5.
ACCLAIM
German Melody

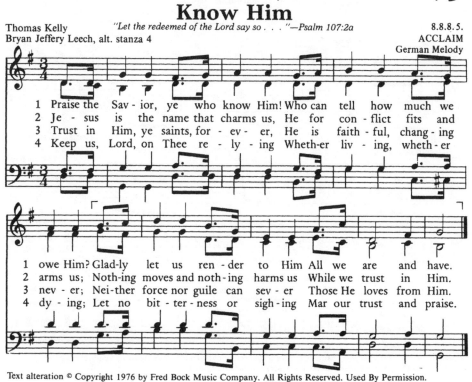

1 Praise the Sav - ior, ye who know Him! Who can tell how much we
2 Je - sus is the name that charms us, He for con - flict fits and
3 Trust in Him, ye saints, for - ev - er, He is faith - ful, chang - ing
4 Keep us, Lord, on Thee re - ly - ing Wheth-er liv - ing, wheth-er

1 owe Him? Glad-ly let us ren - der to Him All we are and have.
2 arms us; Noth-ing moves and noth-ing harms us While we trust in Him.
3 nev - er; Nei-ther force nor guile can sev - er Those He loves from Him.
4 dy - ing; Let no bit - ter-ness or sigh-ing Mar our trust and praise.

PRAISE TO CHRIST, THE ETERNAL WORD

76 Great Is the Lord

"Great is the Lord and most worthy of praise; his greatness no one can fathom."
—Psalm 145:3

Michael W. Smith
Deborah D. Smith

GREAT IS THE LORD
Michael W. Smith
Deborah D. Smith

Great is the Lord, He is ho-ly and just; By His pow-er we trust in His love. Great is the Lord, He is faith-ful and true; By His mer-cy He proves He is love.

1, 2. Great is the Lord and wor-thy of glo-ry!
(D.S.) Great are You, Lord, and wor-thy of glo-ry!

Great is the Lord and wor-thy of praise.
Great are You, Lord, and wor-thy of praise.
Great is the Lord; now
Great are You, Lord; I

lift up your voice, Now lift up your voice: Great is the
lift up my voice, I lift up my voice: Great are You,

PRAISE TO CHRIST, THE ETERNAL WORD

Lord!   Great   is the Lord!   Lord!
Lord!   *Great*   *are You, Lord!*

O for a Thousand Tongues to Sing

77

"My tongue will speak of your righteousness and of your praises all day long."
—Psalm 35:28

Charles Wesley

C.M.
AZMON
Carl G. Gläser
Descant by Eugene Butler

Descant for last stanza

5 O hear His praise,   Your loos-ened tongues em-ploy;

1 O   for a thou-sand tongues to sing My great Re-deem-er's   praise,
2 My gra-cious Mas-ter   and my God, As-sist me to   pro-claim,
3 Je-sus! the name that charms our fears, That bids our sor-rows   cease,
4 He breaks the power of   can-celled sin, He   sets the pris-oner free;
5 Hear Him, ye deaf; His   praise, ye dumb, Your loos-ened tongues em-ploy;

5 Ye blind, be-hold Him come; And   leap   for joy! A-men.

1 The glo-ries of my   God and King, The   tri-umphs of His grace!
2 To   spread through all the earth a-broad The   hon-ors of Thy name.
3 'Tis mu-sic in   the sin-ners' ears, 'Tis life and health and peace.
4 His blood can make the foul-est clean, His   blood a-vailed for me.
5 Ye blind, be-hold your Sav-ior come; And   leap, ye lame, for joy! A-men.

PRAISE TO CHRIST, THE ETERNAL WORD

78 Come, Christians, Join to Sing

"Speak to one another with psalms, hymns and spiritual songs. Sing and make music in your heart to the Lord, always giving thanks to God the Father for everything, in the name of our Lord Jesus Christ."—Ephesians 5:19-20

6.6.6.6.D.
MADRID
Traditional

Christian Henry Bateman

Harmonization by David Evans

1 Come, Chris-tians, join to sing; Al - le - lu - ia! A - men!
2 Come, lift your hearts on high; Al - le - lu - ia! A - men!
3 Praise yet our Christ a - gain; Al - le - lu - ia! A - men!

1 Loud praise to Christ our King; Al - le - lu - ia! A - men!
2 Let prais - es fill the sky; Al - le - lu - ia! A - men!
3 Life shall not end the strain; Al - le - lu - ia! A - men!

1 Let all, with heart and voice, Be - fore His throne re - joice;
2 He is our Guide and Friend; To us He'll con - de - scend;
3 On heav - en's bliss - ful shore His good - ness we'll a - dore,

1 Praise is His gra - cious choice: Al - le - lu - ia! A - men!
2 His love shall nev - er end: Al - le - lu - ia! A - men!
3 Sing - ing for - ev - er - more, "Al - le - lu - ia! A - men!" A-men.

PRAISE TO CHRIST, THE ETERNAL WORD

Everybody Sing Praise to the Lord 79

"... I will exalt thee, I will praise thy name; for thou hast done wonderful things ..." —Isaiah 25:1b,c (RSV)

John W. Peterson

EVERYBODY SING
John W. Peterson

PRAISE TO CHRIST, THE ETERNAL WORD

80 I Will Praise Him, Hallelujah!

"Let us rejoice and be glad and give Him glory!"—Revelation 19:7a

PRAISE HIM, HALLELUJAH

D. Otis Teasley

D. Otis Teasley

1 O I praise the Lord who bought me, hal - le - lu - jah!
2 I will praise Him for sal - va - tion, hal - le - lu - jah!
3 O I'll nev - er cease to praise Him, hal - le - lu - jah!
4 I will praise Him for the strength He dai - ly gives me,

1 I'm a hap - py pil - grim bound for glo - ry land;
2 Rich - est treas - ure hu - man spir - its ev - er found;
3 For He gives me peace a - bound - ing ev - 'ry day;
4 I am run - ning now to gain that heav'n - ly prize;

1 I am sing - ing and I hope to sing for - ev - er
2 Once I wan - dered far a - way, was sad and lone - ly,
3 He re - deemed me from my sins and ful - ly cleansed me,
4 Soon with joy I'll reach the goal of life im - mor - tal

1 When be - fore His throne e - ter - nal I shall stand.
2 But I'm dwell - ing now where pleas - ures e'er a - bound.
3 And I find His ser - vice sweet - er all the way.
4 And go sweep - ing thru the gates of par - a - dise.

PRAISE TO CHRIST, THE ETERNAL WORD

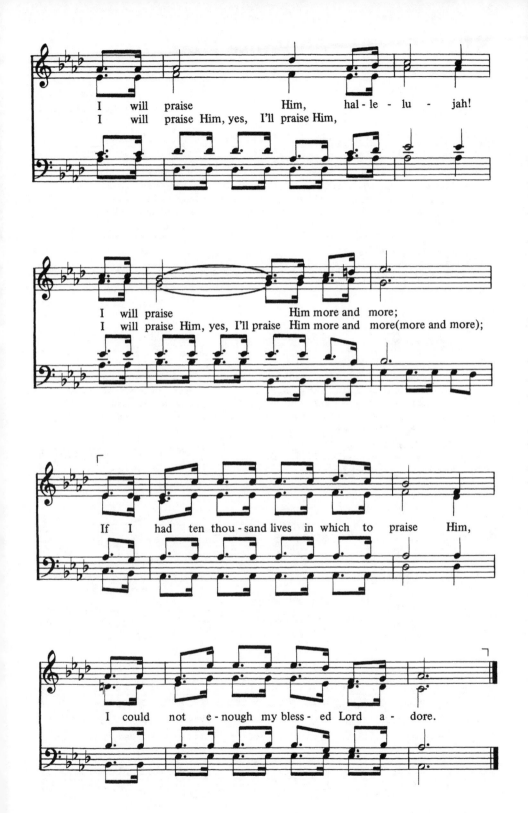

PRAISE TO CHRIST, THE ETERNAL WORD

81 I Will Praise Him!

"To him who loves us and has freed us from our sins by his blood . . . to him be glory and power for ever and ever! Amen."—Revelation 1:5b, 6

8.7.8.7.wR.

Margaret J. Harris

I WILL PRAISE HIM
Margaret J. Harris

1 When I saw the cleans-ing foun-tain O - pen wide for all my sin,
2 Tho the way seems straight and nar-row, All I claimed was swept a -way;
3 Bless-ed be the name of Je - sus! I'm so glad He took me in;
4 Glo - ry, glo - ry to the Fa - ther! Glo - ry, glo - ry to the Son!

1 I o-beyed the Spir - it's call - ing When He said, "Will you be clean?"
2 My am - bi - tions, plans and wish-es At my feet in dis - ar - ray.
3 He's for - giv - en my trans - gres-sions, . He has cleansed my heart from sin.
4 Glo - ry, glo - ry to the Spir - it! Glo - ry to the Three in One!

I will praise Him! I will praise Him! Praise the Lamb for sin-ners slain;

Give Him glo-ry, all ye peo-ple, For His blood can wash a-way each stain.

PRAISE TO CHRIST, THE ETERNAL WORD

We'll Praise the Lord

"For we cannot help speaking about what we have seen and heard."—Acts 4:20

D. Otis Teasley

WE'LL PRAISE THE LORD
D. Otis Teasley

1 We'll praise the Lord for sins for-giv-en, Praise Him ev-er-more;
2 We'll praise the Lord for full sal-va-tion, Hearts made pure and free;
3 We'll praise the Lord that death's dark val-ley Is no long-er drear;

1 Till earth has passed a-way for-ev-er, Christ we will a-dore.
2 We'll praise Him for a blest in-fill-ing, And for vic-to-ry.
3 The light of Love dis-pels the shad-ows, Drives a-way our fear.

We'll tell the sto-ry, And give God glo-ry;
We'll tell the sto-ry all our days, And give God glo-ry, thanks and praise;

For He has saved us by His blood, And we will sing and praise the Lord;
For He has saved us, And we will praise Him;

When like a scroll the sky has van-ished, Still we'll praise the Lord.

PRAISE TO CHRIST, THE ETERNAL WORD

83 Once Again We Come

"I rejoiced with those who said to me, 'Let us go to the house of the Lord.' "
—Psalm 122:1

ONCE AGAIN WE COME

Charles W. Naylor

Charles W. Naylor

1 Once a - gain we come to the house of God, To u - nite in
2 In the days gone by Thou hast been our stay, Thou hast led us
3 May our hearts, O Lord, e'er u - nit - ed be In true fel - low -
4 May our prayers as - cend as an in - cense sweet, And our praise ac -

1 songs of praise; To ex - tol with joy our Re - deem - er's name
2 safe - ly on To the bless - ed light of the pres - ent day,
3 ship and love; May Thy will be done by us here on earth,
4 cept - ed be, As in grat - i - tude all our hearts o'er - flow

1 And to tell His works and ways.
2 Where the dark - ness now is gone.
3 As by an - gel hosts a - bove.
4 In a trib - ute un - to Thee.

To Thy house, O Lord, with re -

joic - ing we come, For we know that we are Thine; We will wor - ship

PRAISE TO CHRIST, THE ETERNAL WORD

Thee in the Bi-ble way,* As the even-ing light doth shine. A-men.

*Optional text: We will seek Thy will divine

A Perfect Heart

84

"I will give them an undivided heart and put a new spirit in them; I will remove from them their heart of stone and give them a heart of flesh."—Ezekiel 11:19

Dony McGuire
Reba Rambo

A PERFECT HEART
Dony McGuire
Reba Rambo

Bless the Lord (bless the Lord) who reigns in beau-ty; Bless the Lord (bless the Lord)

who reigns in wis-dom and with pow'r. Bless the Lord (bless the Lord)

who reigns my life with so much love, He can make a per-fect heart.

PRAISE TO CHRIST, THE ETERNAL WORD

85 Majesty

"Yours, O Lord, is the greatness and the power and the glory and the majesty and the splendor, for everything in heaven and earth is yours."
—I Chronicles 29:11

Jack Hayford

MAJESTY
Jack Hayford

Maj - es - ty, wor - ship His maj - es - ty. Un - to
Ma - jes - tad, a-do-rad - á su ma - jes - tad, á Je -

Je - sus be all glo - ry, pow-er and praise.
sús se - a glo-ria, hon-ray lo - or.

Maj - es - ty, king-dom au - thor - i - ty flow from His
Ma - jes - tad, Rei-no y au - tor - i - dad flu - yen del

throne un - to His own, His an - them raise. So ex -
tro-no ha - cia su pue-blo á el can - tad. Ex - al -

PRAISE TO CHRIST, THE ETERNAL WORD

PRAISE TO CHRIST, THE ETERNAL WORD

86 *God Is for Us*

LEADER: What can we ever say to such wonderful things as these?

PEOPLE: *If God is on our side, who can ever be against us?*

LEADER: Since He did not spare even His own Son for us but gave Him up for us all, won't He also surely give us everything else? Who dares accuse us whom God has chosen for His own? Will God?

PEOPLE: *No! He is the one who has forgiven us and given us right standing with Himself.*

LEADER: Who then will condemn us? Will Christ?

PEOPLE: *No! For He is the one who died for us and came back to life again for us and is sitting at the place of highest honor next to God, pleading for us there in Heaven.*

LEADER: Who then can ever keep Christ's love from us? When we have trouble or calamity, when we are hunted down or destroyed, is it because He doesn't love us anymore? And if we are hungry, or penniless, or in danger, or threatened with death, has God deserted us?

PEOPLE: *No, for the Scriptures tell us that for His sake we must be ready to face death at every moment of the day—we are like sheep awaiting slaughter; but despite all this, the overwhelming victory is ours through Christ who loved us enough to die for us.*

ALL: *For I am convinced that nothing can ever separate us from His love. Death can't, and life can't. The angels won't, and all the powers of hell itself cannot keep God's love away! Our fears for today, our worries about tomorrow, or where we are—high above the sky, or in the deepest ocean—nothing will ever be able to separate us from the love of God demonstrated by our Lord Jesus Christ when He died for us.*

—Romans 8:31–39 (TLB)

When Morning Gilds the Skies 87

"They were also to stand every morning to thank and praise the Lord."
—1 Chronicles 23:30a

6.6.6.6.6.6.

German, 18th century
Tr. by Edward Caswall

LAUDES DOMINI
Joseph Barnby

1 When morn-ing gilds the skies, My heart a - wak - ing
2 Does sad - ness fill my mind? A sol - ace here I
3 The night be - comes as day When from the heart we
4 To God, the Word on High, the hosts of an - gels
5 Be this, while life is mine, My can - ti - cle di -

1 cries, "May Je - sus Christ be praised!" A -
2 find, "May Je - sus Christ be praised!" Or
3 say, "May Je - sus Christ be praised!" The
4 cry, "May Je - sus Christ be praised!" Let
5 vine, "May Je - sus Christ be praised!" Be

1 like at work and prayer To Je - sus I re -
2 fades my earth - ly bliss? My com - fort still is
3 powers of dark - ness fear When this sweet chant they
4 mor - tals, too, up - raise, their voice in hymns of
5 this th'e - ter - nal song Through all the a - ges

1 pair, "May Je - sus Christ be praised!"
2 this, "May Je - sus Christ be praised!"
3 hear, "May Je - sus Christ be praised!"
4 praise: "May Je - sus Christ be praised!"
5 long, "May Je - sus Christ be praised!" A - men.

PRAISE TO CHRIST, THE ETERNAL WORD

88 I Will Call Upon the Lord

"I call to the Lord, who is worthy of praise, and I am saved from my enemies."
—Psalm 18:3

Michael O'Shields

O'SHIELDS
Michael O'Shields

Optional descant

I will call up-on the Lord

Unison

I will call up-on the Lord who is wor-thy to be

who is wor-thy to be praised. So shall I be

praised. So shall I be saved from my en - e - mies.

saved from my en-e-mies. I will call up-on the Lord. Lord. The

I will call up-on the Lord. Lord. The

Harmony

Lord liv - eth, and bless-ed be the Rock, and let the God of my sal-va-tion be ex-

PRAISE TO CHRIST, THE ETERNAL WORD

alt - ed. The Lord liv-eth, and bless-ed be the Rock, and let the God

of my sal - va-tion be ex - alt - ed. The ed.

Jesus Shall Reign

89

"He will rule from sea to sea and from the River to the ends of the earth."
—Psalm 72:8

L.M.

Based on Psalm 72
Isaac Watts

DUKE STREET
John Hatton

1 Je - sus shall reign wher - e'er the sun Does His suc -
2 To Him shall end - less prayer be made, And end - less
3 Peo - ple and realms of ev - ery tongue Dwell on His
4 Let ev - ery crea - ture rise and bring His grate - ful

1 ces - sive jour - neys run, His king-dom spread from
2 prais - es crown His head; His name like sweet per -
3 love with sweet - est song; And in - fant voic - es
4 hon - ors to our King; An - gels de - scend with

1 shore to shore, 'Til moons shall wax and wane no more.
2 fume shall rise With ev - ery morn - ing sac - ri - fice.
3 shall pro - claim Their ear - ly bless - ings on His name.
4 songs a - gain, And earth re - peat the loud "A - men!"

90 Rejoice, the Lord Is King!

"Rejoice in the Lord always. I will say it again: Rejoice!"—Philippians 4:4

6.6.6.6.8.8.

Based on Philippians 4:4
Charles Wesley

DARWALL'S 148TH
John Darwall

1 Re - joice, the Lord is King! Your Lord and King a - dore!
2 The Lord, our Sav - ior, reigns, The God of truth and love;
3 His king - dom can - not fail, He rules o'er earth and heaven;
4 Re - joice in glo - rious hope! Our Lord the Judge, shall come

1 Re - joice, give thanks, and sing, And tri - umph ev - er -
2 When He had purged our stains, He took His seat a -
3 The keys of death and hell Are to our Je - sus
4 And take His serv - ants up To their e - ter - nal

1 more:
2 bove:
3 given:
4 home:

Lift up your heart, lift up your voice! Re -

joice, a - gain I say, re - joice!

PRAISE TO CHRIST, THE ETERNAL WORD

Lamb of God

"The next day John saw Jesus coming toward him and said, 'Look, the Lamb of God, who takes away the sin of the world!' "—John 1:29

Twila Paris

8.8.8.8.wR
LAMB OF GOD
Twila Paris

1 Your on-ly Son no sin to hide, But You have sent Him from Your
2 Your gift of love they cru-ci-fied, They laughed and scorned Him as He
3 I was so lost I should have died, But You have brought me to Your

1 side To walk up-on this guilt-y sod And to be-
2 died, The hum-ble King they named a fraud And sac-ri-
3 side To be led by Your staff and rod, And to be

1 come the Lamb of God.
2 ficed the Lamb of God. O Lamb of God, sweet Lamb of
3 called a lamb of God.

God, I love the ho-ly Lamb of God. O wash me in His pre-cious

blood, My Je-sus Christ, the Lamb of God.
(3) till I am just a lamb of God.

PRAISE TO CHRIST, THE ETERNAL WORD

92 We Will Glorify

" 'I am the Alpha and the Omega,' says the Lord God, 'who is, and who was, and who is to come, the Almighty.' "—Revelation 1:8

9.7.9.6.

Twila Paris

WE WILL GLORIFY
Twila Paris

1 We will glo-ri-fy the King of kings, we will glo-ri-fy the Lamb;
2 Lord Je-ho-vah reigns in maj-es-ty, we will bow be-fore His throne;
3 He is Lord of heav-en, Lord of earth, He is Lord of all who live;

[1,2. 3.
D.C. twice

1 We will glo-ri-fy the Lord of lords, who is the great I Am.
2 We will wor-ship Him in right-eous-ness, we will wor-ship Him a-lone.
3 He is Lord a-bove the u-ni-verse, all praise to Him we give.

4 Hal-le-lu-jah to the King of Kings, hal-le-lu-jah to the Lamb;

4 Hal-le-lu-jah to the Lord of lords, who is the great I Am.

PRAISE TO CHRIST, THE ETERNAL WORD

Holy Ground

93

*" 'Do not come any closer,' God said. 'Take off your sandals, for the place
where you are standing is holy ground.' "—Exodus 3:5*

Geron Davis

HOLY GROUND
Geron Davis

We are stand-ing on ho-ly ground
and I know that there are an-gels all a-round;
Let us praise Je-sus now. We are
stand-ing in His pres-ence on ho-ly ground.
ho-ly ground.

PRAISE TO CHRIST, THE ETERNAL WORD

94 Lamb of Glory

"The next day John saw Jesus coming toward him and said, 'Look, the Lamb of God, who takes away the sin of the world!' "—John 1:29

7.8.7.8.wR.
LAMB OF GLORY

Greg Nelson
Phill McHugh

Greg Nelson
Phill McHugh

1 Hear the sto - ry from God's Word That kings and priests and
2 On the cross God loved the world While all the pow'rs of

1 pro - phets heard; There would be a sac - ri - fice And
2 hell were hurled; No one there could un - der - stand The

rit.   *a tempo*

1 blood would flow to pay sin's price. Pre - cious Lamb of
2 One they saw was Christ the Lamb.

glo - ry, Love's most won - drous sto - ry.

Heart of God's re - demp - tion of man; Wor - ship the Lamb of glo - ry.

PRAISE TO CHRIST, THE ETERNAL WORD

I Love You, Lord

95

" . . . the man who loves God is known by God."—I Corinthians 8:3

Laurie Klein

I LOVE YOU, LORD
Laurie Klein

I love You, Lord, and I lift my voice to wor - ship You; O my soul, re - joice! Take joy, my King, in what You hear: May it be a sweet, sweet sound in Your ear.

Lord, We Praise You

96

"I will praise the Lord all my life; I will sing praise to my God as long as I live."—Psalm 146:2

Otis Skillings

LORD, WE PRAISE YOU
Otis Skillings

1 Lord, we praise You, Lord, we praise You,
2 Lord, we thank You, Lord, we thank You,
3 Lord, we love You, Lord, we love You,

1 Lord, we praise You, We praise You, Lord!
2 Lord, we thank You, We thank You, Lord!
3 Lord, we love You, We love You, Lord!

PRAISE TO CHRIST, THE ETERNAL WORD

97 Alleluia, Praise the Lamb!

" . . . to him who sits on the throne and to the Lamb be praise and honor and glory and power, for ever and ever!"—Revelation 5:13b

Pamela Starr Thum

PRAISE THE LAMB
Pamela Starr Thum

Al-le-lu - ia, praise the Lamb! Al-le-lu - ia, praise the Lamb! My heart sings His praise a - gain: Al - le- lu - ia, praise the Lamb! Al - le - lu - ia, praise the Lamb! Al - le - lu - ia, praise the Lamb! My heart

PRAISE TO CHRIST, THE ETERNAL WORD

sings His praise a - gain: Al - le - lu - ia, praise the Lamb!

Come, Lord Jesus, Be Among Us

98

" . . . and surely I will be with you always, to the very end of the age."
—Matthew 28:20b

8.7.8.7.

James L. Edwards

BE AMONG US
Lloyd Larson

1 Come, Lord Je - sus, be a - mong us;
2 Turn us from the things that bind us,

1 Fill our lives with hope and power; Now re - ceive our
                                     O now re-ceive our
2 and the trou - bles that we face; To a mo - ment
                                     Turn to a mo - ment

1 lov - ing ser - vice, make us one with Thee this hour.
2 filled with won - der, in the splen - dor of Thy grace.

PRAISE TO CHRIST, THE ETERNAL WORD

99 Alleluia

" . . . Hallelujah! Salvation and glory and power belong to our God . . . "
—Revelation 19:1b

Jerry Sinclair

L.M.
ALLELUIA
Jerry Sinclair

1 Al - le - lu - ia, al - le - lu - ia, Al - le - lu - ia, al - le - lu - ia,
2 He's my Sav - ior, He's my Sav - ior, He's my Sav - ior, He's my Sav - ior,
3 I will praise Him, I will praise Him, I will praise Him, I will praise Him,

1,2
D.C. twice

1 Al - le - lu - ia, al - le - lu - ia, Al - le - lu - ia, al - le - lu - ia.
2 He's my Sav - ior, He's my Sav - ior, He's my Sav - ior, He's my Sav - ior.
3 I will praise Him, I will praise Him, I will praise Him, I will

3

praise Him. 4 He is wor - thy, He is wor - thy, He is
5 I will serve Him, I will serve Him, I will

4 wor - thy, He is wor - thy, He is wor - thy, He is
5 serve Him, I will serve Him, I will serve Him, I will

PRAISE TO CHRIST, THE ETERNAL WORD

4 wor - thy, He is wor - thy, He is wor - thy.
5 serve Him, I will serve Him, I will serve Him.

Fairest Lord Jesus   **100**

"I, Jesus, have sent My angel to testify to you . . . I am the Root and the
Offspring of David, the Bright and Morning Star."—Revelation 22:16

5.6.8.5.5.8.
CRUSADERS' HYMN

From *Münster Gesangbuch*

Silesian Folk Melody

1 Fair - est Lord Je - sus, Rul - er of all na - ture,
2 Fair are the mead - ows, Fair - er still the wood - lands,
3 Fair is the sun - 'shine, Fair - er still the moon - light,
4 Beau - ti - ful Sav - ior! Lord of the na - tions!

1 O Thou of God and man the Son: Thee will I cher - ish,
2 Robed in the bloom-ing garb of spring: Je - sus is fair - er,
3 And all the twin - kling star - ry host: Je - sus shines bright - er,
4 Son of God and Son of Man! Glo - ry and hon - or,

1 Thee will I hon - or, Thou my soul's glo - ry, joy, and crown.
2 Je - sus is pur - er, Who makes the woe - ful heart to sing.
3 Je - sus shines pur - er Than all the an - gels heaven can boast.
4 Praise, ad - o - ra - tion, Now and for - ev - er - more be Thine!

PRAISE TO CHRIST, THE ETERNAL WORD

101 Sing Hallelujah to the Lord

"... sing and make music in your heart to the Lord."—Ephesians 5:19b

Linda Stassen

SING HALLELUJAH
Linda Stassen

1 Sing hal - le - lu - jah to the
2 Je - sus is ris - en from the
3 Christ is the Lord of heav'n and
4 Praise be to God for - ev - er -
5 Sing hal - le - lu - jah to the
Can - ta al - le - lu - ia al Se -

1 & 5 Sing hal - le - lu - jah to the Lord.
2-4 *(Echo each verse)*

1 Lord.
2 dead.
3 earth.
4 more.
5 Lord.
fior.

Sing hal - le - lu - jah to the
Je - sus is ris - en from the
Christ is the Lord of heav'n and
Praise be to God for - ev - er -
Sing hal - le - lu - jah to the
Can - ta al - le - lu - ia al Se -

PRAISE TO CHRIST, THE ETERNAL WORD

Sing hal-le-lu-jah, hal - le - lu - jah,

1	Lord.		Sing hal-le-lu-jah,	sing hal-le-lu-jah,
2	dead.		Sing hal-le-lu-jah,	sing hal-le-lu-jah,
3	earth.		Sing hal-le-lu-jah,	sing hal-le-lu-jah,
4	more.		Sing hal-le-lu-jah,	sing hal-le-lu-jah,
5	Lord.		Sing hal-le-lu-jah,	sing hal-le-lu-jah,
	ñor.		Can-ta al-le-lu - ia,	can-ta al-le-lu - ia,

1 & 5 Sing hal-le-lu-jah to the Lord.
2 – 4 *(Echo again)*

1	Sing	hal - le - lu - jah	to	the	Lord.
2	Je -	sus is ris - en	from	the	dead.
3	Christ	is the Lord of	heav'n and	earth.
4	Praise	be to God for -	ev - er - more.
5	Sing	hal - le - lu - jah	to	the	Lord.
	Can -	ta al-le-lu - ia	al	Se -	ñor.

PRAISE TO CHRIST, THE ETERNAL WORD

102

God Is Love

"God is love."—1 John 4:16c

8.7.8.7.wR.
GOD IS LOVE
D. Otis Teasley

D. Otis Teasley

1 Hark! my soul, an-gel-ic mu-sic From the heav'n-ly
2 See the depths of His com-pas-sion, Giv-ing heav-en's
3 Lo, I feel the Ho-ly Spir-it, Like a peace-ful
4 Sing, my soul, and all with-in me, Sing till all the
Con se-re-ni-dad es-cu-cha Cán-ti-co con-

1 choirs a-bove Breaks to earth the joy-ful ti-dings
2 best to prove, By a life of pain and sor-row,
3 heav'n-ly dove, Wit-ness-ing with-in my bos-om,
4 clouds re-move; Sing and praise and shout for-ev-er,
so la-dor, Que nos trae la dul-ce nue-va

1 That the Lord our God is love.
2 That the Lord our God is love.
3 That the Lord our God is love.
4 For the Lord our God is love.
Que el Se-ñor Dios es a-mor.

God is love, God is love;
God is love, yes, God is love. Hal-le-lu-jah! God is love;
Es a-mor, Es a-mor,
Es a-mor, Dios es a-mor, Es a-mor, Dios es a-mor,

GOD'S LOVE

Song of an - gel choirs a - bove; Hal - le - lu - jah! God is love.
Co - ro an-gé - li - co, en-to - nad, Con fer -vor a Dios lo - ad;

Par - a - dise now helps to swell it, Saints on earth, a-
En - to - nan - do mil can - ta - res Por la tie - rra y

far go tell it; Sa - tan's host can nev - er quell it,
por los ma - res, Re - ve - lan - do a los mi - lla - res

For the Lord our God is love. A - men.
Que el Se - ñor Dios es a - mor.

GOD'S LOVE

103 The Love of God

"How great is the love the Father has lavished on us, that we should be called children of God!"—I John 3:1a

F. M. Lehman

LOVE OF GOD
F. M. Lehman

1 The love of God is great-er far Than tongue or pen can ev - er tell;
2 When years of time shall pass a - way, And earth-ly thrones and king-doms fall,
3 Could we with ink the o-cean fill, And were the skies of parchment made,

1 It goes be - yond the high-est star, And reach-es to the low - est hell;
2 When men, who here re-fuse to pray, On rocks and hills and moun-tains call,
3 Were ev-ery stalk on earth a quill, And ev-ery man a scribe by trade,

1 The guilt-y pair, bowed down with care, God gave His Son to win;
2 God's love so sure, shall still en - dure, All mea-sure - less and strong;
3 To write the love of God a - bove Would drain the o - cean dry.

1 His err - ing child He rec-on - ciled, And par - doned from his sin.
2 Re-deem-ing grace to A - dam's race— The saints' and an - gels' song.
3 Nor could the scroll con-tain the whole, Though stretched from sky to sky.

GOD'S LOVE

O love of God, how rich and pure! How mea-sure-less and strong!

It shall for-ev-er-more en-dure— The saints' and an-gels' song.

To Know God's Love ## 104

I feel like singing this morning, O Lord.
I feel like telling everyone about me
how great You are.

If only they could know the depths of Your love
and Your eternal concern for those who
will follow You!

But my songs are so often off-key.
My speech is so inadequate.
I simply cannot express what I feel,
what I know to be true about Your love
for Your creatures upon this world.

But even the songs of the birds
proclaim Your praises.

The heavens and the earth beneath them,
the trees that reach toward You,
the flowers that glow in colorful beauty,
the green hills and soaring mountains,
the valleys and the plains,
the lakes and the rivers,
the great oceans that pound our shores,
they proclaim Your greatness, O God,
and Your love for the sons of men.

How glorious it is to be alive, O Lord!
May every breath of my body,
every beat of my heart,
be dedicated to Your praise and glory.

—Leslie Brandt
Based on Psalm 89

105
It's God

"The heavens declare the glory of God; the skies proclaim the work of his hands."—Psalm 19:1

Peggy Clark

IT'S GOD
Peggy Clark

1 See the sun giv - ing light— It's God!
2 In the midst of the storm— It's God!

1 Feel the breeze in the trees— It's God!
2 There I feel no a - larm— It's God!

1 And the love that I feel— It's God!
2 For I know all is well— It's God!

1 It's God, it's God— O it's God!
2 It's God, it's God— O it's God!

GOD'S LOVE

For God So Loved the World 106

"For God so loved the world that he gave his one and only Son, that whoever believes in him shall not perish but have eternal life."—John 3:16

12.12.12.7.

Based on John 3:16
Frances Townsend

GOD LOVED THE WORLD
Alfred B. Smith

For God so loved the world He gave His on-ly Son To die on Cal-vary's
Some day He's com-ing back—What glo-ry that will

tree, From sin to set me free; be! Won-der-ful His love to me.

There's a Wideness in God's Mercy 107

"Let me fall into the hands of the Lord, for his mercy is very great . . . "
—1 Chronicles 21:13b

8.7.8.7.
WELLESLEY
Lizzie S. Tourjeé

Frederick W. Faber

1 There's a wide-ness in God's mer-cy Like the wide-ness of the sea;
2 There is wel-come for the sin-ner And more grac-es for the good;
3 For the love of God is broad-er Than the meas-ure of one's mind;
4 If our love were but more sim-ple We should take Him at His word,

1 There's a kind-ness in His jus-tice Which is more than lib-er-ty.
2 There is mer-cy with the Sav-ior; There is heal-ing in His blood.
3 And the heart of the E-ter-nal Is most won-der-ful-ly kind.
4 And our lives would be all sun-shine In the sweet-ness of our Lord. A-men.

GOD'S LOVE

108 The Wonder of It All

" . . . What is man that you are mindful of him, the son of man that you care for him?"—Hebrews 2:6b

George Beverly Shea

WONDER OF IT ALL
George Beverly Shea

1 There's the won-der of sun-set at eve-ning, The won-der as
2 There's the won-der of spring-time and har-vest, The sky, the

1 sun-rise I see; But the won-der of won-ders that thrills my soul
2 stars, the sun; But the won-der of won-ders that thrills my soul

1 Is the won-der that God loves me. O the won-der of it all! The
2 Is a won-der that's on-ly be-gun.

won-der of it all! Just to think that God loves me. O the won-der of it

all! The won-der of it all! Just to think that God loves me.

GOD'S LOVE

None Is Like God Who Reigns Above 109

" . . . you are right in saying that God is one and there is no other but him."
—Mark 12:32b

C.M.

John Burton

ST. AGNES
John B. Dykes

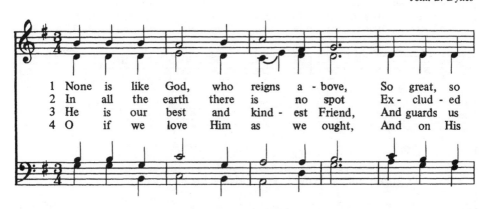

1 None is like God, who reigns a - bove, So great, so
2 In all the earth there is no spot Ex - clud - ed
3 He is our best and kind - est Friend, And guards us
4 O if we love Him as we ought, And on His

1 pure, so high; None is like God, whose name is
2 from His care; We can - not go where God is
3 night and day; To all our wants He will at -
4 grace re - ly, We shall be joy - ful at the

1 Love, And who is al - ways nigh.
2 not, For He is ev - 'ry where.
3 tend, And an - swer when we pray.
4 thought That God is al - ways nigh. A - men.

GOD'S LOVE

110 Wonderful Grace of Jesus

"When He arrived and saw the evidence of the grace of God . . . "—Acts 11:23a

Haldor Lillenas

WONDERFUL GRACE
Haldor Lillenas

1 Won - der-ful grace of Je - sus, Great - er than all my sin;
2 Won - der-ful grace of Je - sus, Reach-ing to all the lost—
3 Won - der-ful grace of Je - sus, Reach-ing the most de - filed,

1 How shall my tongue de - scribe it? Where shall His praise be - gin?
2 By it I have been par - doned, Saved to the ut - ter - most.
3 By its trans-form-ing pow - er Mak - ing him God's dear child.

1 Tak - ing a - way my bur - den, Set - ting my spir - it free;
2 Chains have been torn a - sun - der, Giv - ing me lib - er - ty;
3 Pur - chas-ing peace and heav - en For all e - ter - ni - ty;

1 For the won - der - ful grace of Je - sus reach - es me.
2 For the won - der - ful grace of Je - sus reach - es me.
3 For the won - der - ful grace of Je - sus reach - es me.

the match - less grace of Je - sus,
Won - der - ful the match-less grace of Je - sus,

GRATITUDE FOR GOD'S FAITHFULNESS AND GRACE

the roll - ing sea!

Deep - er than the might - y, roll - ing sea!

Won - der - ful grace, all - suf - fi -
High - er than the moun-tain, spar-kling like a foun-tain, All suf-fi-cient

cient for me, for e - ven me! Broad - er than the scope of my trans-
grace for e - ven me!

gres - sions, Great - er far than all my sin and shame!
gres-sions, sing it! my sin and shame!

O mag - ni - fy the pre - cious name of Je - sus! Praise His name!

GRATITUDE FOR GOD'S FAITHFULNESS AND GRACE

111 Now Thank We All Our God

"In that day you will say: 'Give thanks to the Lord, call on his name; make known among the nations what he has done, and proclaim that his name is exalted.' "—Isaiah 12:4

Martin Rinkart
Tr. by Catherine Winkworth

6.7.6.7.6.6.6.6.
NUN DANKET
Johann Crüger

1 Now thank we all our God With hearts and hands and voic - es,
2 O may this boun-teous God Through all our life be near us,
3 All praise and thanks to God The Fa - ther now be giv - en,

1 Who won-drous things hath done, In whom His world re - joic - es;
2 With ev - er joy - ful hearts And bless - ed peace to cheer us;
3 The Son, and Him who reigns With them in high - est heav - en,

1 Who, from our moth-ers' arms, Hath blessed us on our way
2 And keep us in His grace, And guide us when per - plexed,
3 The one e - ter - nal God, Whom earth and heaven a - dore;

1 With count-less gifts of love, And still is ours to - day.
2 And free us from all ills In this world and the next.
3 For thus it was, is now, And shall be ev - er - more.

GRATITUDE FOR GOD'S FAITHFULNESS AND GRACE

In Thanksgiving Let Us Praise Him 112

"With praise and thanksgiving they sang to the Lord."—Ezra 3:11a

8.7.8.7.D.

Claire Cloninger

AUSTRIAN HYMN
Franz Joseph Haydn

1 From the first bright light of morn-ing, To the last warm glow of dusk,
2 In the sea - son of our plen - ty, In the sea - son of our need,
3 Safe with-in His hand that guides us, Hid - den in His heal-ing wings,

1 Ev - 'ry breath we take is sa - cred, For it is God's gift to us.
2 We will find His grace suf - fi - cient, We will find His love com-plete.
3 Day by day His love pro-vides us Ev - 'ry good and per-fect thing.

In thanks-giv-ing, let us praise Him; In thanks-giv-ing, let us sing

Songs of praise and ad - o - ra - tion To our gra-cious Lord and King. A - men.

GRATITUDE FOR GOD'S FAITHFULNESS AND GRACE

113 Come, Ye Thankful People, Come

"Praise the Lord. Give thanks to the Lord, for he is good; his love endures forever."—Psalm 106:1

7.7.7.7.D.

Henry Alford

ST. GEORGE'S WINDSOR
George J. Elvey

1 Come, ye thank-ful peo - ple, come, Raise the song of har - vest-home;
2 All the world is God's own field, Fruit un - to His praise to yield;
3 For the Lord our God shall come And shall take His har - vest-home;
4 E - ven so, Lord, quick-ly come To Thy fi - nal har - vest-home;

1 All is safe - ly gath - ered in, Ere the win - ter storms be - gin:
2 Wheat and tares to - geth - er sown, Un - to joy or sor - rows grown:
3 From His field shall in that day All of - fens-es purge a - way,
4 Gath - er Thou Thy peo - ple in, Free from sor - row, free from sin:

1 God, our Mak - er, doth pro - vide For our wants to be sup - plied;
2 First the blade, and then the ear, Then the full corn shall ap - pear;
3 Give His an - gels charge at last In the fire the tares to cast,
4 There for - ev - er pu - ri - fied, In Thy pres-ence to a - bide;

1 Come to God's own tem - ple, come, Raise the song of har-vest-home.
2 Lord of har - vest, grant that we Whole-some grain and pure may be.
3 But the fruit-ful ears to store In His gar - ner ev - er-more.
4 Come, with all Thine an - gels, come, Raise the glo - rious har-vest-home. A-men.

GRATITUDE FOR GOD'S FAITHFULNESS AND GRACE

For the message of Christ and the shared life which can never be exhausted;
O God, we give You thanks.
For seeking minds, for searching hearts, for all who strive for truth;
O God, we give You thanks.
For our nation and its leaders and for all martyrs and unknowns who have served mankind;
O God, we give You thanks.
For the love of a man and woman, for the laughter of a child, for all that in our lives gives meaning;

O God, we give You thanks.
For those occasions which cause us to humble ourselves, and for the strength that has come to us in our hour of weakness and despair;
We rejoice and give thanks. Let the work of our hands declare the gladness of our hearts, and may kindly deeds speak forth our inner gratitude.

—James Earl Massey

For All the Blessings of the Year 115

"Let the peace of Christ rule in your hearts, since as members of one body you were called to peace. And be thankful."—Colossians 3:15

8.8.8.4.
OLDBRIDGE

Albert H. Hutchinson

Robert N. Quaile

1 For all the bless - ings of the year, For all the
2 For life and health, those com - mon things Which ev - 'ry
3 For love of Thine, which nev - er tires, Which all our

1 friends we hold so dear, For peace on earth, both
2 day and hour brings, For home, where our af -
3 bet - ter thought in - spires, And warms our lives with

1 far and near, We thank Thee, Lord.
2 fec - tion clings, We thank Thee, Lord.
3 heaven - ly fires, We thank Thee, Lord. A - men.

GRATITUDE FOR GOD'S FAITHFULNESS AND GRACE

116 Not Alone for Mighty Empire

"Some trust in chariots and some in horses, but we trust in the name of the Lord our God."—Psalm 20:7

8.7.8.7.D.
HYFRYDOL

William P. Merrill

Rowland H. Prichard
Arr. by Ralph Vaughan Williams

1 Not a - lone for might - y em - pire, Stretch-ing far o'er
2 Not for bat - tle - ship and for - tress, Not for con - quests
3 For the ar - mies of the faith - ful, Souls that passed and

1 land and sea; Not a - lone for boun-teous har - vests, Lift we
2 of the sword; But for con-quests of the spir - it Give we
3 left no name; For the glo - ry that il - lu - mines Pa - triot

1 up our hearts to Thee. Stand-ing in the liv - ing pre - sent,
2 thanks to Thee, O Lord; For the her - i - tage of lib - er - ty,
3 lives of death-less fame; For our proph - ets and a - pos - tles,

1 Mem - o - ry and hope be - tween, Lord, we would with deep thanks-
2 For the home, the church, the school; For the o - pen door to
3 Loy - al to the liv - ing Word; For all he - roes of the

GRATITUDE FOR GOD'S FAITHFULNESS AND GRACE

1 giv - ing Praise Thee most for things un - seen.
2 free - dom In a land the peo - ple rule.
3 Spir - it, Give we thanks to Thee, O Lord. A - men.

Give Thanks to the Lord 117

It is good to give thanks to the Lord,
for His love endures forever.

Give thanks to the God of gods;
His love endures forever.

Give thanks to the Lord of lords;
His love endures forever.

Alone He works great marvels;
His love endures forever.

In wisdom He made the heavens;
His love endures forever.

He laid the earth upon the waters;
His love endures forever.

He made the great lights,
His love endures forever.

The sun to rule by day,
His love endures forever,

The moon and the stars to rule by night;
His love endures forever.

He remembered us when we were cast down,
His love endures forever,

and rescued us from our enemies;
His love endures forever.

He gives food to all His creatures;
His love endures forever.

Give thanks to the God of heaven,
for His love endures forever.

—*From Psalm 136 (NEB)*

118   We Gather Together

"May God be gracious to us and bless us and make his face shine upon us."
—Psalm 67:1

12.11.12.11.
KREMSER

Netherlands Folk Song
Tr. by Theodore Baker

Netherlands Folk Song
Harmonized by Edward Kremser

1 We gath-er to-geth-er to ask the Lord's bless-ing— He
2 Be-side us to guide us, our God with us join-ing, Or-
3 We all do ex-tol Thee, Thou lead-er tri-um-phant, And

1 chas-tens and has-tens His will to make known; The
2 dain-ing, main-tain-ing His king-dom di-vine; So
3 pray that Thou still our de-fend-er wilt be; Let

1 wick-ed op-press-ing now cease from dis-tress-ing: Sing
2 from the be-gin-ning the fight we were win-ning: Thou,
3 Thy con-gre-ga-tion es-cape trib-u-la-tion: Thy

1 prais-es to His name— He for-gets not His own.
2 Lord, wast at our side— all glo-ry be Thine.
3 name be ev-er praised! O Lord, make us free! A-men.

GRATITUDE FOR GOD'S FAITHFULNESS AND GRACE

Rejoice, Ye Pure in Heart 119

"Rejoice in the Lord and be glad, you righteous; sing, all you who are upright in heart!"—Psalm 32:11

S.M.wR.
MARION

Edward H. Plumptre

Arthur H. Messiter

1 Re - joice, ye pure in heart, Re - joice, give thanks and sing;
2 Go on through life's long path, Still chant - ing as ye go;
3 Then on, ye pure in heart, Re - joice, give thanks and sing;

1 Your fes - tive ban - ner wave on high, The cross of Christ your King:
2 From youth to age, by night and day, In glad - ness and in woe:
3 Your glo - rious ban - ner wave on high, The cross of Christ your King:

Re - joice, re - joice, Re - joice, give thanks and sing. A - men.
Re - joice, re - joice,

Giving Thanks 120

"O Lord my God, I will give you thanks forever."—Psalm 30:12b

GIVING THANKS
Denny Cagle

Denny Cagle

Giv - ing thanks, giv - ing thanks, To God, through Christ, the Lord.

Giv - ing thanks, giv - ing thanks, To God, through Christ, the Lord.

GRATITUDE FOR GOD'S FAITHFULNESS AND GRACE

121 Great Is Thy Faithfulness

"Because of the Lord's great love we are not consumed, for his compassions never fail. They are new every morning: great is your faithfulness."
—Lamentations 3:22,23

Based on Lamentations 3:22, 23
Thomas O. Chisholm

11.10.11.10.wR.
FAITHFULNESS
William M. Runyan

1 Great is Thy faith-ful-ness, O God my Fa-ther! There is no
2 Sum-mer and win-ter, and spring-time and har-vest, Sun, moon, and
3 Par-don for sin and a peace that en-dur-eth, Thine own dear

1 shad-ow of turn-ing with Thee; Thou chang-est not, Thy com-
2 stars in their cours-es a - bove, Join with all na - ture in
3 pres-ence to cheer and to guide, Strength for to - day and bright

1 pas-sions, they fail not: As Thou hast been Thou for - ev - er wilt be.
2 man-i-fold wit-ness To Thy great faith - ful-ness, mer-cy, and love.
3 hope for to - mor-row— Bless-ings all mine, with ten thou-sand be - side!

Great is Thy faith-ful-ness, Great is Thy faith-ful-ness, Morn-ing by

GRATITUDE FOR GOD'S FAITHFULNESS AND GRACE

morn-ing new mer-cies I see; All I have need-ed Thy

hand hath pro-vid-ed— Great is Thy faith-ful-ness, Lord, un-to me! A-men.

God Is So Good

122

"Give thanks to the Lord, for he is good; his love endures forever."
—I Chronicles 16:34

GOD IS SO GOOD
Traditional

Traditional

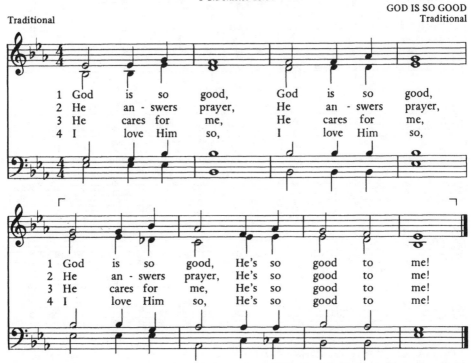

1 God is so good, God is so good,
2 He an-swers prayer, He an-swers prayer,
3 He cares for me, He cares for me,
4 I love Him so, I love Him so,

1 God is so good, He's so good to me!
2 He an-swers prayer, He's so good to me!
3 He cares for me, He's so good to me!
4 I love Him so, He's so good to me!

GRATITUDE FOR GOD'S FAITHFULNESS AND GRACE

123 We Are So Blessed

"Praise be to the God and Father of our Lord Jesus Christ, who has blessed us in the heavenly realms with every spiritual blessing in Christ."—Ephesians 1:3

SO BLESSED

William J. Gaither
Gloria Gaither

William J. Gaither
Greg Nelson

We are so blessed by the gifts from Your hand, I just
so blessed, we just can't find a way or the

can't un-der-stand Why You've loved us so much. We are
words that can say. Thank You

Lord, for Your

touch. When we're emp-ty, You fill us 'Til we o-ver-

flow; When we're hun-gry, You feed us and cause us to

know We are so blessed, Take what we have to

GRATITUDE FOR GOD'S FAITHFULNESS AND GRACE

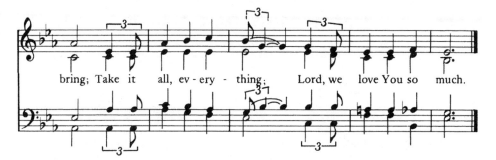

bring; Take it all, ev-ery-thing; Lord, we love You so much.

Gratitude 124

O God, You have given me so much . . . all at once I know these things I
call common are daily miracles!

Eyes that behold . . . the uncharted universe above me, and a busy robin
building a nest for its young;

Ears that hear . . . the pounding of a mighty sea, and the clear, sweet
strains of a violin;

The ability . . . to appreciate the fragrance of a dew-laden dawn, and the
pungent sweetness of a fresh gardenia;

The warmth . . . in the handclasp of a friend;

The light . . . in the glance of a loved one turned my way;

The trust . . . in the arms of a child tight around me.

. . . Purpose

. . . Work

. . . Rest

Father, all this You have given me. What can I do for You?

—Marvin J. Hartman
from *He Restoreth My Soul*

Thank You, Lord 125

"Thanks be to God for His indescribable gift!"—II Corinthians 9:15

8.8.8.9.
THANK YOU, LORD
Seth Sykes
Bessie Sykes

Seth Sykes

Thank you, Lord, for sav-ing my soul, Thank you, Lord, for mak-ing me whole;

Thank you, Lord, for giv-ing to me Thy great sal-va-tion so rich and free.

GRATITUDE FOR GOD'S FAITHFULNESS AND GRACE

126 Count Your Blessings

"Many, O Lord my God, are the wonders you have done. The things you planned for us no one can recount to you; were I to speak and tell of them, they would be too many to declare."—Psalm 40:5

Johnson Oatman, Jr.

11.11.11.11.wR.
BLESSINGS
Edwin O. Excell

1 When up-on life's bil-lows you are tem-pest-tossed, When you are dis-
2 Are you ev-er bur-dened with a load of care? Does the cross seem
3 When you look at oth-ers with their lands and gold, Think that Christ has
4 So, a-mid the con-flict, wheth-er great or small, Do not be dis-

1 cour-aged, think-ing all is lost, Count your man-y bless-ings, name them
2 heav-y you are called to bear? Count your man-y bless-ings, ev-ery
3 prom-ised you His wealth un-told; Count your man-y bless-ings, mon-ey
4 cour-aged, God is o-ver all; Count your man-y bless-ings, an-gels

1 one by one, And it will sur-prise you what the Lord hath done.
2 doubt will fly, And you will be sing-ing as the days go by.
3 can-not buy Your re-ward in heav-en, nor your home on high.
4 will at-tend, Help and com-fort give you to your jour-ney's end.

Count your bless-ings, Name them one by one; Count your
Count your man-y bless-ings, Name them one by one; Count your man-y

GRATITUDE FOR GOD'S FAITHFULNESS AND GRACE

bless-ings, See what God hath done. Count your bless-ings,
bless-ings, See what God hath done. Count your man-y bless-ings,

Name them one by one; Count your man-y bless-ings, See what God hath done.

Amazing Grace! How Sweet **127**
the Sound

"He replied, 'Whether he is a sinner or not, I don't know. One thing I do know.
I was blind but now I see!' "—John 9:25

C.M.

John Newton
John P. Rees, stanza 4

AMAZING GRACE
American Melody
Carrell and Clayton's *Virginia Harmony*

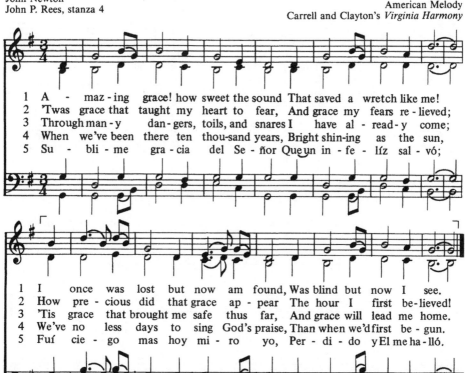

1 A - maz-ing grace! how sweet the sound That saved a wretch like me!
2 'Twas grace that taught my heart to fear, And grace my fears re - lieved;
3 Through man-y dan-gers, toils, and snares I have al - read-y come;
4 When we've been there ten thou-sand years, Bright shin-ing as the sun,
5 Su - bli - me gra - cia del Se - ñor Que un in - fe - líz sal - vó;

1 I once was lost but now am found, Was blind but now I see.
2 How pre - cious did that grace ap - pear The hour I first be-lieved!
3 'Tis grace that brought me safe thus far, And grace will lead me home.
4 We've no less days to sing God's praise, Than when we'd first be - gun.
5 Fuí cie - go mas hoy mi - ro yo, Per - di - do y El me ha-lló.

GRATITUDE FOR GOD'S FAITHFULNESS AND GRACE

128 Grace Greater than Our Sin

"But where sin increased, grace increased all the more."—Romans 5:20b

9.9.9.9.wR.
MOODY

Julia H. Johnston

Daniel B. Towner

1. Mar-vel-ous grace of our lov-ing Lord, Grace that ex-ceeds our
2. Sin and de-spair, like the sea-waves cold, Threat-en the soul with
3. Dark is the stain that we can-not hide, What can a-vail to
4. Mar-vel-ous, in-fi-nite, match-less grace, Free-ly be-stowed on

1. sin and our guilt! Yon-der on Cal-va-ry's mount out-poured—
2. in-fi-nite loss; Grace that is great-er—yes, grace un-told—
3. wash it a-way? Look! There is flow-ing a crim-son tide—
4. all who be-lieve! You that are long-ing to see His face,

1. There where the blood of the Lamb was spilt.
2. Points to the Ref-uge, the might-y Cross. Grace, grace,
3. Free from all sin you may be to-day.
4. Will you this mo-ment His grace re-ceive?

God's grace, Grace that will par-don and cleanse with-in; Grace,

grace, God's grace, Grace that is great-er than all our sin!

GRATITUDE FOR GOD'S FAITHFULNESS AND GRACE

I Will Sing of the Mercies of the Lord

"I will sing of the Lord's great love forever; with my mouth I will make your faithfulness known through all generations."—Psalm 89:1

James H. Fillmore

FILLMORE
James H. Fillmore

I will sing of the mer-cies of the Lord for-ev-er, I will

sing, I will sing; I will sing of the mer-cies of the

Lord. With my mouth will I make known Thy

faith-ful-ness, Thy faith-ful-ness; With my mouth will I make

known Thy faith-ful-ness to all gen-er - a - tions. I will

GRATITUDE FOR GOD'S FAITHFULNESS AND GRACE

130 Thank the Lord

"Give thanks to the Lord, for he is good; his love endures forever."
—I Chronicles 16:34

Source Unknown

THANK THE LORD
Folk Tune
Harmonization by Bernadette Blount Salley

Thank the Lord and sing His praise. Tell ev-'ry-one what He has done. Let

ev-'ry-one who loves the Lord re - joice and glad - ly bear His name.

bear His name. He re - calls His prom - i - ses And

leads His peo - ple forth in joy with shouts of thanks - giv - ing:

GRATITUDE FOR GOD'S FAITHFULNESS AND GRACE

Jesus, We Just Want to Thank You 131

"Thanks be to God for his indescribable gift!"—II Corinthians 9:15

Gloria Gaither
William J. Gaither

THANK YOU
William J. Gaither

1 Je - sus, we just want to thank You, Je - sus, we just want to thank You, Je - sus, we just want to thank You, Thank You for be - ing so good.

2 Je - sus, we just want to praise You, Je - sus, we just want to praise You, Je - sus, we just want to praise You, Praise You for be - ing so good.

3 Je - sus, we just want to tell You, Je - sus, we just want to tell You, tell You, We love You for be - ing so good.

4 Sav - ior, we just want to serve You, Sav - ior, we just want to serve You, Sav - ior, we just want to serve You, Serve You for be - ing so good.

Cris - to, yo quie - ro dar gra - cias, Cris - to, yo quie - ro dar gra - cias; Cris - to, yo quie - ro dar gra - cias, Gra - cias por tu gran bon - dad.

GRATITUDE FOR GOD'S FAITHFULNESS AND GRACE

32 This Is My Father's World

"If I were hungry I would not tell you, for the world is mine, and all that is in it."—Psalm 50:12

Maltbie D. Babcock

S.M.D.
TERRA BEATA
English Melody

1 This is my Fa-ther's world, And to my lis-tening ears
2 This is my Fa-ther's world, The birds their car-ols raise,
3 This is my Fa-ther's world, O let me ne'er for - get

1 All na - ture sings, and 'round me rings The mu - sic of the spheres.
2 The morn-ing light, the lil - y white, De - clare their Mak-er's praise.
3 That though the wrong seems oft so strong, God is the rul - er yet.

1 This is my Fa-ther's world: I rest me in the thought Of
2 This is my Fa-ther's world: He shines in all that's fair; In the
3 This is my Fa-ther's world: Why should my heart be sad? The

1 rocks and trees, of skies and seas— His hand the won - ders wrought.
2 rus - tling grass I hear Him pass, He speaks to me ev-ery - where.
3 Lord is King let the heav-ens ring. God reigns let the earth be glad.

We Sing the Greatness of Our God

"Praise him, sun and moon, praise him, all you shining stars."—Psalm 148:3

Isaac Watts
Jeff Redd, alt.

C.M.D.
ELLACOMBE
"Gesängbuch der Herzogl," Württemburg

1 We sing the great-ness of our God That made the moun-tains rise,
2 We sing the good-ness of the Lord That filled the earth with food;
3 There's not a plant or flower be-low But makes Thy glo-ries known;

1 That spread the flow-ing sea a-broad And built the loft-y skies.
2 He formed the crea-tures with His word And then pro-nounced them good.
3 And clouds a-rise and tem-pests blow By or-der from Thy throne,

1 We sing the wis-dom that or-dained The sun to rule the day;
2 Lord, how Thy won-ders are dis-played Wher-e'er we turn our eyes:
3 While all that bor-rows life from Thee Is ev-er in Thy care,

1 The moon shines full at His com-mand, And all the stars o-bey.
2 In ev-ery sea-son of the year, And through the changing skies.
3 And ev-ery-where that we can be, Lord, Thou art pres-ent there. A-men.

GRATITUDE FOR GOD'S CREATION

134 All Things Bright and Beautiful

"God saw all that he had made, and it was very good. And there was evening, and there was morning—the sixth day."—Genesis 1:31

7.6.7.6.wRPT.
ROYAL OAK

Cecil F. Alexander

Traditional English Melody

Unison

All things bright and beau-ti-ful, All crea-tures great and small,

All things wise and won-der-ful; The Lord God made them all.

1 Each lit-tle flow'r that o-pens, Each lit-tle bird that sings,
2 The pur-ple-head-ed moun-tain, The riv-er run-ning by,
3 The cold wind in the win-ter, The pleas-ant sum-mer sun,
4 God gave us eyes to see them, And lips that we might tell

D.C. al Fine

1 God made their glow-ing col - ors, He made their ti - ny wings.
2 The sun - set, and the morn - ing That bright-ens up the sky.
3 The ripe fruits in the gar - den: He made them, ev - ery one.
4 How great is God Al - might - y, Who has made all things well.

GRATITUDE FOR GOD'S CREATION

It Is Good to Sing Thy Praises 135

"It is good to praise the Lord and make music to your name, O Most High."
—Psalm 92:1

8.7.8.7.D.
ELLESDIE
Leavitt's *The Christian Lyre*, 1831
Attributed to Wolfgang A. Mozart

From Psalm 92
The Psalter

1 It is good to sing Thy prais-es And to thank Thee, O Most High,
2 Thou hast filled my heart with glad-ness Thru the works Thy hands have wrought;
3 But the good shall live be-fore Thee, Plant-ed in Thy dwell-ing place,

1 Show-ing forth Thy lov-ing-kind-ness When the morn-ing lights the sky.
2 Thou hast made my life vic-to-rious, Great Thy works and deep Thy thought.
3 Fruit-ful trees and ev-er ver-dant, Nour-ished by Thy bound-less grace.

1 It is good when night is fall-ing Of Thy faith-ful-ness to tell,
2 Thou, O Lord, on high ex-alt-ed, Reign-est ev-er-more in might;
3 In His good-ness to the right-eous God His right-eous-ness dis-plays;

1 While with sweet, me-lo-dious prais-es Songs of ad-o-ra-tion swell.
2 All Thy en-e-mies shall per-ish, Sin be ban-ished from Thy sight.
3 God my rock, my strength, my ref-uge, Just and true are all His ways. A-men.

136 Let All Things Now Living

"You will go out in joy and be led forth in peace; the mountains and hills will burst into song before you."—Isaiah 55:12

Katherine K. Davis
Previously attributed to
John Cowley

6.6.11.6.6.11.D.
ASH GROVE
Traditional Welsh Melody
Descant by Katherine K. Davis

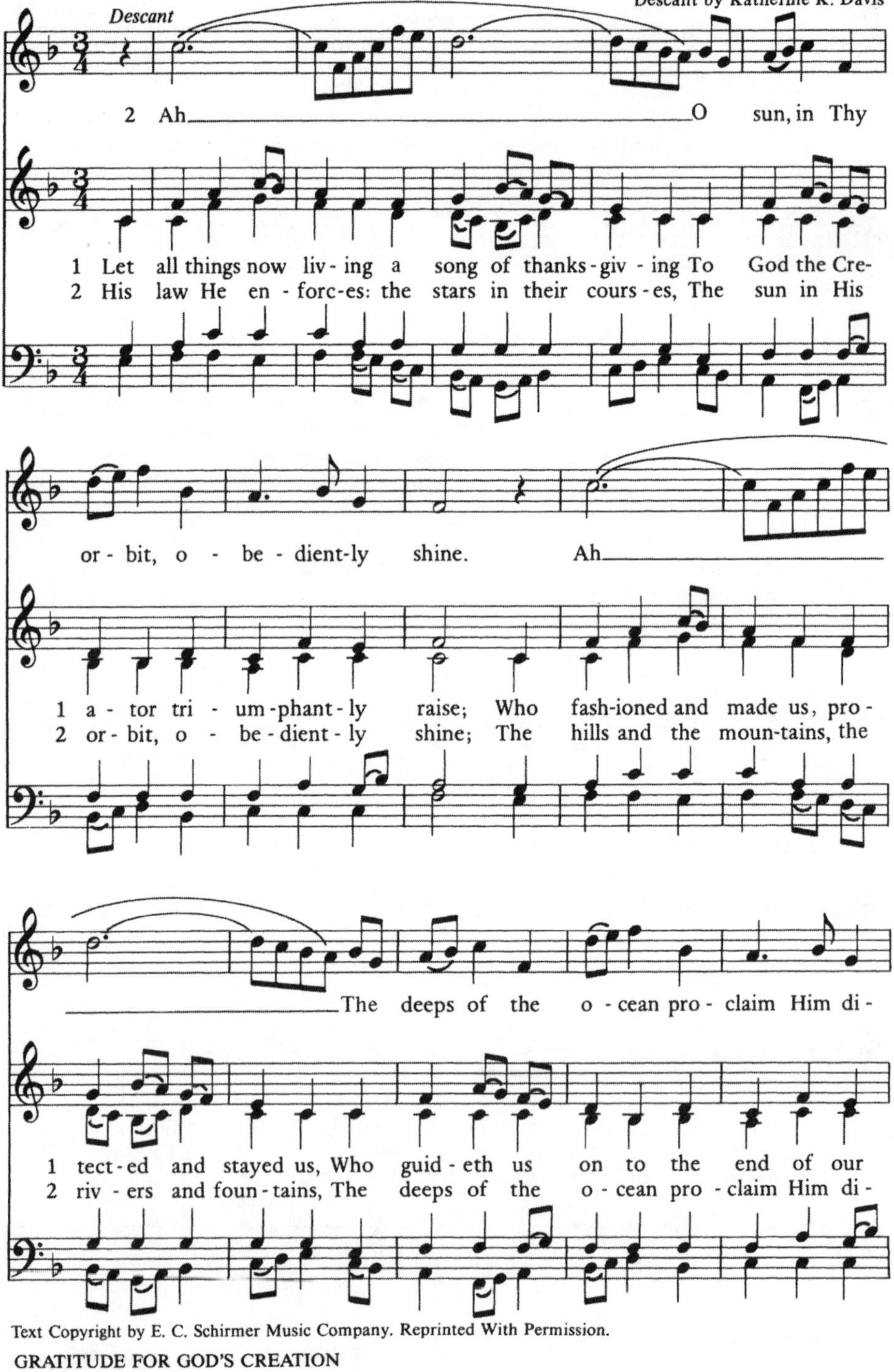

Descant

2 Ah_____O sun, in Thy

1 Let all things now liv-ing a song of thanks-giv-ing To God the Cre-
2 His law He en-forc-es: the stars in their cours-es, The sun in His

1 or-bit, o-be-dient-ly shine. Ah_____

1 a-tor tri-um-phant-ly raise; Who fash-ioned and made us, pro-
2 or-bit, o-be-dient-ly shine; The hills and the moun-tains, the

_____The deeps of the o-cean pro-claim Him di-

1 tect-ed and stayed us, Who guid-eth us on to the end of our
2 riv-ers and foun-tains, The deeps of the o-cean pro-claim Him di-

GRATITUDE FOR GOD'S CREATION

vine. Re - joice,_____ re - joice! With glad ad - o -

1 days. His ban-ners are o'er us, His light goes be - fore us, A pil - lar of
2 vine. We too, should be voic -ing our love and re - joic-ing, With glad ad - o -

ra -tion a song let us raise; Ah_____

1 fire shin-ing forth in the night; 'Til shad-ows have van-ished and dark-ness is
2 ra - tion a song let us raise; 'Til all things now liv - ing u - nite in thanks-

_____ To God in the high-est, ho - san - na and praise. A - men.

1 ban-ished, As for - ward we trav - el from light in - to light.
2 giv - ing To God in the high-est, ho - san - na and praise! A - men.

137   For the Beauty of the Earth

"Let them give thanks to the Lord for his unfailing love and his wonderful deeds for men."—Psalm 107.8

Folliott S. Pierpoint, alt.

7.7.7.7.7.7.
DIX
Adapted by Conrad Kocher

1 For the beau-ty of the earth, For the glo-ry of the skies,
2 For the won-der of each hour Of the day and of the night,
3 For the joy of hu-man love, Broth-er, sis-ter, par-ent, child;
4 For Thy Church that ev-er-more Lift-eth ho-ly hands a-bove,
5 For Thy-self, best gift di-vine, To our race so free-ly given;

1 For the love which from our birth O-ver and a-round us lies:
2 Hill and vale and tree and flower, Sun and moon and stars of light:
3 Friends on earth and friends a-bove; For all gen-tle thoughts and mild:
4 Of-fering up on ev-ery shore Her pure sac-ri-fice of love:
5 For that great, great love of Thine, Peace on earth and joy in heaven:

Lord of all, to Thee we raise This our hymn of grate-ful praise. A-men.

138   Morning Has Broken

"Awake, my soul! Awake, harp and lyre! I will awaken the dawn."
—Psalm 57:8-9

Eleanor Farjeon

10.9.10.9.
BUNESSAN
Traditional Gaelic Melody

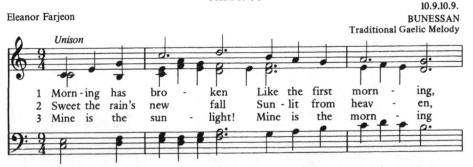

Unison

1 Morn-ing has bro-ken Like the first morn-ing,
2 Sweet the rain's new fall Sun-lit from heav-en,
3 Mine is the sun-light! Mine is the morn-ing

GRATITUDE FOR GOD'S CREATION

1 Black-bird has spo - ken Like the first bird.
2 Like the first dew - fall On the first grass.
3 Born of the one light E - den saw play!

1 Praise for the sing - ing! Praise for the morn - ing!
2 Praise for the sweet - ness Of the wet gar - den,
3 Praise with e - la - tion, Praise ev - ery morn - ing,

1 Praise for them, spring - ing Fresh from the Word!
2 Sprung in com - plete - ness Where His feet pass.
3 God's re - cre - a - tion Of the new day!

We Thank You, God 139

We thank You
   for the promise of a wondrous sunrise;
   for the peaceful benediction of the setting sun.
   for the moody sea filled with unexplored mystery,
   for the tinted loveliness of the sky at dusk.

We thank You
   for the gold of the persistant dandelion;
   for the giant oak with leafy arms raised in prayer.
   for the graceful rhythm of a breeze-blown tree bending in worship to its Maker.
   for the pungent spring, the abundant summer,
   for the quiet winter, the rustling autumn.

We thank You
   for the never-failing promise of the seed;
   for the lush-laden offering of the fruit tree.
   for the quiet simplicity of the prairie,
   for the royal majesty of the mountains;
   for immeasurable space; unfathomable time.

For all these, O God, an inexpressible gratitude floods our being.

—Marvin J. and Madelyn Hartman
from *He Restoreth My Soul*

GRATITUDE FOR GOD'S CREATION

140 For the Fruit of All Creation

"Give thanks to the Lord, for he is good; his love endures forever."—Psalm 107:1

Fred Pratt Green

8.4.8.4.8.8.8.4.
AR HYD Y NOS
Traditional Welsh Melody

Unison

1 For the fruit of all cre-a-tion, thanks be to God.
2 In the just re-ward of la-bor, God's will is done.
3 For the har-vest of the Spir-it, thanks be to God.

1 For His gifts to ev-ery na-tion, thanks be to God.
2 In the help we give our neigh-bor, God's will is done.
3 For the good we all in-her-it, thanks be to God.

1 For the plow-ing, sow-ing, reap-ing, si-lent growth while we are sleep-ing,
2 In our world-wide task of car-ing for the hun-gry and de-spair-ing,
3 For the won-ders that as-tound us, for the truths that still con-found us,

1 Fu-ture needs in earth's safe-keep-ing, thanks be to God.
2 In the har-vest we are shar-ing, God's will is done.
3 Most of all, that Love has found us, thanks be to God.

GRATITUDE FOR GOD'S CREATION

God of the Fertile Fields 141

"And God is able to make all grace abound to you, so that in all things at all times, having all that you need, you will abound in every good work."
—II Corinthians 9:8

6.6.4.6.6.6.4.
AMERICA

Georgia Harkness

Source Unknown

1 God of the fer - tile fields, Lord of the earth that yields
2 We would Thy stew - ards be, Hold - ing in trust from Thee
3 As grows the hid - den seed To fruit that serves our need,
4 God of the coun - try-side, Dear to our Lord who died

1 Our dai - ly bread; Forth from Thy boun-teous hand Come gifts Thy
2 All Thou dost give; Help us in love to share, Teach us like
3 Thy King-dom grows. So let our toil be used, No gift of
4 To make us one; We pledge our lives to Thee, To serve Thee

1 love has planned, That all through-out the land Be clothed and fed.
2 Thee to care, That earth may all be fair, And we may live.
3 Thine a - bused, No hum-blest task re-fused, Thy love be - stows.
4 faith - ful - ly Till in e - ter - ni - ty Our day is done. A - men.

Awareness 142

LEADER: Almighty God, whose love is evident everywhere, We see Thy handiwork In the brilliance of a noonday sun, In the somber silence of a harvest moon.

PEOPLE: *We see Thy touch In the kindly, wrinkled face of an elderly saint, In the inquisitive eyes of a growing child.*

LEADER: We see Thy artistry In the bursting bud of a daffodil and In the colorful beauty of an autumn leaf.

PEOPLE: *We see Thy stately strength in the majestic sequoia and Thy love and gentleness in a straw-filled manger.*

LEADER: But most of all, our Father, we see Thee in a ransomed life drawn from the depth of sin and misery to the heights of purity and peace.

PEOPLE: *Make us, we pray, sensitive to all evidence of Thee. Most of all, keep us aware of the guiding Voice within.*

ALL: *In the name of Christ, Thy gift to us, we pray. Amen.*

—Marvin J. and Madelyn Hartman

STEWARDSHIP OF GOD'S CREATION

143 God, Our Father and Creator

"Give thanks to the Lord, for he is good; his love endures forever."—Psalm 107:1

8.7.8.7.8.7.7.

CWM RHONDDA
John Hughes

Edward K. Ziegler

1 God, our Fa - ther and Cre - a - tor, Lord of land and
2 Thou art giv - er of the har - vest, Where is shown Thy
3 Teach us, Lord, the joy of giv - ing; Tune our hearts to

1 sky and sea; From earth's poles to the E - qua - tor Hymns of praise as -
2 bound - less love; Field and or - chard, mine and for - est Thine un - end - ing
3 grate - ful praise; Stir us to un - self - ish liv - ing, Serv - ing Thee in

1 cend to Thee. Glo - ry, hon - or and thanks-giv-ing Sing we to Thy maj - es -
2 good-ness prove. Glo - ry, hon - or and thanks-giv-ing Bring we now, O God A -
3 all our ways. Glo - ry, hon - or and thanks-giv-ing Of - fer we through end - less

1 ty, Sing we to Thy maj - es - ty.
2 bove, Bring we now, O God A - bove.
3 days, Of - fer we through end - less days. A - men.

STEWARDSHIP OF GOD'S CREATION

God Who Stretched the Spangled Heavens

144

"As God's fellow workers we urge you not to receive God's grace in vain."
—II Corinthians 6:1

8.7.8.7.D.

Catherine Cameron

HYMN TO JOY
Ludwig van Beethoven

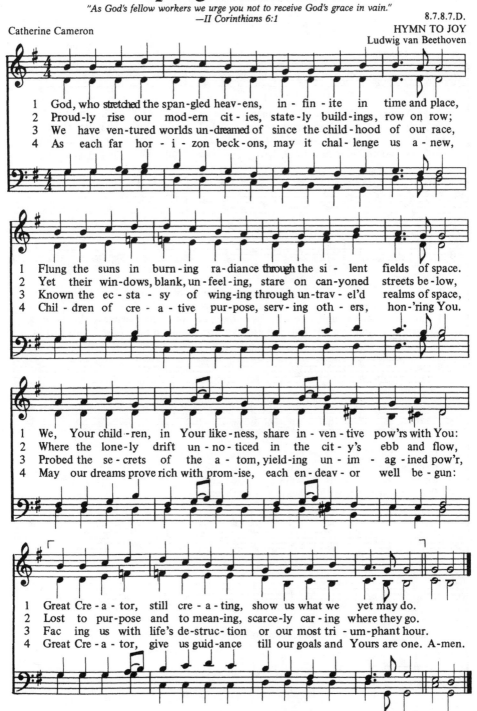

1 God, who stretched the span-gled heav-ens, in - fin - ite in time and place,
2 Proud-ly rise our mod-ern cit - ies, state-ly build-ings, row on row;
3 We have ven-tured worlds un-dreamed of since the child-hood of our race,
4 As each far hor - i - zon beck-ons, may it chal - lenge us a - new,

1 Flung the suns in burn-ing ra-diance through the si - lent fields of space.
2 Yet their win-dows, blank, un-feel-ing, stare on can-yoned streets be-low,
3 Known the ec - sta - sy of wing-ing through un-trav - el'd realms of space,
4 Chil - dren of cre - a - tive pur-pose, serv-ing oth - ers, hon-'ring You.

1 We, Your child - ren, in Your like-ness, share in - ven - tive pow'rs with You:
2 Where the lone-ly drift un - no - ticed in the cit - y's ebb and flow,
3 Probed the se - crets of the a - tom, yield-ing un - im - ag - ined pow'r,
4 May our dreams prove rich with prom-ise, each en - deav - or well be - gun:

1 Great Cre - a - tor, still cre - a - ting, show us what we yet may do.
2 Lost to pur-pose and to mean-ing, scarce-ly car - ing where they go.
3 Fac ing us with life's de-struc - tion or our most tri - um-phant hour.
4 Great Cre - a - tor, give us guid-ance till our goals and Yours are one. A-men.

STEWARDSHIP OF GOD'S CREATION

145 O Come, O Come, Emmanuel

"Therefore the Lord himself will give you a sign: The virgin will be with child and will give birth to a son, and will call him Immanuel."—Isaiah 7:14

Latin c. 9th century
Tr. by John M. Neale, stanzas 1, 2, alt.
Tr. by Henry S. Coffin, stanzas 3 & 4

L.M.wR.
VENI EMMANUEL
Thomas Helmore
Adapted from Plainsong, Mode I

1 O come, O come, Em - man - u - el, And ran-som cap-tive
2 O come, thou Day-spring, come and cheer Our spir-its by Thine
3 O come, thou Wis-dom from on high, And or -der all things
4 O come, De-sire of na - tions, bind All peo - ples in one

1 Is - ra - el, That mourns in lone- ly ex - ile here, Un -
2 ad - vent here; Dis - perse the gloom-y clouds of night, And
3 far and nigh; To us the path of knowl-edge show, And
4 heart and mind; Bid en - vy, strife and quar - rels cease; Fill

1 til the Son of God ap - pear.
2 death's dark shad - ows put to flight. Re -joice! Re - joice! Em -
3 cause us in its ways to go.
4 the whole earth with heav - en's peace.

man - u - el Shall come to thee, O Is - ra - el! A -men.

JESUS CHRIST: ADVENT AND NATIVITY

What Child Is This?   **146**

"When they had seen him, they spread the word concerning what had been told them about this child."—Luke 2:17

8.7.8.7.wR.

GREENSLEEVES
English Melody
Harmonized by John Stainer

William C. Dix

1 What child is this, who, laid to rest, On Ma-ry's lap is sleep-ing?
2 Why lies He in such mean es-tate Where ox and ass are feed-ing?
3 So bring Him in-cense, gold, and myrrh, Come peas-ant, king, to own Him;

1 Whom an-gels greet with an-thems sweet, While shep-herds watch are keep-ing?
2 Good Chris-tian, fear: for sin-ners here The si-lent Word is plead-ing.
3 The King of kings sal-va-tion brings, Let lov-ing hearts en-throne Him.

This, this is Christ the King, Whom shep-herds guard and an-gels sing:

Haste, haste to bring Him laud, The Babe, the son of Ma-ry.

JESUS CHRIST: ADVENT AND NATIVITY

147 O Holy Night

"The angel answered, 'The Holy Spirit will come upon you, and the power of the Most High will overshadow you. So the holy one to be born will be called the Son of God.' "—Luke 1:35

John S. Dwight

CANTIQUE DE NOEL
Adolphe C. Adam

1 O ho-ly night the stars are bright-ly shin-ing, It is the night of the dear Sav-ior's birth; Long lay the world in sin and er-ror* pin-ing, 'Til He ap-peared and the soul felt its worth. A thrill of hope the wea-ry world re-joic-es, For yon-der breaks a new and glo-rious morn! Fall on your knees! O

2 Led by the light of Faith se-rene-ly beam-ing, With glow-ing heart by His cra-dle we stand; So led by light of a star sweet-ly gleam-ing, Here came the Wise Men from the O-rient land. The King of kings lay thus in low-ly man-ger, In all our tri-als born to be our Friend; He knows our need, He

3 Tru-ly He taught us to love one an-oth-er; His law is Love and His gos-pel is Peace; Chains shall He break, for the slave is our broth-er, And in His Name, all op-pres-sion shall cease. With hymns of joy in grate-ful cho-rus rais-ing, Let ev-ery heart a-dore His Ho-ly Name! Christ is the Lord! With

*or sorrow

JESUS CHRIST: ADVENT AND NATIVITY

1 hear the an-gel voic-es O night di - vine! O night when Christ was
2 guards us from all dan-ger, Be - hold your King! be - fore Him low-ly
3 saint and ser-aph prais-ing, His pow'r and glo - ry ev - er-more pro-

1 born! O night di - vine! O night, O night di - vine!
2 bend! Be - hold your King! Be - fore Him low-ly bend!
3 claim! His pow'r and glo - ry ev - er-more pro - claim!

The Birth of Christ   148

This is how the birth of Jesus Christ came about.

> *His mother Mary was pledged to be married to Joseph,*
> *but before they came together,*
> *she was found to be with child through the Holy Spirit.*

An angel of the Lord appeared to him in a dream and said,
"Joseph, son of David,
do not be afraid to take Mary home as your wife,
because what is conceived in her is from the Holy Spirit.

> *"She will give birth to a son,*
> *and you are to give Him the name Jesus,*
> *because He will save His people from their sins."*

And there were shepherds living out in the fields nearby,
keeping watch over their flocks at night.

An angel of the Lord appeared to them, and the glory of the Lord shone around them, and they were terrified.

> *But the angel said to them,*
> *"Do not be afraid.*
> *I bring you good news of great joy that will be for all the people.*

"Today, in the town of David, a Savior has been born to you;
He is Christ the Lord.
This will be a sign to you:
You will find a baby wrapped in strips of cloth and lying in a manger."

> *Suddenly a great company of the heavenly host appeared with the angel, praising God and saying,*
> *"Glory to God in the highest,*
> *and on earth peace to men on whom His favor rests."*

—*Selected from Matthew 1 and Luke 2 (NIV)*

149 We Three Kings of Orient Are

" . . . Magi came from the east to Jerusalem and asked,'Where is the one who has been born king of the Jews? We saw his star in the east and have come to worship him . . . ' "—Matthew 2:1

8.8.8.6.wR.

KINGS OF ORIENT

John H. Hopkins, Jr.

John H. Hopkins, Jr.

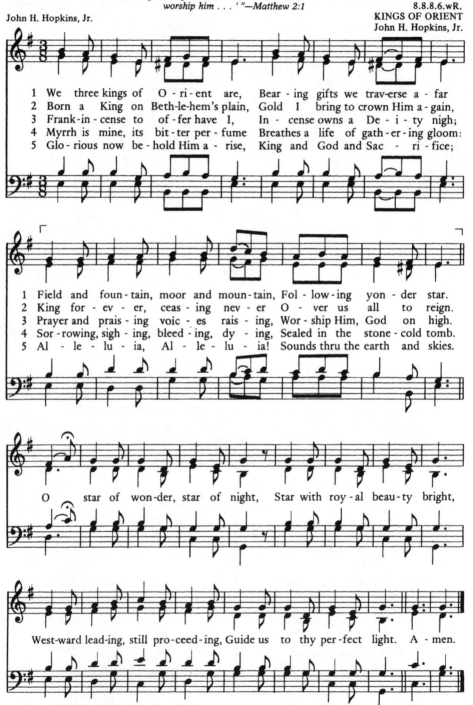

1 We three kings of O-ri-ent are, Bear-ing gifts we trav-erse a-far
2 Born a King on Beth-le-hem's plain, Gold I bring to crown Him a-gain,
3 Frank-in-cense to of-fer have I, In-cense owns a De-i-ty nigh;
4 Myrrh is mine, its bit-ter per-fume Breathes a life of gath-er-ing gloom:
5 Glo-rious now be-hold Him a-rise, King and God and Sac-ri-fice;

1 Field and foun-tain, moor and moun-tain, Fol-low-ing yon-der star.
2 King for-ev-er, ceas-ing nev-er O-ver us all to reign.
3 Prayer and prais-ing voic-es rais-ing, Wor-ship Him, God on high.
4 Sor-row-ing, sigh-ing, bleed-ing, dy-ing, Sealed in the stone-cold tomb.
5 Al-le-lu-ia, Al-le-lu-ia! Sounds thru the earth and skies.

O star of won-der, star of night, Star with roy-al beau-ty bright,

West-ward lead-ing, still pro-ceed-ing, Guide us to thy per-fect light. A-men.

Joy to the World!

150

"Shout for joy to the Lord, all the earth, burst into jubilant song with music . . . "—Psalm 98:4

C.M.
ANTIOCH
George Friedrich Handel
Arr. by Fred Bock & Ralph Carmichael

Psalm 98
Adapted by Isaac Watts

1 Joy to the world! the Lord is come: Let earth re-
2 Joy to the world! the Sav - ior reigns: Let men their
3 No more let sins and sor - rows grow, Nor thorns in -
4 He rules the world with truth and grace, And makes the

1 ceive her King; Let ev - ery heart pre - pare Him
2 songs em - ploy; While fields and flocks, rocks, hills, and
3 fest the ground; He comes to make His bless - ings
4 na - tions prove The glo - ries of His right - eous -

1 room, And heaven and na-ture sing, And heaven and na-ture sing, And
2 plains Re - peat the sound-ing joy, Re - peat the sound-ing joy, Re -
3 flow Far as the curse is found, Far as the curse is found, Far
4 ness, And won-ders of His love, And won-ders of His love, And

And heaven and na-ture sing,

And heaven and na-ture

1 heaven, and heaven and na - ture sing.
2 peat, re - peat the sound - ing joy.
3 as, far as the curse is found.
4 won - ders, won - ders of His love. A - men.

sing,

JESUS CHRIST: ADVENT AND NATIVITY

151

The First Noel

" . . . Where is the one who has been born king of the Jews? We saw his star in
the east and have come to worship him."—Matthew 2:2

English Carol

THE FIRST NOEL
English Melody
From Sandys' Christmas Carols

1 The first No - el the an - gel did say Was to cer - tain poor
2 They look - ed up and saw a star Shin - ing in the
3 And by the light of that same star, Three wise men
4 This star drew nigh to the north - west, O - ver Beth - le -
5 Then en - tered in those wise men three, Full rev - erent -
6 Then let us all with one ac - cord Sing prais - es

1 shep-herds in fields as they lay— In fields where they lay keep-ing their
2 east, be - yond them far; And to the earth it gave great
3 came from coun - try far; To seek for a king was their in -
4 hem it took its rest; And there it did both stop and
5 ly up - on their knee, And of - fered there, in His pres -
6 to our heaven - ly Lord, That hath made heaven and earth of

1 sheep, On a cold win-ter's night that was so deep.
2 light, And so it con - tin-ued both day and night.
3 tent, And to fol - low the star wher - ev - er it went.
4 stay, Right o - ver the place where Je - sus lay.
5 ence, Their gold and myrrh and frank - in - cense.
6 naught, And with His blood man - kind hath bought.

No - el, no -

JESUS CHRIST: ADVENT AND NATIVITY

There's a Song in the Air   152

"and she gave birth to her firstborn, a son. She wrapped him in cloths
and placed him in a manger, because there was no room for them in
the inn."—Luke 2:7

Josiah G. Holland

6.6.6.6.D.
CHRISTMAS SONG
Karl P. Harrington

1 There's a song in the air! There's a star in the sky! There's a moth-er's deep
2 There's a tu-mult of joy O'er the won-der-ful birth, For a Vir-gin's sweet
3 In the light of that star Lie the a-ges im-pearled; And that song from a-
4 We re-joice in the light, And we ech-o the song That comes down thro' the

1 prayer And a ba-by's low cry! And the star rains its fire while the
2 boy Is the Lord of the earth. Ay! the star rains its fire while the
3 far Has swept o-ver the world. Ev-ery hearth is a-flame, and the
4 night From the heav-en-ly throng. Ay! we shout to the love-ly e-

1 beau-ti-ful sing, For the man-ger of Beth-le-hem cra-dles a King!
2 beau-ti-ful sing, For the man-ger of Beth-le-hem cra-dles a King!
3 beau-ti-ful sing In the homes of the na-tions that Je-sus is King!
4 van-gel they bring, And we greet in His cra-dle our Sav-ior and King!

153 Come, Thou Long-Expected Jesus

"The Spirit of the Sovereign Lord is on me, because the Lord has anointed me to preach good news to the poor. He has sent me to bind up the brokenhearted, to proclaim freedom for the captives and release for the prisoners."—Isaiah 61:1

8.7.8.7.D.
HYFRYDOL

Charles Wesley

Rowland Hugh Prichard

1 Come, Thou long - ex - pect - ed Je - sus, Born to
2 Born Thy peo - ple to de - liv - er, Born a

1 set Thy peo - ple free; From our fears and
2 child and yet a King, Born to reign in

1 sins re - lease us; Let us find our rest in Thee.
2 us for - ev - er, Now Thy gra - cious King - dom bring.

1 Is - rael's Strength and Con - so - la - tion, Hope of
2 By Thine own e - ter - nal Spir - it Rule in

1 all the earth Thou art; Dear De - sire of ev - 'ry
2 all our hearts a - lone; By Thine all suf - fi - cient

JESUS CHRIST: ADVENT AND NATIVITY

1 na - tion, Joy of ev - 'ry long - ing heart.
2 mer - it Raise us to Thy glo - rious throne.

While Shepherds Watched Their Flocks   154

Nahum Tate

"Then shepherds returned, glorifying and praising God . . ."—Luke 2:20

C.M.
CHRISTMAS

Arranged from George Friedrich Handel

1 While shep - herds watched their flocks by night, All seat - ed on the
2 "Fear not!" said he, for might - y dread Had seized their trou - bled
3 "To you in Da - vid's town this day Is born, of Da - vid's
4 "The heaven - ly Babe you there shall find To hu - man view dis -
5 "All glo - ry be to God on high, And to the earth be

1 ground, The an - gel of the Lord came down, And
2 mind; "Glad ti - dings of great joy I bring To
3 line, The Sav - ior, who is Christ the Lord, And
4 played, All mean - ly wrapt in swath - ing - bands And
5 peace: Good will hence - forth from heaven to earth Be -

1 glo - ry shone a - round, And glo - ry shone a - round.
2 you and all man - kind, To you and all man - kind.
3 this shall be the sign— And this shall be the sign:
4 in a man - ger laid, And in a man - ger laid.
5 gin and nev - er cease! Be - gin and nev - er cease!"

JESUS CHRIST: ADVENT AND NATIVITY

155 Away in a Manger

"So they hurried off and found Mary and Joseph, and the baby, who was lying in the manger."—Luke 2:16

Source unknown, stanzas 1, 2
John Thomas McFarland, stanza 3

11.11.11.11.
AWAY IN A MANGER
James R. Murray

1 A - way in a man-ger, no crib for a bed, The lit - tle Lord
2 The cat - tle are low-ing, the Ba - by a - wakes, But lit - tle Lord
3 Be near me, Lord Je - sus, I ask Thee to stay Close by me for -

1 Je - sus laid down His sweet head; The stars in the sky looked
2 Je - sus no cry - ing He makes, I love Thee, Lord Je - sus, look
3 ev - er, and love me, I pray. Bless all the dear chil-dren in

1 down where He lay, The lit - tle Lord Je - sus, a - sleep on the hay.
2 down from the sky, And stay by my cra-dle till morn-ing is nigh.
3 Thy ten-der care, And fit us for heav-en, to live with Thee there.

156 Away in a Manger

". . . there was no room for them in the inn."—Luke 2:7

Source unknown, stanzas 1, 2
John Thomas McFarland, stanza 3

11.11.11.11.
CRADLE SONG
William J. Kirkpatrick

Unison

1 A - way in a man-ger, no crib for a bed, The lit - tle Lord
2 The cat - tle are low - ing, the ba - by a - wakes, But lit - tle Lord
3 Be near me, Lord Je - sus! I ask Thee to stay Close by me for -

JESUS CHRIST: ADVENT AND NATIVITY

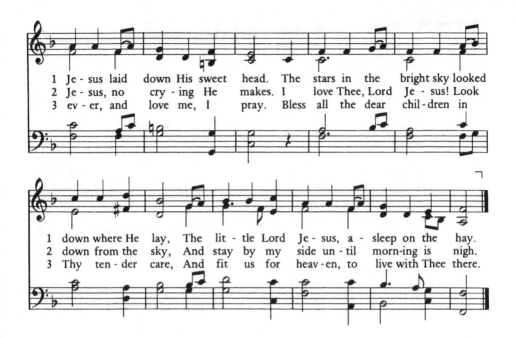

1 Je - sus laid down His sweet head. The stars in the bright sky looked
2 Je - sus, no cry - ing He makes. I love Thee, Lord Je - sus! Look
3 ev - er, and love me, I pray. Bless all the dear chil - dren in

1 down where He lay, The lit - tle Lord Je - sus, a - sleep on the hay.
2 down from the sky, And stay by my side un - til morn - ing is nigh.
3 Thy ten - der care, And fit us for heav - en, to live with Thee there.

In the Beginning Was . . . 157

In the beginning was the Word:
the Word was with God
and the Word was God.

He was with God in the beginning.

Through Him all things came to be,
not one thing had its being but through Him.

All that came to be had life in Him
and that life was the light of men,
a light that shines in the dark,
a light that darkness could not overpower.

A man came, sent by God.
His name was John.
He came as a witness,
as a witness to speak for the light,
so that everyone might believe through Him.

He was not the light,
only a witness to speak for the light.

The Word was the true light
that enlightens all men;
and He was coming into the world.

He was in the world
that had its being through Him,
and the world did not know Him.

He came to His own domain
and His own people did not accept Him.

But to all who did accept Him
He gave power to become children of God,
to all who believe in the name of Him
who was born not out of human stock,
or urge of the flesh,
or will of man,
but of God Himself.

The Word was made flesh,
He lived among us,
and we saw His glory,
the glory that is His as the only
    Son of the Father,
full of grace and truth.

—John 1:1-14 (TJB)

A Spoken Messiah

LEADER: Comfort ye, comfort ye my people, saith your God; speak ye comfortably to Jerusalem; and cry unto her, that her warfare is accomplished, that her iniquity is pardoned.

The voice of him that crieth in the wilderness, "Prepare ye the way of the Lord, make straight in the desert a highway for our God." *(Isaiah 40:1-3)*

MEN: *Every valley shall be exalted, and every mountain and hill made low; the crooked straight, and the rough places plain. (Isaiah 40:4)*

ALL: *And the glory of the Lord shall be revealed, and all flesh shall see it together; for the mouth of the Lord hath spoken it. (Isaiah 40:5)*

LEADER: Behold, a virgin shall conceive, and bear a Son, and shall call His name Emmanuel, God with us. *(Isaiah 7:14)*

WOMEN: *O thou that tellest good tidings to Zion, get thee up into the high mountain; O thou that tellest good tidings to Jerusalem, lift up thy voice with strength; lift it up, be not afraid; say unto the cities of Judah, "Behold your God!" (Isaiah 40:9)*

MEN: *Arise, shine, for thy light is come, and the glory of the Lord is risen upon thee. (Isaiah 60:1)*

ALL: *For unto us a Child is born, unto us a Son is given, and the government shall be upon His shoulder: and His name shall be called Wonderful,*
  Counselor,
    the Mighty God,
      the Everlasting Father,
        the Prince of Peace.
          (Isaiah 9:6)

LEADER: There were shepherds abiding in the field, keeping watch over their flocks by night. *(Luke 2:8)*

CHOIR: *And lo! the angel of the Lord came upon them, and the glory of the Lord shone round about them, and they were sore afraid.*
(Luke 2:9)

LEADER: And the angel said unto them, "Fear not; for, behold, I bring you good tidings of great joy, which shall be to all people.

"For unto you is born this day in the city of David a Savior, which is Christ the Lord."
(Luke 2:10, 11)

ALL: *Hallelujah, for the Lord God omnipotent reigneth. The kingdom of this world is become the kingdom of our Lord, and of His Christ; and He shall reign forever and ever. King of kings, and Lord of lords. Hallelujah! Hallelujah! (Revelation 19:6; 11:15; 19:16)*

—from *Messiah* by George Frederic Handel
—libretto by Charles Jennens

JESUS CHRIST: ADVENT AND NATIVITY

The Birthday of a King

159

" 'The days are coming' declares the Lord, 'when I will raise up to David a righteous Branch, a King who will reign wisely and do what is just and right in the land.' "—Jeremiah 23:5

10.6.10.7.wR.
NEIDLINGER

William Harold Neidlinger

William Harold Neidlinger

1 In the lit - tle vil - lage of Beth - le - hem, there lay a Child one
2 'Twas a hum - ble birth-place, but O how much God gave to us that

1 day, And the sky was bright with a ho - ly light o'er the
2 day, From the man - ger bed what a path has led, what a

1 place where Je - sus lay. Al - le - lu - ia! O how the
2 per - fect ho - ly way.

an - gels sang. Al - le - lu - ia! How it rang! And the

sky was bright with a ho - ly light, 'twas the birth - day of a King.

160

How Great Our Joy

"But the angel said to them, 'Do not be afraid. I bring you good news of great
joy that will be for all the people.' "—Luke 2:10

German Carol

JÜNGST
German Melody
Arranged by Hugo Jüngst

1 While by the sheep we watched at night, Glad tid-ings brought an
2 There shall be born, so he did say, In Beth-le-hem a
3 There shall the Child lie in a stall, This Child who shall re-
4 This gift of God we'll cher-ish well, That ev-er joy our

f   *p* echo

1 an - gel bright. How great our joy! Great our joy!
2 Child to - day. How great our joy! Great our joy!
3 deem us all. How great our joy! Great our joy!
4 hearts shall fill. How great our joy! Great our joy!

f   *p* echo   *f*

1 Joy, joy, joy! Joy, joy, joy! Praise we the Lord in
2 Joy, joy, joy! Joy, joy, joy! Praise we the Lord in
3 Joy, joy, joy! Joy, joy, joy! Praise we the Lord in
4 Joy, joy, joy! Joy, joy, joy! Praise we the Lord in

p echo

1 heaven on high! Praise we the Lord in heaven on high!
2 heaven on high! Praise we the Lord in heaven on high!
3 heaven on high! Praise we the Lord in heaven on high!
4 heaven on high! Praise we the Lord in heaven on high!

JESUS CHRIST: ADVENT AND NATIVITY

Angels We Have Heard on High 161

"Let's go to Bethlehem and see this thing that has happened, which the Lord has told us about."—Luke 2:15b

7.7.7.7.wR.
GLORIA
French Carol

French Carol

1 An - gels we have heard on high Sweet-ly sing - ing o'er the plains,
2 Shep-herds, why this ju - bi - lee? Why your joy - ous strains pro-long?
3 Come to Beth - le - hem and see Him whose birth the an - gels sing;

1 And the moun-tains in re - ply Ech - o back their joy - ous strains.
2 Say what may the ti - dings be, Which in - spire your heaven - ly song?
3 Come a - dore, on bend - ed knee, Christ, the Lord, the new - born King.

Glo - - - - - - ri - a

in ex - cel - sis De - o, Glo - - - -

- - ri - a in ex - cel - sis De - o.

JESUS CHRIST: ADVENT AND NATIVITY

162 Hark! the Herald Angels Sing

"Suddenly a great company of the heavenly host appeared with the angel, praising God and saying . . . "—Luke 2:13

7.7.7.7.D.wR.
MENDELSSOHN
Felix Mendelssohn
Descant by Paul Liljestrand

Charles Wesley

1 Hark! the her-ald an-gels sing, "Glo-ry to the new-born King:
2 Christ, by high-est heaven a-dored; Christ, the ev-er-last-ing Lord!
3 Hail the heaven-born Prince of Peace! Hail the Sun of Right-eous-ness!

1 Peace on earth, and mer-cy mild, God and sin-ners
2 Late in time be-hold Him come, Off-spring of the
3 Light and life to all He brings, Risen with heal-ing

1 rec-on-ciled!" Joy-ful, all ye na-tions, rise, Join the tri-umph
2 Vir-gin's womb. Veiled in flesh the God-head see; Hail th'in-car-nate
3 in His wings. Mild He lays His glo-ry by, Born that we no

1 of the skies; With the an-gel-ic host pro-claim,
2 De-i-ty, Pleased as man with us to dwell,
3 more may die; Born to raise the souls of earth,

JESUS CHRIST: ADVENT AND NATIVITY

sons of earth to sec - ond birth.

1 "Christ is born in Beth - le - hem!" Hark! the her - ald
2 Je - sus, our Em - man - u - el. Hark! the her - ald
3 Born to give them sec - ond birth. Hark! the her - ald

Hark! the her - ald an - gels sing to the new - born King.

1 an - gels sing, "Glo - ry to the new - born King."
2 an - gels sing, "Glo - ry to the new - born King."
3 an - gels sing, "Glo - ry to the new - born King."

His Love . . . Reaching 163

Right from the beginning God's love has reached, and from the beginning man has refused to understand. But love went on reaching, offering itself. Love offered the eternal . . . we wanted the immediate. Love offered deep joy . . . we wanted thrills. Love offered freedom . . . we wanted license. Love offered communion with God Himself . . . we wanted to worship at the shrine of our own minds. Love offered peace . . . we wanted approval for our wars. Even yet, love went on reaching. And still after two thousand years , patiently , lovingly , Christ is reaching out to us today. Right through the chaos of our world, through the confusion of our minds. He is reaching . . . longing to share with us . . . the very being of God.

His love still is longing, His love still is reaching, right past the shackles of my mind. And the Word of the Father became Mary's little Son. And His love reached all the way to where I was.

—Gloria Gaither

164 Glory in the Highest

"Glory to God in the highest, and on earth peace to men on whom his favor rests."—Luke 2:14

HIGHEST GLORY
William J. Gaither
Bill George
Billy Smiley

Gloria Gaither

1 Glo - ry in the high - est! Glo - ry to His name!
2 Je - sus, You have found us When we wan - dered far;
3 Glo - ry in the high - est! Let the song be - gin!
4 Glo - ry in the high - est! Glo - ry to His name!

1 Joy has come in - to our lives; We'll nev - er be the same.
2 When we could not find our - selves You came to where we are.
3 Joy has come in - to our world; Let us wor - ship Him!
4 Joy has come in - to our lives; We'll nev - er be the same.

1 Glo - ry in the high - est! Wor - thy is our King!
2 "Glo - ry in the high - est!" Is more than just a phrase.
3 Glo - ry in the high - est! Wor - thy is our King!
4 Glo - ry in the high - est! Wor - thy is our King!

1 Come let us a - dore Him, And give Him ev - ery - thing.
2 Lord, we fall be - fore You now, Your ho - ly name we praise.
3 Come let us a - dore Him, And bring Him ev - ery - thing.
4 Come let us a - dore Him, And give Him ev - ery - thing.

JESUS CHRIST: ADVENT AND NATIVITY

O Little Town of Bethlehem 165

*"But you, Bethlehem Ephrathah, though you are small among the clans of
Judah, out of you will come for me one who will be ruler over Israel, whose
origins are from old, from ancient times."—Micah 5:2*

8.6.8.6.7.6.8.6.

Phillips Brooks

ST. LOUIS
Lewis H. Redner

1 O lit-tle town of Beth-le-hem, How still we see thee lie!
2 For Christ is born of Ma-ry, And gath-ered all a-bove,
3 How si-lent-ly, how si-lent-ly, The won-drous gift is given!
4 O ho-ly Child of Beth-le-hem! De-scend to us, we pray;

1 A-bove thy deep and dream-less sleep The si-lent stars go by;
2 While mor-tals sleep, the an-gels keep Their watch of won-dering love.
3 So God im-parts to hu-man hearts The bless-ings of His heaven.
4 Cast out our sin and en-ter in, Be born in us to-day.

1 Yet in thy dark streets shin-eth The ev-er-last-ing Light:
2 O morn-ing stars, to-geth-er Pro-claim the ho-ly birth!
3 No ear may hear His com-ing, But in this world of sin,
4 We hear the Christ-mas an-gels The great glad ti-dings tell;

1 The hopes and fears of all the years Are met in thee to-night.
2 And prais-es sing to God the King, And peace to all on earth.
3 Where meek souls will re-ceive Him still, The dear Christ en-ters in.
4 O come to us, a-bide with us, Our Lord Em-man-u-el! A-men.

JESUS CHRIST: ADVENT AND NATIVITY

166 He Started the Whole World Singing

"The Spirit of the Sovereign Lord is on me, because the Lord has anointed me to preach good news to the poor."—Isaiah 61:1

Gloria Gaither

ALEXANDRIA
William J. Gaither
Chris Waters

1 Be - fore the song start - ed, the world, bro - ken heart - ed, was
2 A new Word was spo - ken, and chords that were bro - ken wove

1 dream - less - ly pass - ing the long, emp - ty days; Then a
2 gen - tly to - geth - er to make a new song. It was

1 dark, lone - ly hill - side was span - gled with light, and a
2 more than a car - ol to greet the new morn— for the

1 song burst in - to the night! He
2 Source of all mu - sic was born!

JESUS CHRIST: ADVENT AND NATIVITY

start-ed   the   whole world   sing - ing   a   song.   The

words and   the   mu - sic   were there   all   a   -   long! What the

song   had to   say   was that   love   found a   way   to

start   the world   sing - ing   a   song.

167 Silent Night, Holy Night

*"For unto us a child is born, to us a son is given, and the government will be
on his shoulders. And he will be called Wonderful Counselor, Mighty God,
Everlasting Father, Prince of Peace."—Isaiah 9:6*

Joseph Mohr
Tr. by John F. Young

STILLE NACHT
Franz Grüber

1 Si - lent night, ho - ly night! All is calm, all is bright
2 Si - lent night, ho - ly night! Shep-herds quake at the sight.
3 Si - lent night, ho - ly night! Son of God, love's pure light

1 'Round yon vir - gin moth-er and child. Ho - ly in-fant so ten-der and mild,
2 Glo - ries stream from heav-en a - far, Heaven-ly hosts sing al - le - lu - ia;
3 Ra - diant beams from Thy ho-ly face With the dawn of re - deem - ing grace,

1 Sleep in heav - en-ly peace, Sleep in heav - en-ly peace.
2 Christ, the Sav - ior is born! Christ, the Sav - ior is born!
3 Je - sus, Lord, at Thy birth, Je - sus, Lord, at Thy birth.

168 *The First Christmas*

There she was. The young woman with the radiant smile. She was leaning against one of the stalls, and the eyes in the happy face were closed. The man was at her side. And behind them, in the manger where the cows came for their food, was the Baby.

He was a tiny thing, wrapped tightly in a long linen band and sleeping as soundly as any newborn baby. Sleeping as though the world had not waited thousands of years for this moment. As soundly as though your life and my life and the life of everyone on earth were not wrapped up in His birth. As though from this moment on all the sin and sorrow of the world were not His problem.

Should you speak to His mother resting so quietly there? Should you ask her if you might touch the Baby—not to wake Him, but just to touch His hand?

What a moment that would have been! To have reached out your own hand and touched the Son of God!

—Ruth Bell Graham
From *Our Christmas Story*
by Mrs. Billy Graham

JESUS CHRIST: ADVENT AND NATIVITY

The Star Carol

169

"When they saw the star, they were overjoyed."—Matthew 2:10

Wihla Hutson

STAR CAROL
Alfred S. Burt

1 Long years a - go on a deep win - ter night,
2 Je - sus, the Lord, was that Ba - by so small,
3 Dear Ba - by Je - sus, How ti - ny Thou art,

1 High in the heav'ns a star shone bright,
2 Laid down to sleep in a hum - ble stall;
3 I'll make a place for Thee in my heart,

1 While in a man - ger a wee Ba - by lay,
2 Then came the star and it stood o - ver - head,
3 And when the stars in the heav - ens I see,

1 Sweet - ly a - sleep on a bed of hay.
2 Shed - ding its light 'round His lit - tle bed.
3 Ev - er and al - ways I'll think of Thee.

JESUS CHRIST: ADVENT AND NATIVITY

I Heard the Bells on Christmas Day

"And he will be their peace."—Micah 5:5

Henry W. Longfellow

L.M.
WALTHAM
J. Baptiste Calkin

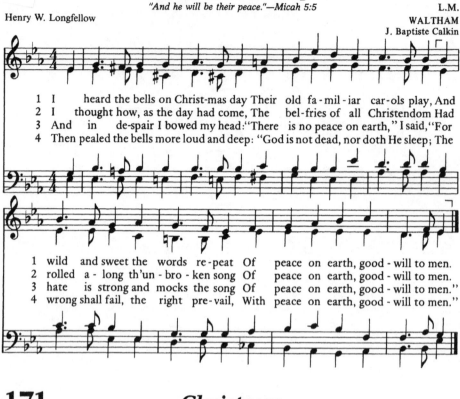

1 I heard the bells on Christ-mas day Their old fa-mil-iar car-ols play, And
2 I thought how, as the day had come, The bel-fries of all Christendom Had
3 And in de-spair I bowed my head:"There is no peace on earth," I said,"For
4 Then pealed the bells more loud and deep: "God is not dead, nor doth He sleep; The

1 wild and sweet the words re-peat Of peace on earth, good-will to men.
2 rolled a-long th'un-bro-ken song Of peace on earth, good-will to men.
3 hate is strong and mocks the song Of peace on earth, good-will to men."
4 wrong shall fail, the right pre-vail, With peace on earth, good-will to men."

171 *Christmas*

Are you willing to forget what you have done for other people, and to remember what other people have done for you, to ignore what the world owes you, to think what you owe the world?

We are willing, with the help of God.

To put your rights in the background, and your duties in the middle distance, and your chances to do a little more than your duty in the foreground?

We are willing, with the help of God.

To see that your fellowmen are just as real as you are, and try to look behind their faces to their hearts, hungry for joy?

We are willing, with the help of God.

To close your book of complaints against the management of the universe, and look around you for a place where you can sow a few seeds of happiness—are you willing to do these things even for a day?

We are willing, with the help of God.

Then—you can keep Christmas. Are you willing to believe that love is the strongest thing in the world—stronger than hate, stronger than evil, stronger than death—and that the blessed life which began in Bethlehem 2,000 years ago is the image and brightness of the eternal love?

We are willing, with the help of God.

Then you can keep Christmas. And if you keep it for a day, why not always?

—James Earl Massey

Good Christians, Now Rejoice 172

"I delight greatly in the Lord; my soul rejoices in my God."—Isaiah 61:10a

Latin Carol
Tr. by John M. Neale

IN DULCI JUBILO
German Melody
Harmonized by John Stainer

1 Good Chris-tians, now re-joice   With heart and soul and voice;
2 Good Chris-tians, now re-joice   With heart and soul and voice;
3 Good Chris-tians, now re-joice   With heart and soul and voice;

1 Give ye heed to what we say: News! news! Je - sus Christ is born to-day!
2 Now ye hear of end-less bliss: Joy! joy!   Je - sus Christ was born for this!
3 Now ye need not fear the grave: Peace! peace! Je - sus Christ was born to save!

1 Ox   and ass be - fore Him bow, And He   is in   the man - ger now.
2 He   has o - pened heav-en's door, And man is bless - ed ev - er-more.
3 Calls you one and calls you all To gain His ev - er - last - ing hall.

1 Christ is born to - day!   Christ is born to - day!
2 Christ was born for this!   Christ was born for this!
3 Christ was born to save!   Christ was born to save!

173   O Christmas Tree

"Sing joyfully to the Lord, you righteous; it is fitting for the upright to praise him."—Psalm 33:1

Bryan Jeffery Leech

8.7.8.7.8.8.8.7.
TANNENBAUM
German Carol

1 O Christ-mas tree, O Christ-mas tree, your branch-es are up-lift-ed. You
2 O Christ-mas tree, O Christ-mas tree, you shine like stars a-bove us; And
3 O Christ-mas tree, O Christ-mas tree, in plain-ness you were grow-ing un-

1 seem to say that on this day our world's su-preme-ly gift-ed. The
2 with your beau-ty si-lent say, "How great-ly God must love us!" You
3 til we came and brought you here and set your branch-es glow-ing. Your

1 shin-ing of your can-dles bright, re-minds us Light has come to-night. O
2 show us Him who with God's face, brought to our hearts the gift of grace. O
3 liv-ing beau-ty helps us see how clothed with Christ our lives can be. O

1 Christ-mas tree, O Christ-mas tree, you lift our eyes to heav-en.
2 Christ-mas tree, O Christ-mas tree, you lift our eyes to heav-en.
3 Christ-mas tree, O Christ-mas tree, you lift our eyes to heav-en.

JESUS CHRIST: ADVENT AND NATIVITY

Now when Jesus was born in
  Bethlehem of Judea
in the days of Herod the king,
  behold,
wise men from the East came
  to Jerusalem, saying

> *"Where is He who has been born*
>   *King of the Jews?*
> *For we have seen His star in the East,*
> *and have come to worship Him."*

When Herod the king heard this,
he was troubled, and all Jerusalem
  with him;
and assembling all the chief priests
  and scribes of the people,
he inquired of them where the
  Christ was to be born.

> *They told him, "In Bethlehem*
>   *of Judea;*
> *for so it is written by the prophet:*
> *'And you, O Bethlehem, in the*
>   *land of Judah,*
> *are by no means least among the*
>   *rulers of Judah;*
> *for from you shall come a ruler*
> *who will govern my*
>   *people Israel.' "*

Then Herod summoned the wise
  men secretly
and ascertained from them
what time the star appeared;
and he sent them to Bethlehem,
  saying,
"Go and search diligently for
  the Child,
and when you have found Him bring
  me word,
that I too may come and
  worship Him."

> *When they had heard the king*
> *they went their way;*
> *and lo, the star which they had seen*
>   *in the East*
> *went before them,*
> *till it came to rest over the place*
>   *where the Child was.*

When they saw the star, they rejoiced
  exceedingly with great joy;
and going into the house they saw
  the Child with Mary His mother,
and they fell down and
  worshiped Him.

> *Then, opening their treasures,*
> *they offered Him gifts,*
> *gold and frankincense and myrrh.*

—From Matthew 2 (RSV)

175 As with Gladness Men of Old

*"When they saw the star, they were overjoyed. On coming to the house, they
saw the child with his mother Mary, and they bowed down and worshiped him.
Then they opened their treasures and presented him with gifts of gold and of
incense and of myrrh."—Matthew 2:10-11*

7.7.7.7.7.7.
DIX

William C. Dix

Adapted from a chorale by Conrad Kocher

1 As with glad - ness men of old Did the guid - ing
2 As with joy - ful steps they sped To that low - ly
3 As they of - fered gifts most rare At the man - ger
4 Ho - ly Je - sus, ev - 'ry day Keep us in the

1 star be - hold; As with joy they hailed its light,
2 man - ger - bed, There to bend the knee be - fore
3 rude and bare, So may we with ho - ly joy,
4 nar - row way; And, when earth - ly things are past,

1 Lead - ing on - ward, beam - ing bright; So, most gra - cious
2 Him whom heaven and earth a - dore; So may we with
3 Pure and free from sin's al - loy, All our cost - liest
4 Bring our ran - somed souls at last Where they need no

1 Lord, may we Ev - er - more be led to Thee.
2 will - ing feet Ev - er seek Thy mer - cy seat.
3 treas - ures bring, Christ, to Thee, our heaven - ly King.
4 star to guide, Where no clouds Thy glo - ry hide. A - men.

JESUS CHRIST: ADVENT AND NATIVITY

Go, Tell It on the Mountain 176

"Let the desert and its towns raise their voices; let the settlements where Kedar lives rejoice. Let the people of Sela sing for joy; let them shout from the mountaintops. Let them give glory to the Lord and proclaim his praise in the islands."—Isaiah 42:11-12

John W. Work

GO, TELL IT ON THE MOUNTAIN
American Folk Song

Go, tell it on the moun-tain, O-ver the hills and ev-ery-where;

Go, tell it on the moun-tain That Je-sus Christ is born!

1 While shep-herds kept their watch-ing O'er si-lent flocks by night, Be-
2 The shep-herds feared and trem-bled When lo! a-bove the earth Rang
3 Down in a low-ly man-ger The hum-ble Christ was born, And

1 hold through-out the heav-ens There shone a ho-ly light.
2 out the an-gel cho-rus That hailed our Sav-ior's birth.
3 brought us God's sal-va-tion That bless-ed Christ-mas morn.

JESUS CHRIST: ADVENT AND NATIVITY

177 Child in the Manger

"So they hurried off and found Mary and Joseph, and the baby, who was lying in the manger."—Luke 2:16

10.9.10.9.

Mary MacDonald
Fred Bock

BUNESSAN
Traditional Gaelic Melody

1 Child in the man - ger, In - fant of Ma - ry,
2 Proph-ets fore - told Him, In - fant of won - der,

1 Came as a stran - ger born in the stall;
2 An - gels be - hold Him there on His throne;

1 Sweet lit - tle Je - sus sent down from heav - en,
2 Wor - thy the Sav - ior of all our prais - es,

1 God's gift of new life of - fered to all.
2 Hap - py and ev - er blest are His own. A - men.

JESUS CHRIST: ADVENT AND NATIVITY

Emmanuel

178

"The virgin will be with child and will give birth to a son, and they will call him 'Immanuel'—which means, 'God with us.' "—Matthew 1:23

Robert McGee

EMMANUEL
Robert McGee

Em-man - u - el, Em-man - u - el,

His name is called Em-man-u - el;

God with us, re - vealed in us;

His name is called Em-man-u - el.

179 Once in Royal David's City

"He will reign on David's throne . . . "—Isaiah 9:7

8.7.8.7.7.7.
IRBY

Cecil F. Alexander

Henry J. Gauntlett

1 Once in roy - al Da - vid's cit - y Stood a low - ly cat - tle
2 He came down to earth from heav - en Who is God and Lord of
3 Je - sus is our child - hood's pat - tern, Day by day like us He
4 And our eyes at last shall see Him Thro' His own re - deem - ing

1 shed, Where a moth - er laid her Ba - by In a
2 all, And His shel - ter was a sta - ble, And His
3 grew; He was lit - tle, weak, and help - less, Tears and
4 love; For that Child so dear and gen - tle Is our

1 man - ger for His bed; Ma - ry was that moth - er
2 cra - dle was a stall: With the poor and mean and
3 smiles like us He knew: And He feel - eth for our
4 Lord in heav'n a - bove, And He leads His chil - dren

1 mild, Je - sus Christ her lit - tle Child.
2 low - ly Lived on earth, our Sav - ior ho - ly.
3 sad - ness, And He shar - eth in our glad - ness.
4 on To the place where He is gone.

JESUS CHRIST: ADVENT AND NATIVITY

Of the Father's Love Begotten 180

"I am the Alpha and the Omega, the First and the Last, the Beginning and the End."—Revelation 22:13

Aurelius C. Prudentius
Tr. by John M. Neale, stanza 1.
Henry W. Baker, stanzas 2 and 3

8.7.8.7.8.7.7.
DIVINUM MYSTERIUM
13th Century Plainsong

Unison

1 Of the Fa - ther's love be - got - ten, Ere the worlds be - gan
2 O ye heights of heav'n, a - dore Him; An - gel hosts, His prais -
3 Christ, to Thee with God the Fa - ther, And, O Ho - ly Ghost,

1 to be, He is Al - pha and O - me - ga, He the Source, the
2 es sing; Pow'rs, do - min - ions, bow be - fore Him And ex - tol our
3 to Thee, Hymn and chant and high thanks-giv - ing And un - wea - ried

1 End - ing He, Of the things that are, that have been,
2 God and King; Let no tongue on earth be si - lent,
3 prais - es be: Hon - or, glo - ry, and do - min - ion,

1 And that future years shall see, Ev - er-more and ev-er-more!
2 Ev - 'ry voice in con-cert ring, Ev - er-more and ev-er-more!
3 And e - ter - nal vic - to - ry, Ev - er-more and ev-er-more! A - men.

181 Infant Holy, Infant Lowly

" . . . and she gave birth to her firstborn, a son."—Luke 2:7a

8.7.8.7.8.8.7.7.
W ZLOBIE LEZY
Polish Carol

Traditional
Paraphrase by Edith M. G. Reed

1 In - fant ho - ly, in - fant low - ly, for His bed a cat - tle stall;
2 Flocks were sleep - ing: shep-herds keep - ing vig - il till the morn-ing new

1 Ox - en low - ing, lit - tle know-ing Christ, the babe, is Lord of all.
2 Saw the glo - ry, heard the sto - ry, ti - dings of a gos - pel true.

1 Swift are wing - ing an - gels sing - ing, No - els ring - ing,
2 Thus re - joic - ing, free from sor - row, Prais - es voic - ing

1 tid - ings bring - ing: Christ, the babe, is Lord of all.
2 greet the mor - row: Christ, the babe, was born for you.

JESUS CHRIST: ADVENT AND NATIVITY

It Came Upon the Midnight Clear   182

"An angel of the Lord appeared to them, and the glory of the Lord shone around them, and they were terrified."—Luke 2:9

Edmund H. Sears

C.M.D.
CAROL
Richard S. Willis

1 It came up-on the mid-night clear, That glo-rious song of old,
2 And ye, be-neath life's crush-ing load, Whose forms are bend-ing low,
3 For lo, the days are has-tening on, By proph-et seen of old,

1 From an-gels bend-ing near the earth To touch their harps of gold:
2 Who toil a-long the climb-ing way With pain-ful steps and slow,
3 When, with the ev-er-cir-cling years, Shall come the time fore-told,

1 "Peace on the earth, good-will to men, From heaven's all-gra-cious King":
2 Look now! for glad and gold-en hours Come swift-ly on the wing:
3 When the new heaven and earth shall own The Prince of Peace their King,

1 The world in sol-emn still-ness lay To hear the an-gels sing.
2 O rest be-side the wea-ry load, And hear the an-gels sing.
3 And the whole world send back the song Which now the an-gels sing.

JESUS CHRIST: ADVENT AND NATIVITY

183 Angels, from the Realms of Glory

"Suddenly a great company of the heavenly host appeared with the angel, praising God and saying . . . "—Luke 2:13

James Montgomery

8.7.8.7.8.7.
REGENT SQUARE
Henry T. Smart

1 An - gels, from the realms of glo - ry, Wing your flight o'er all the earth;
2 Shep-herds, in the fields a - bid - ing, Watch-ing o'er your flocks by night,
3 Wise men, leave your con - tem-pla-tion, Bright-er vi - sions beam a - far;
4 Saints be - fore the al - tar bend-ing, Watch-ing long in hope and fear,

1 Ye who sang cre - a - tion's sto - ry, Now pro-claim Mes - si - ah's birth:
2 God with man is now re - sid - ing, Yon-der shines the in - fant light:
3 Seek the great De - sire of na - tions, Ye have seen His na - tal star:
4 Sud - den - ly the Lord, de-scend-ing, In His tem - ple shall ap - pear:

Come and wor-ship, come and wor-ship, Wor-ship Christ, the new-born King. A-men.

184 O Come, All Ye Faithful

"When the angels had left them and gone into heaven, the shepherds said to one another, 'Let's go to Bethlehem and see this thing that has happened, which the Lord has told us about.' "—Luke 2:15

Latin: John F. Wade
Tr. by Frederick Oakeley

ADESTE FIDELES
John F. Wade's *Cantus Diversi*
Descant by Fred Bock

1 O come, all ye faith - ful, joy-ful and tri - um-phant, O come ye, O
2   Sing, choirs of an - gels, sing in ex - ul - ta - tion, O sing, all ye
3   Yea, Lord, we greet Thee, born this hap-py morn - ing, O Je - sus, to

JESUS CHRIST: ADVENT AND NATIVITY

1 come ye to Beth - le - hem; Come and be-hold Him, born the King of an - gels;
2 cit - i-zens of heaven a - bove; Glo - ry to God, all glo-ry in the high - est;
3 Thee be all glo - ry given; Word of the Fa - ther, now in flesh ap -pear-ing;

Descant

O come, O come,

O come, let us a - dore Him, O come, let us a - dore Him,

O come, let us a - dore Him, Christ, the Lord. A -men.

O come, let us a - dore Him, Christ, the Lord. A -men.

185 Thou Didst Leave Thy Throne

"He came to that which was his own, but his own did not receive him."
—John 1:11

Emily E. S. Elliott

MARGARET
Timothy R. Matthews

1 Thou didst leave Thy throne and Thy king - ly crown When Thou
2 Heav - en's arch - es rang when the an - gels sang, Pro -
3 The fox - es found rest, and the birds their nest In the
4 Thou cam - est, O Lord, with the liv - ing word That should
5 When the heavens shall ring and the an - gels sing At Thy

1 cam - est to earth for me, But in Beth - le-hem's home there was
2 claim - ing Thy roy - al de - gree, But in low - ly birth didst Thou
3 shade of the for - est tree, But Thy couch was the sod, O Thou
4 set Thy peo - ple free, But with mock - ing scorn and with
5 com - ing to vic - to - ry, Let Thy voice call me home, say - ing,

1 found no room For Thy ho - ly na - tiv - i - ty. O come to my
2 come to earth And in great hu - mil - i - ty. O come to my
3 Son of God, In the des - erts of Gal - i - lee. O come to my
4 crown of thorn They bore Thee to Cal - va - ry. O come to my
5 "Yet there is room, There is room at My side for thee." And my heart shall re-

1 heart, Lord Je - sus: There is room in my heart for Thee!
2 heart, Lord Je - sus: There is room in my heart for Thee!
3 heart, Lord Je - sus: There is room in my heart for Thee!
4 heart, Lord Je - sus: There is room in my heart for Thee!
5 joice, Lord Je - sus, When Thou com - est and call - est me.

JESUS CHRIST: LIFE AND MINISTRY

Tell Me the Stories of Jesus 186

*"But go and learn what this means: 'I desire mercy, not sacrifice.' For I have
not come to call the righteous, but sinners."—Matthew 9:13*

William H. Parker

STORIES OF JESUS
Frederic A. Challinor

Unison or duet

1 Tell me the sto - ries of Je - sus I love to hear;
2 First let me hear how the chil - dren Stood 'round His knee,
3 In - to the cit - y I'd fol - low The chil - dren's band,

1 Things I would ask Him to tell me If He were here:
2 I shall im - ag - ine His bless - ing Rest - ing on me;
3 Wav - ing a branch of the palm - tree High in my hand;

1 Scenes by the way - side, Tales of the sea,
2 Words full of kind - ness, Deeds full of grace,
3 One of His her - alds, Yes, I would sing

1 Sto - ries of Je - sus, Tell them to me.
2 All in the bright - ness Of Je - sus' face.
3 Loud - est ho - san - nas, "Je - sus is King!"

JESUS CHRIST: LIFE AND MINISTRY

187 Hosanna, Loud Hosanna

"The crowds that went ahead of him and those that followed shouted, 'Hosanna to the Son of David!' "—Matthew 21:9a

Based on Matthew 21:15, 16
Jennette Threlfall
Jeff Redd, stanza 2

7.6.7.6.D.
ELLACOMBE
"Gesängbuch der Herzogl," Württemburg

1 Ho - san - na, loud ho - san - na, The lit - tle chil - dren sang;
2 From Ol - i - vet they fol - lowed, A hap - py, joy - ous crowd,
3 "Ho - san - na in the high - est!" That an - cient song we sing,

1 Through pil - lared court and tem - ple The love - ly an - them rang:
2 Their large palm branch - es wav - ing, And sing - ing clear and loud;
3 For Christ is our Re - deem - er, The Lord of heaven our King;

1 To Je - sus, who had blessed them Close fold - ed to His breast,
2 The Lord of earth and heav - en Rode on in sim - ple joy,
3 O may we ev - er praise Him With heart and life and voice,

1 The chil - dren sang their prais - es, The sim - plest and the best.
2 And wel - comed all the chil - dren: Each lit - tle girl and boy.
3 And in His ho - ly pres - ence E - ter - nal - ly re - joice!

JESUS CHRIST: TRIUMPHAL ENTRY

All Glory, Laud and Honor 188

"They took palm branches and went out to meet him, shouting, 'Hosanna!'
'Blessed is he who comes in the name of the lord!' 'Blessed is the King of
Israel!' "—John 12:13

Theodulph of Orleans
Tr. by John M. Neale

7.6.7.6.D.
ST. THEODULPH
Melchior Teschner

1 All glo - ry, laud and hon - or To Thee, Re - deem - er, King,
2 The com - pa - ny of an - gels Are prais - ing Thee on high,
3 To Thee, be - fore Thy pas - sion, They sang their hymns of praise;

1 To whom the lips of chil - dren Made sweet ho - san - nas ring:
2 And we, with all cre - a - tion, In cho - rus make re - ply:
3 To Thee, now high ex - alt - ed, Our mel - o - dy we raise:

1 Thou art the King of Is - ra - el, Thou Da - vid's roy - al Son,
2 The peo - ple of the He - brews With palms be - fore Thee went,
3 Thou didst ac - cept their prais - es— Ac - cept the praise we bring,

1 Who in the Lord's name com - est, The King and bless - ed one!
2 Our praise and prayer and an - thems Be - fore Thee we pre - sent.
3 Who in all good de - light - est, Thou good and gra - cious King!

JESUS CHRIST: TRIUMPHAL ENTRY

189 Lead Me to Calvary

"I have been crucified with Christ and I no longer live, but Christ lives in me."
—Galatians 2:20

Jennie Evelyn Hussey

C.M.wR.
DUNCANNON
John T. Grape

1 King of my life I crown Thee now— Thine shall the glo - ry be;
2 Show me the tomb where Thou wast laid, Ten - der - ly mourned and wept,
3 Let me like Ma - ry, through the gloom, Come with a gift to Thee;
4 May I be will - ing, Lord, to bear Dai - ly my cross for Thee;

1 Lest I for-get Thy thorn-crowned brow, Lead me to Cal - va - ry.
2 An - gels in robes of light ar - rayed Guard-ed Thee whilst Thou slept.
3 Show to me now the emp - ty tomb— Lead me to Cal - va - ry.
4 E - ven Thy cup of grief to share— Thou hast borne all for me.

Lest I for-get Geth - sem - a - ne, Lest I for-get Thine ag - o - ny,

Lest I for-get Thy love for me, Lead me to Cal - va - ry.

JESUS CHRIST: SUFFERING AND DEATH ON THE CROSS

At the Cross

"For the message of the cross is foolishness to those who are perishing, but to us who are being saved it is the power of God."—I Corinthians 1:18

Isaac Watts
Refrain added by Ralph E. Hudson

C.M.wR.
HUDSON
Ralph E. Hudson

1 A - las, and did my Sav - ior bleed? And did my Sov-ereign die?
2 Was it for crimes that I have done, He suf - fered on the tree?
3 Well might the sun in dark - ness hide And shut His glo - ries in,
4 But drops of grief can ne'er re - pay The debt of love I owe:

1 Would He de - vote that sa - cred head For some-one such as I?
2 A - maz - ing pit - y! grace un-known! And love be - yond de - gree!
3 When Christ, the great Re - deem - er, died To set me free from sin.
4 Here, Lord, I give my - self a - way, 'Tis all that I can do!

At the cross, at the cross where I first saw the light, And the
bur - den of my heart rolled a - way, It was there by faith
I re - ceived my sight, And now I am hap-py all the day!

JESUS CHRIST: SUFFERING AND DEATH ON THE CROSS

191 Down at the Cross

"In fact, the law requires that nearly everything be cleansed with blood, and without the shedding of blood there is no forgiveness."—Hebrews 9:22

GLORY TO HIS NAME

Elisha A. Hoffman

John H. Stockton

1 Down at the cross where my Sav-ior died, Down where for cleans-ing from
2 I am so won-drous-ly saved from sin, Je - sus so sweet-ly a-
3 O pre-cious foun-tain that saves from sin, I am so glad I have
4 Come to this foun-tain so rich and sweet; Cast your poor soul at the

1 sin I cried, There to my heart was the blood ap - plied;
2 bides with - in; There at the cross where He took me in;
3 en - tered in; There Je - sus saves me and keeps me clean;
4 Sav - ior's feet; Plunge in to-day, and be made com - plete;

Glo - ry to His name. Glo - ry to His name, Glo - ry to His name!

There to my heart was the blood ap - plied; Glo - ry to His name.

JESUS CHRIST: SUFFERING AND DEATH ON THE CROSS

There Is a Fountain Filled with Blood

192

"On that day a fountain will be opened to the house of David and the inhabitants of Jerusalem, to cleanse them from sin and impurity."
—Zechariah 13:1

C.M.D.

CLEANSING FOUNTAIN
Traditional American Melody
Arranged by Lowell Mason

William Cowper

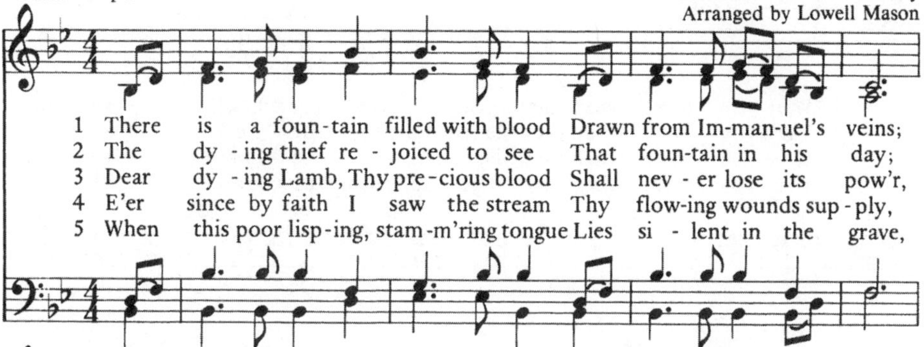

1 There is a foun-tain filled with blood Drawn from Im-man-uel's veins;
2 The dy-ing thief re-joiced to see That foun-tain in his day;
3 Dear dy-ing Lamb, Thy pre-cious blood Shall nev-er lose its pow'r,
4 E'er since by faith I saw the stream Thy flow-ing wounds sup-ply,
5 When this poor lisp-ing, stam-m'ring tongue Lies si-lent in the grave,

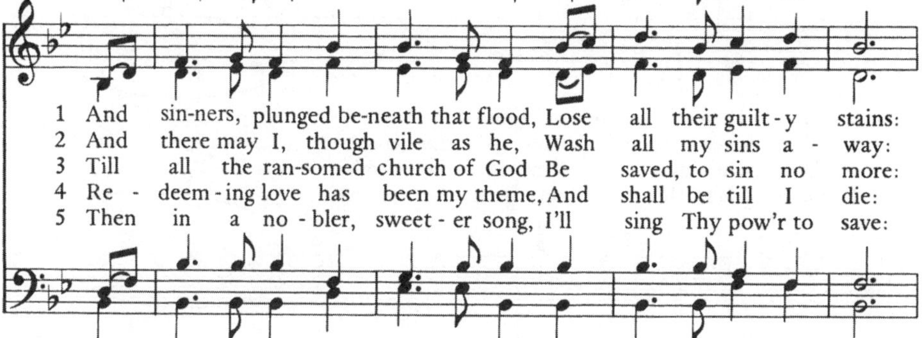

1 And sin-ners, plunged be-neath that flood, Lose all their guilt-y stains:
2 And there may I, though vile as he, Wash all my sins a-way:
3 Till all the ran-somed church of God Be saved, to sin no more:
4 Re-deem-ing love has been my theme, And shall be till I die:
5 Then in a no-bler, sweet-er song, I'll sing Thy pow'r to save:

1 Lose all their guilt-y stains, Lose all their guilt-y stains; And
2 Wash all my sins a-way, Wash all my sins a-way; And
3 Be saved, to sin no more, Be saved, to sin no more; Till
4 And shall be till I die, And shall be till I die; Re-
5 I'll sing Thy pow'r to save, I'll sing Thy pow'r to save; Then

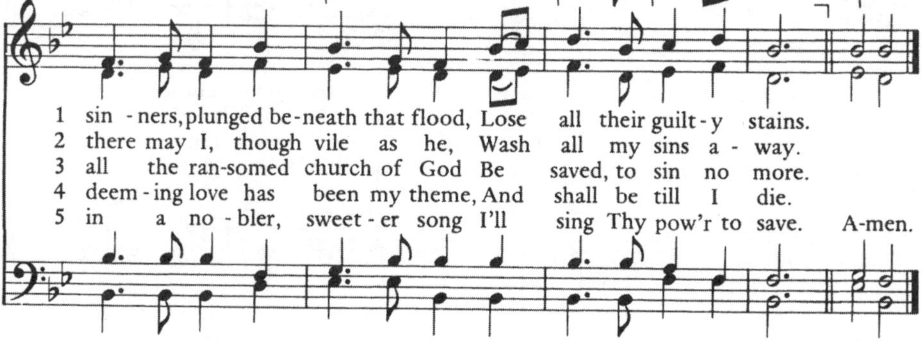

1 sin-ners, plunged be-neath that flood, Lose all their guilt-y stains.
2 there may I, though vile as he, Wash all my sins a-way.
3 all the ran-somed church of God Be saved, to sin no more.
4 deem-ing love has been my theme, And shall be till I die.
5 in a no-bler, sweet-er song I'll sing Thy pow'r to save. A-men.

JESUS CHRIST: SUFFERING AND DEATH ON THE CROSS

193

Were You There?

*"We all, like sheep, have gone astray, each of us has turned to his own way;
and the Lord has laid on him the iniquity of us all."—Isaiah 53:6*

American Folk Hymn

WERE YOU THERE
American Folk Melody

1 Were you there when they cru-ci-fied my Lord? Were you
2 Were you there when they nailed Him to the tree? Were you
3 Were you there when they laid Him in the tomb? Were you
4 Were you there when He rose up from the grave? Were you

1 there when they cru-ci-fied my Lord?
2 there when they nailed Him to the tree?
3 there when they laid Him in the tomb? O!
4 there when He rose up from the grave?

Some-times it caus-es me to trem-ble, trem-ble, trem-ble.

1 Were you there when they cru-ci-fied my Lord?
2 Were you there when they nailed Him to the tree?
3 Were you there when they laid Him in the tomb?
4 Were you there when He rose up from the grave?

JESUS CHRIST: SUFFERING AND DEATH ON THE CROSS

Behold the Lamb

194

"The next day John saw Jesus coming toward him and said, 'Look, the Lamb of God, who takes away the sin of the world!' "—John 1:29

BEHOLD THE LAMB
Dottie Rambo

Dottie Rambo

Be - hold the Lamb, Be - hold the Lamb,

slain from the foun - da - tion of the world. For sin - ners

cru - ci - fied, O ho - ly sac - ri - fice, be - hold the

Lamb of God be - hold the Lamb.
Lamb, the Lamb of God,

JESUS CHRIST: SUFFERING AND DEATH ON THE CROSS

195   The Old Rugged Cross

"And being found in appearance as a man, he humbled himself and became obedient to death—even death on a cross!"—Philippians 2:8

RUGGED CROSS
George Bennard

George Bennard

1 On a hill far a-way stood an old rug-ged cross, The em-blem of
2 O that old rug-ged cross, so de-spised by the world, Has a won-drous at-
3 In the old rug-ged cross, stained with blood so di-vine, A won-drous
4 To the old rug-ged cross I will ev-er be true, Its shame and re-

1 suf-fering and shame; And I love that old cross where the dear-est and best
2 trac-tion for me; For the dear Lamb of God left His glo-ry a-bove
3 beau-ty I see; For 'twas on that old cross Je-sus suf-fered and died
4 proach glad-ly bear; Then He'll call me some day to my home far a-way,

1 For a world of lost sin-ners was slain.
2 To bear it to dark Cal-va-ry.
3 To par-don and sanc-ti-fy me.
4 Where His glo-ry for-ev-er I'll share.   So I'll cher-ish the old rug-ged

cross, 'Til my tro-phies at last I lay down; I will cling to the

JESUS CHRIST: SUFFERING AND DEATH ON THE CROSS

old rug-ged cross, And ex-change it some day for a crown.

In the Cross of Christ I Glory 196

"Let us fix our eyes on Jesus, the author and perfecter of our faith, who for the joy set before him endured the cross, scorning its shame, and sat down at the right hand of the throne of God."—Hebrews 12:2

John Bowring

8.7.8.7.
RATHBUN
Ithamar Conkey

1 In the cross of Christ I glo-ry, Tower-ing
2 When the woes of life o'er-take me, Hopes de-
3 When the sun of bliss is beam-ing Light and
4 Bane and bless-ing, pain and pleas-ure, By the

1 o'er the wrecks of time; All the light of
2 ceive, and fears an-noy, Nev-er shall the
3 love up-on my way, From the cross the
4 cross are sanc-ti-fied; Peace is there that

1 sa-cred sto-ry Gath-ers round its head sub-lime.
2 cross for-sake me: Lo! it glows with peace and joy.
3 ra-diance stream-ing Adds more lus-ter to the day.
4 knows no meas-ure, Joys that through all time a-bide.

197 O Sacred Head, Now Wounded

"They put a purple robe on him, then wove a crown of thorns and set it on him."—Mark 15:17

Latin: 12th Century
German: Paul Gerhardt
Tr. by James W. Alexander, alt.

7.6.7.6.D.
PASSION CHORALE
Hans Leo Hassler
Harmonized by J. S. Bach

1 O sa-cred Head, now wound-ed, With grief and shame weighed down,
2 What Thou, my Lord, hast suf-fered Was all for sin-ners' gain;
3 What lan-guage shall I bor-row To thank Thee, dear-est friend,

1 Now scorn-ful-ly sur-round-ed With thorns, Thy on-ly crown,
2 Mine, mine was the trans-gres-sion, But Thine the dead-ly pain.
3 For this Thy dy-ing sor-row, Thy pit-y with-out end?

1 How art Thou pale with an-guish, With sore a-buse and scorn!
2 Lo, here I fall, my Sav-ior! 'Tis I de-serve Thy place;
3 O make me Thine for-ev-er; And, should I faint-ing be,

1 How does that vis-age lan-guish Which once was bright as morn!
2 Look on me with Thy fa-vor, Vouch-safe to me Thy grace.
3 Lord, let me nev-er, nev-er Out-live my love for Thee! A-men.

JESUS CHRIST: SUFFERING AND DEATH ON THE CROSS

Beneath the Cross of Jesus 198

"And anyone who does not take his cross and follow me is not worthy of me."
—Matthew 10:38

7.6.8.6.8.6.8.6.
ST. CHRISTOPHER
Elizabeth C. Clephane
Frederick C. Maker

1 Beneath the cross of Jesus I gladly take my stand:
2 Upon that cross of Jesus My eyes at times can see
3 I take, O cross, thy shadow For my abiding place;

1 The shadow of a mighty rock Within a weary land,
2 The very dying form of One Who suffered there for me;
3 I ask no other sunshine than The sunshine of His face,

1 A home within the wilderness, A rest upon the way,
2 And from my smitten heart, with tears, Two wonders I confess—
3 Content to let the world go by, To know no gain or loss,

1 From the burning of the noontide heat And the burden of the day.
2 The wonders of His glorious love And my unworthiness.
3 My sinful self my only shame, My glory all the cross.

199 Calvary Covers It All

"When you were dead in your sins and in the uncircumcision of your sinful nature, God made you alive with Christ. He forgave us all our sins."
—Colossians 2:13

Mrs. Walter G. Taylor

CALVARY COVERS IT ALL
Mrs. Walter G. Taylor

1 Far dear-er than all that the world can im-part Was the mes-sage that
2 The stripes that He bore and the thorns that He wore Told His mer-cy and
3 How match-less the grace, when I looked in the face Of this Je-sus, my
4 How bless-ed the thought, that my soul by Him bought, Shall be His in the

1 came to my heart; How that Je-sus a-lone for my
2 love ev-er-more; And my heart bowed in shame as I
3 cru-ci-fied Lord; My re-demp-tion com-plete I then
4 glo-ry on high, Where with glad-ness and song I'll be

1 sin did a-tone, And Cal-va-ry cov-ers it all.
2 called on His name, And Cal-va-ry cov-ers it all.
3 found at His feet, And Cal-va-ry cov-ers it all.
4 one of the throng, And Cal-va-ry cov-ers it all.

Cal-va-ry cov-ers it all, My past with its sin and stain; My

JESUS CHRIST: SUFFERING AND DEATH ON THE CROSS

guilt and de-spair Je-sus took on Him there, and Cal - va - ry cov-ers it all.

Hallelujah, What a Savior! 200

"He was despised and rejected by men, a man of sorrows, and familiar with suffering."—Isaiah 53:3

7.7.7.8.

Philip P. Bliss

MAN OF SORROWS
Philip P. Bliss

1 "Man of sor-rows!" what a name   For the Son of   God who came
2 Bear-ing shame and scoff-ing rude,   In my place con- demned He stood,
3 Guilt-y, vile, and help-less we,   Spot-less Lamb of   God was He;
4 Lift-ed up was   He to die,   "It is fin-ished," was His cry;
5 When He comes, our glo-rious King,   All His ran-somed home to bring,

1 Ru - ined sin - ners   to re-claim! Hal-le - lu - jah, what a   Sav - ior!
2 Sealed my par-don   with His blood; Hal-le - lu - jah, what a   Sav - ior!
3 Full a - tone-ment! Can it be?   Hal-le - lu - jah, what a   Sav - ior!
4 Now in heaven ex - alt-ed high,   Hal-le - lu - jah, what a   Sav - ior!
5 Then a - new this   song we'll sing: Hal-le - lu - jah, what a   Sav - ior!

JESUS CHRIST: SUFFERING AND DEATH ON THE CROSS

01 When I Survey the Wondrous Cross

"What is more, I consider everything a loss compared to the surpassing greatness of knowing Christ Jesus my Lord, for whose sake I have lost all things."—Philippians 3:8a

Isaac Watts

L.M.
HAMBURG
Based On Gregorian Chant
Arr. by Lowell Mason

1 When I sur - vey the won - drous cross On which the
2 For - bid it, Lord, that I should boast, Save in the
3 See, from His head, His hands, His feet, Sor - row and
4 Were the whole realm of na - ture mine, That were a

1 Prince of glo - ry died, My rich - est gain I
2 death of Christ my God; All the vain things that
3 love flow min - gled down: Did e'er such love and
4 pres - ent far too small; Love so a - maz - ing,

1 count but loss, And pour con - tempt on all my pride.
2 charm me most, I sac - ri - fice them to His blood.
3 sor - row meet, Or thorns com - pose so rich a crown?
4 so di - vine, De - mands my soul, my life, my all.

JESUS CHRIST: SUFFERING AND DEATH ON THE CROSS

MINISTER: The Lord is risen!

CHOIR: *He is risen indeed!*

MINISTER: The Lord is risen!

CONGREGATION: *He is risen indeed!*

MINISTER: The Lord is risen!

ALL: *HE IS RISEN INDEED!*

MINISTER: Surely this is the best of all news. It transformed those who first heard it and excites us when we think about the extraordinary wonder of Christ rising from the dead.

PEOPLE: *"He is risen" is the marvelous proclamation which has reverberated through the ages. It shows God's masterful ability to bring triumph out of tragedy.*

MINISTER: Christ has been raised and we shall be raised with Him. This affects how we see death and dying. We resent death as an alien intruder—it robs us of loved ones—it leaves grievous holes in our families. But death, like an ignited fuse, has been extinguished.

PEOPLE: *Death, where is your victory? Death, where is your sting? Thanks be to God for giving us the victory through our Lord Jesus Christ!*

MINISTER: Because of Christ's resurrection, Christians always have hope, always believe in a bright tomorrow, always rely on the promise of reunion with our families in Christ Jesus.

PEOPLE: *The tragedy of Jesus' death brought us pardon for our sins. The triumph of Jesus' resurrection gives us a resilient life on earth and resurrected life in the world beyond.*

MINISTER: When life is going well, we know that any earthly pleasure is but a pale foretaste of future delights.

PEOPLE: *When life is painful, we know that it's only for a moment. Very soon we shall be where hurts and hardships cannot be remembered.*

ALL: *THE LORD IS RISEN.*
WE SHALL BE RAISED WITH HIM.
PRAISE TO THE RISEN SON.
AMEN!

—Adapted by Bryan Jeffery Leech

JESUS CHRIST: RESURRECTION AND ASCENSION

203 Christ the Lord Is Risen Today

"But Christ has indeed been raised from the dead, the firstfruits of those who have fallen asleep."—I Corinthians 15:20

7.7.7.7.with Alleluias
EASTER HYMN
"Lyra Davidica"

Charles Wesley

1 Christ the Lord is risen to-day,
2 Lives a-gain our glo-rious King,
3 Love's re-deem-ing work is done,
4 Sing we to our God a-bove,

Al - le - lu - ia!

1 *Sons of men and an-gels say:
2 Where, O death, is now thy sting?
3 Fought the fight, the bat-tle won,
4 Praise e-ter-nal as His love;

Al - le - lu - ia!

1 Raise your joys and tri-umphs high,
2 Dy-ing once, He all doth save,
3 Death in vain for-bids Him rise,
4 Praise Him, all ye heaven-ly host,

Al - le - lu - ia!

1 Sing, ye heavens, and earth re-ply:
2 Where thy vic - to - ry, O grave?
3 Christ has o-pened par-a-dise,
4 Fa-ther, Son, and Ho-ly Ghost.

Al - le - lu - ia! A-men.

*Earth and heav'n in chor-us say:

JESUS CHRIST: RESURRECTION AND ASCENSION

Jesus Christ Is Risen Today 204

" . . . Jesus rose early on the first day of the week . . . "—Mark 16:9a

Latin: 14th century
English translation, *New Version*
Charles Wesley, Stanza 4

7.7.7.7. with Alleluias
LLANFAIR
Robert Williams
Harmonized by John Roberts

1 Je - sus Christ is risen to - day,
2 Hymns of praise then let us sing,
3 But the pains which He en - dured,
4 Sing we to our God a - bove,

Al - le - lu - ia!

1 Our tri - um - phant ho - ly day,
2 Un - to Christ, our heav'n - ly King,
3 Our sal - va - tion have pro - cured;
4 Praise e - ter - nal as His love;

Al - le - lu - ia!

1 Who did once up - on the cross,
2 Who en - dured the cross and grave,
3 Now a - bove the sky He's King,
4 Praise Him, all ye heav'n - ly host,

Al - le - lu - ia!

1 Suf - fer to re - deem our loss.
2 Sin - ners to re - deem and save.
3 Where the an - gels ev - er sing.
4 Fa - ther, Son and Ho - ly Ghost.

Al - le - lu - ia!

A-men.

JESUS CHRIST: RESURRECTION AND ASCENSION

205 Easter Song

*" 'Don't be alarmed,' he said. 'You are looking for Jesus the Nazarene, who was
crucified. He has risen! He is not here. See the place where they laid him.' "*
—Mark 16:6-7

Anne Herring

EASTER SONG
Anne Herring

1 Hear the bells ring-ing, they're sing-ing that we can be
2 Hear the bells ring-ing, they're sing-ing, "Christ is ris-en

1 born a - gain!
2 from the dead!"

The an - gel up - on the tomb-stone said, "He is

ris - en just as He said. Quick-ly now go tell His dis-

JESUS CHRIST: RESURRECTION AND ASCENSION

ci - ples that Je - sus Christ is no long - er dead!"

Joy to the world, He is ris - en, Al -

le - lu - ia! He's ris - en, Al - le - lu - ia! He's

ris - en, Al - le - lu - ia!

JESUS CHRIST: RESURRECTION AND ASCENSION

206

Alleluia! Alleluia!

" 'Where, O death, is your victory? Where, O death, is your sting?' "
—I Corinthians 15:55

8.7.8.7.D.
HYMN TO JOY
Ludwig van Beethoven
Adapted by Edward Hodges

Christopher Wordsworth

1 Al - le - lu - ia! al - le - lu - ia! Hearts to heav'n and voic - es raise;
2 Now the i - ron bars are bro - ken, Christ from death to life is born,
3 Al - le - lu - ia! al - le - lu - ia! Glo - ry be to God on high;

1 Sing to God a hymn of glad - ness, Sing to God a hymn of praise.
2 Glo - rious life, and life im - mor - tal, On this ho - ly Eas - ter morn;
3 Al - le - lu - ia to the Sav - ior Who has won the vic - to - ry;

1 He who on the cross as Sav - ior For the world's sal - va - tion bled,
2 Christ has tri - umphed, and we con - quer By His might - y en - ter - prise;
3 Al - le - lu - ia to the Spir - it, Fount of love and sanc - ti - ty;

1 Je - sus Christ, the King of Glo - ry, Now is ris - en from the dead.
2 We with Him to life e - ter - nal By His res - ur - rec - tion rise.
3 Al - le - lu - ia! al - le - lu - ia! To the Tri - une Maj - es - ty. A - men.

JESUS CHRIST: RESURRECTION AND ASCENSION

Rejoice and Be Glad

207

"But go, tell his disciples and Peter, 'He is going ahead of you into Galilee.
There you will see him, just as he told you.' "—Mark 16:7

Horatius Bonar

REVIVE US AGAIN
John J. Husband

1 Re - joice and be glad! The Re - deem - er has come!
2 Re - joice and be glad! It is sun - shine at last!
3 Re - joice and be glad! For the blood hath been shed;
4 Re - joice and be glad! Now the par - don is free!
5 Re - joice and be glad! For the Lamb that was slain

1 Go, look on His cra - dle, His cross and His tomb.
2 The clouds have de - part - ed, The shad - ows are past.
3 Re - demp-tion is fin - ished, The price has been paid.
4 The Just for the un - just Has died on the tree.
5 O'er death is tri - um - phant, And liv - eth a - gain.

Sound His prais - es, tell the sto - ry Of Him who was slain;

Sound His prais - es, tell with glad - ness, He liv - eth a - gain.

JESUS CHRIST: RESURRECTION AND ASCENSION

208 I Live

*"Before long, the world will not see me anymore, but you will see me. Because I
live, you also will live."—John 14:19*

Rich Cook

I LIVE
Rich Cook

I live, I live be-cause He is ris-en; I live, I live, with pow'r o-ver sin. I live, I live be-cause He is ris-en; I live, I live to wor-ship Him. Thank you, Je-sus, thank you, Je-sus; Be-cause You're a-live, be-cause You're a-live, Be-cause You're a-live, I live!

JESUS CHRIST: RESURRECTION AND ASCENSION

I live, I live be-cause He is ris-en; I live, I live, I live, with pow'r o-ver sin. I live, I live be-cause He is ris-en; I live, I live to wor-ship Him. Thank you, Je-sus, thank you, Je-sus; Be-cause You're a-live, be-cause You're a-live, Be-cause You're a-live, I live!

209 Because He Lives

"And he died for all, that those who live should no longer live for themselves but for him who died for them and was raised again."—II Corinthians 5:15

Gloria Gaither
William J. Gaither

RESURRECTION
William J. Gaither

1 God sent His Son, they called Him Je - sus, He came to love,
2 How sweet to hold a new-born ba - by, And feel the pride
3 And then one day I'll cross the riv - er, I'll fight life's fi -

1 heal, and for - give; He lived and died to buy my
2 and joy He gives; But great - er still the calm as -
3 nal war with pain; And then as death gives way to

1 par - don, An emp-ty grave is there to prove my Sav-ior lives.
2 sur - ance, This child can face un-cer-tain days be-cause He lives.
3 vic - tory, I'll see the lights of glo-ry and I'll know He reigns.

Be-cause He lives I can face to - mor-row, Be-cause He lives

all fear is gone; Be-cause I know He holds the

JESUS CHRIST: RESURRECTION AND ASCENSION

210

He Lives!

"I am the Living One; I was dead, and behold I am alive for ever and ever!
And I hold the keys of death and Hades."—Revelation 1:18

Alfred H. Ackley

ACKLEY
Alfred H. Ackley

1 I serve a ris - en Sav - ior, He's in the world to - day;
2 In all the world a - round me I see His lov - ing care,
3 Re - joice, re - joice, O Chris - tian, lift up your voice and sing

1 I know that He is liv - ing, what - ev - er foes may say;
2 And though my heart grows wea - ry I nev - er will de - spair;
3 E - ter - nal hal - le - lu - jahs to Je - sus Christ the King!

1 I see His hand of mer - cy, I hear His voice of cheer,
2 I know that He is lead - ing through all the storm - y blast,
3 The Hope of all who seek Him, the Help of all who find,

1 And just the time I need Him He's al - ways near.
2 The day of His ap - pear - ing will come at last.
3 None oth - er is so lov - ing, so good and kind.

He lives, He lives, Christ Je - sus lives to - day!
He lives, He lives,

JESUS CHRIST: RESURRECTION AND ASCENSION

He walks with me and talks with me a - long life's nar - row way.

He lives, He lives, sal - va - tion to im - part!
He lives, He lives,

You ask me how I know He lives? He lives with-in my heart.

Death, Where Is Thy Victory? **211**

For I delivered to you as of first importance what I also received, that Christ died for our sins in accordance with the Scriptures.

That He was buried, that He was raised on the third day in accordance with the Scriptures.

Now if Christ is preached as raised from the dead, how can some of you say that there is no resurrection of the dead?

But if there is no resurrection of the dead, then Christ has not been raised; if Christ has not been raised, then our preaching is in vain and your faith is in vain.

But in fact Christ has been raised from the dead, the first fruits of those who have fallen asleep.

For as by a man came death, by a man has come also the resurrection of the dead.

Lo! I tell you a mystery. We shall not all sleep, but we shall all be changed, in a moment, in the twinkling of an eye, at the last trumpet.

For the trumpet will sound, and the dead will be raised imperishable, and we shall be changed.

For this perishable nature must put on the imperishable, and this mortal nature must put on immortality.

When the perishable puts on the imperishable, and the mortal puts on immortality, then shall come to pass the saying that is written: "Death is swallowed up in victory."

"O death, where is thy victory? O death, where is thy sting?"

The sting of death is sin, and the power of sin is the law. But thanks be to God, who gives us the victory through our Lord Jesus Christ.

—*Adapted from I Corinthians 15*

212 Christ Arose!

"But God raised him from the dead, freeing him from the agony of death, because it was impossible for death to keep its hold on him."—Acts 2:24

Robert Lowry

CHRIST AROSE
Robert Lowry

1 Low in the grave He lay, Je - sus, my Sav - ior! Wait - ing the
2 Vain - ly they watched His bed, Je - sus, my Sav - ior! Vain - ly they
3 Death could not keep his prey, Je - sus, my Sav - ior! He tore the

1 com - ing day, Je - sus, my Lord!
2 sealed the dead, Je - sus, my Lord! Up from the grave He a - rose,
3 bars a - way, Je - sus, my Lord!
He a-rose,

With a might - y tri-umph o'er His foes;
He a-rose;
He a - rose a vic-tor from the

dark do - main, And He lives for - ev- er with His saints to reign; He a-

rose! He a - rose!
He a-rose!
Hal - le - lu - jah! Christ a - rose!
He a-rose!

I Know That My Redeemer Lives

213

"I know that my Redeemer lives, and that in the end he will stand upon the earth."—Job 19:25

L.M.
DUKE STREET
John Hatton

Samuel Medley

1 I know that my Re - deem - er lives: What joy the blest as -
2 He lives, to bless me with His love; He lives to plead for
3 He lives, and grants me dai - ly breath; He lives, and I shall
4 He lives, all glo - ry to His Name; He lives, my Sav - ior,

1 sur - ance gives! He lives, He lives, who once was dead;
2 me a - bove; He lives, my hun - gry soul to feed;
3 con - quer death; He lives, my fu - ture to pre - pare;
4 still the same; What joy the blest as - sur - ance gives;

1 He lives, my ev - er - last - ing Head!
2 He lives, to help in time of need.
3 He lives, to bring me safe - ly there.
4 I know that my Re - deem - er lives! A-men.

He Is Risen! He Is Risen, Indeed! 214

LEADER:	He is risen.
LEFT SIDE:	He is risen.
RIGHT SIDE:	He is risen.
WOMEN (LOUD):	He is risen.
MEN (LOUDER):	He is risen.
ALL (*SHOUTED*):	He is risen, indeed!

215 Crown Him with Many Crowns

" . . . the twenty-four elders fall down before him who sits on the throne, and worship him who lives for ever and ever."—Revelation 4:10

Matthew Bridges
Godfrey Thring

S.M.D.
DIADEMATA
George J. Elvey
Descant by Paul Sjolund

Descant: 5 Crown Him, crown Him the Lord of years: The Lord of time, Cre-a-tor of the roll-ing spheres, In-ef-fa-bly sub-lime. All hail, Re-deem-er

1 Crown Him with man-y crowns, The Lamb up-on His throne: Hark! how the heaven-ly an-them drowns All mu-sic but its own! A-wake, my soul, and sing Of
2 Crown Him the Lord of love: Be-hold His hands and side, Rich wounds, yet vis-i-ble a-bove, In beau-ty glo-ri-fied; No an-gel in the sky Can
3 Crown Him the Lord of life: Who tri-umphed o'er the grave, Who rose vic-to-rious to the strife For those He came to save; His glo-ries now we sing, Who
4 Crown Him the Lord of heaven: One with the Fa-ther known, One with the Spir-it through Him given From yon-der glo-rious throne. To Thee be end-less praise, For
5 Crown Him the Lord of years: The po-ten-tate of time, Cre-a-tor of the roll-ing spheres, In-ef-fa-bly sub-lime. All hail, Re-deem-er, hail! For

JESUS CHRIST: LORDSHIP AND REIGN

hail! For Thou all praise, glory

1 Him who died for thee; And hail Him as thy
2 ful - ly bear that sight, But down - ward bends His
3 died and rose on high, Who died e - ter - nal
4 Thou for us hast died; Be Thou, O Lord, through
5 Thou hast died for me; Thy praise and glo - ry

shall not fail Through - out e - ter - ni - ty. A-men.

1 match - less King Through all e - ter - ni - ty.
2 won - dering eye At mys - ter - ies so bright.
3 life to bring, And lives that death may die.
4 end - less days A - dored and mag - ni - fied.
5 shall not fail Through - out e - ter - ni - ty. A-men.

Future Glory 216

I consider that our present sufferings are not worth comparing with the glory that will be revealed in us. The creation waits in eager expectation for the sons of God to be revealed. For the creation was subjected to frustration, not by its own choice, but by the will of the one who subjected it, in hope that the creation itself will be liberated from its bondage to decay and brought into the glorious freedom of the children of God.

We know that the whole creation has been groaning as in the pains of childbirth right up to the present time. Not only so, but we our-selves, who have the firstfruits of the Spirit, grown inwardly as we wait eagerly for our adoption as sons, the redemption of our bodies. For in this hope we were saved. But hope that is seen is no hope at all. Who hopes for what he already has? But if we hope for what we do not yet have, we wait for it patiently.

In the same way, the Spirit helps us in our weakness. We do not know what we ought to pray, but the Spirit himself intercedes for us with groans that words cannot express. And he who searches our hearts knows the mind of the Spirit, because the Spirit intercedes for the saints in accordance with God's will.

—Romans 8:18-27 (NIV)

JESUS CHRIST: LORDSHIP AND REIGN

217 We'll Crown Him Lord of All

"To Him who loves us and has freed us from our sins by his blood, and has made us to be a kingdom and priests to serve his God and Father—to him be glory and power forever and ever! Amen."—Revelation 1:5b-6

D. Otis Teasley

CROWN HIM LORD OF ALL
D. Otis Teasley

1 We'll shout and sing our Redeemer's praise, Contending for the truth and right; We'll crown Him King in ev'ry heart, And conquer in Jehovah's might.

2 Tho' the hosts of sin should about us camp, We'll shout and sing the victor's song; For Christ, our Savior, withdwells, To save and keep us from the wrong.

3 To Christ all power on earth is giv'n, See now His mighty scepter's sway; While others dream of an age to come, He's reigning in our hearts today.

4 Soon Christ shall come with the trumpet sound, To raise the dead from land and sea; Then we shall meet Him in the air And reign with Him eternally.

5 Then in that heaven and earth anew Where love's eternal blessings fall, We'll sing His praise while the ages roll, And crown the Savior Lord of all.

Crown Him, we'll crown Him,
Crown Him Lord of all, crown Him Lord of all,

Crown the bless-ed Sav-ior Lord of all; We'll crown Him, yes
Crown Him Lord of all,

crown Him, Crown the bless-ed Sav-ior Lord of all.
crown Him Lord of all, Lord of all.

King of Kings 218

" . . . because he is Lord of lords and King of kings . . . "—Revelation 17:14b

Sophie Conty
Naomi Batya

KING OF KINGS
Ancient Hebrew Folk Song

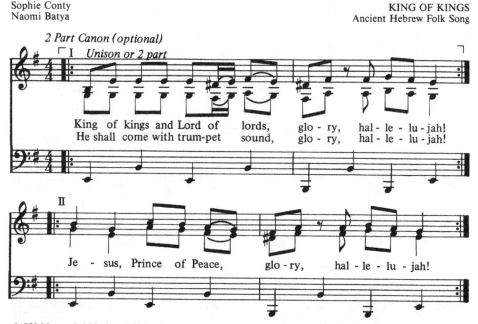

2 Part Canon (optional)

I *Unison or 2 part*

King of kings and Lord of lords, glo - ry, hal - le - lu - jah!
He shall come with trum-pet sound, glo - ry, hal - le - lu - jah!

II

Je - sus, Prince of Peace, glo - ry, hal - le - lu - jah!

JESUS CHRIST: LORDSHIP AND REIGN

219

Christ Is Alive!

L.M.
TRURO

Brian Wren
From "Psalmodia Evangelica" 1789

"God has raised this Jesus to life, and we are all witnesses of the fact."
—Acts 2:32

Psalmodia Evangelica (1789)

1 Christ is a - live! Let Chris - tians sing.
2 Christ is a - live! No long - er bound
3 Not throned a - bove re - mote - ly high,
4 In ev - 'ry in - sult, rift, and war,
5 Christ is a - live! His Spir - it burns

1 His cross stands emp - ty to the sky.
2 To dis - tant years in Pal - es - tine,
3 Un - touched, un - moved by hu - man pains,
4 Where col - or, scorn or wealth di - vide,
5 Through this, and ev - 'ry fu - ture age,

1 Let streets and homes with prais - es ring.
2 He comes to claim the here and now
3 But dai - ly, in the midst of life,
4 He suf - fers still, yet loves the more,
5 Till all cre - a - tion lives and learns

1 His love in death shall nev - er die.
2 And con - quer ev - 'ry place and time.
3 Our Sav - ior with the Fa - ther reigns.
4 And lives, though ev - er cru - ci - fied.
5 His joy, His jus - tice, love, and praise.

JESUS CHRIST: LORDSHIP AND REIGN

Christ Is the World's Light

220

"In him was life, and that life was the light of men."—John 1:4

10.11.11.6.

Fred Pratt Green

CHRISTE SANCTORUM
French Church Melody, *Antiphoner*, Paris, 1681

Unison

1 Christ is the world's light; Christ and none oth - er; Born in our dark - ness, He be - came our Broth - er. If we have seen Him, We have seen the Fa - ther: Glo - ry to God on high!

2 Christ is the world's peace; Christ and none oth - er; No one can serve Him And de - spise an - oth - er. Who else u - nites us One in God the Fa - ther? Glo - ry to God on high!

3 Christ is the world's life, Christ and none oth - er; Sold once for sil - ver, Mur - dered here, our Broth - er — He who re - deems us Reigns with God the Fa - ther: Glo - ry to God on high!

4 Give God the glo - ry, God and none oth - er; Give God the glo - ry, Spir - it, Son and Fa - ther; Give God the glo - ry, "God with Us" our Broth - er: Glo - ry to God on high!

JESUS CHRIST: LORDSHIP AND REIGN

221 Every Eye Shall See

*" . . . that at the name of Jesus every knee should bow, in heaven and on earth
and under the earth, and every tongue confess that Jesus Christ is Lord, to the
glory of God the Father."—Philippians 2:10-11*

Gloria Gaither
William J. Gaither

EVERY EYE
William J. Gaither

JESUS CHRIST: LORDSHIP AND REIGN

Jesus, Lord to Me

222

"Thomas said to him, 'My Lord and my God!' "—John 20:28

Gary McSpadden
Greg Nelson

JESUS, LORD TO ME
Gary McSpadden
Greg Nelson

Je-sus, Je-sus, Lord to me. Mas-ter, Sav-ior, Prince of
Peace. Rul-er of my heart to-day, Je-sus, Lord to me.

He Is Lord

223

" . . . and every tongue confess that Jesus Christ is Lord, to the glory of God the Father."—Philippians 2:11

Traditional
Based on Philippians 2:11

HE IS LORD
Traditional

He is Lord, He is Lord! He is ris-en from the dead and He is Lord!
Ev-'ry knee shall bow, ev-'ry tongue con-fess That Je-sus Christ is Lord.

224 Jesus Is Lord of All

" . . . the King of Kings, and Lord of Lords . . . "—I Timothy 6:15b

Gloria Gaither
William J. Gaither

LORD OF ALL
William J. Gaither

1 All my to-mor-rows, all my past— Je-sus is Lord of
2 All of my con-flicts, all my thoughts— Je-sus is Lord of
3 All of my long-ings, all my dreams— Je-sus is Lord of

1 all. I've quit my strug-gles, con-tent-ment at last!
2 all. His love wins the bat-tles I could not have fought;
3 all. All of my fail-ures His pow-er re-deems;

1 Je-sus is Lord of all.
2 Je-sus is Lord of all.
3 Je-sus is Lord of all.

King of kings, Lord of lords,

Je-sus is Lord of all; All my pos-ses-sions and

all my life, Je-sus is Lord of all.

JESUS CHRIST: LORDSHIP AND REIGN

Our God Reigns

"How beautiful on the mountains are the feet of those who bring good news . . .
'Your God reigns!' "—Isaiah 52:7a,c

Leonard W. Smith

OUR GOD REIGNS
Leonard W. Smith

1 How love-ly on the moun-tains are the feet of those
2 He had no state-ly form, He had no maj-es-ty,
3 Out from the tomb He came with grace and maj-es-ty,

1 Who bring good news, good news An-nounc-ing
2 That we should be drawn to Him. He was de-
3 He is a-live, He is a-live. God loves us

1 peace, pro-claim-ing news of hap-pi-ness. Our God
2 spised and we took no ac-count of Him, Yet now He
3 so, see here His hands, His feet, His side. Yes, we

1 reigns, our God reigns! Our God reigns!
2 reigns with the Most High. Our God reigns!
3 know, He is a-live.

Our God reigns! Our God reigns! Our God reigns!

JESUS CHRIST: LORDSHIP AND REIGN

226 Jesus Loves Even Me

" 'As the Father has loved me, so have I loved you. Now remain in my love.' "
—John 15:9

10.10.10.10.wR.
GLADNESS

Philip P. Bliss

Philip P. Bliss

1 I am so glad that my Fa-ther in heaven Tells of His love in the Book He has given; Won-der-ful things in the Bi-ble I see— This is the dear-est, that Je-sus loves me.

2 Though I for-get Him and wan-der a-way, Still Je-sus loves me wher-ev-er I stray; Back to His dear lov-ing arms I would flee, When I re-mem-ber that Je-sus loves me.

3 O if there's on-ly one song I can sing, When in His beau-ty I see the great King, This shall my song in e-ter-ni-ty be: "O what a won-der that Je-sus loves me!"

I am so glad that Je-sus loves me, Je-sus loves me, Je-sus loves me;
I am so glad that Je-sus loves me, Je-sus loves e-ven me.

JESUS CHRIST: FRIENDSHIP AND LOVE

My Savior's Love

227

"But God demonstrates his own love for us in this: While we were still sinners, Christ died for us."—Romans 5:8

8.7.8.7.wR.
MY SAVIOR'S LOVE
Charles H. Gabriel

Charles H. Gabriel

1 I stand a-mazed in the pres-ence Of Je-sus the Naz-a-rene,
2 For me it was in the gar-den He prayed, "Not my will, but Thine;"
3 He took my sins and my sor-rows, He made them His ver-y own;
4 When with the ran-somed in glo-ry His face I at last shall see,

1 And won-der how He could love me, A sin-ner, con-demned un-clean.
2 He had no tears for His own griefs, But sweat drops of blood for mine.
3 He bore the bur-den to Cal-vary, And suf-fered and died a-lone.
4 'Twill be my joy through the a-ges To sing of His love for me.

How mar-vel-ous! how won-der-ful! And my song shall ev-er be:

How mar-vel-ous! how won-der-ful Is my Sav-ior's love for me!

JESUS CHRIST: FRIENDSHIP AND LOVE

228 O, How He Loves You and Me

" 'As the Father has loved me, so have I loved you. Now remain in my love.' "
—John 15:9

Kurt Kaiser

HE LOVES YOU AND ME
Kurt Kaiser

1 O how He loves you and me,
2 Je - sus to Cal - vary did go,

1 O how He loves you and me;
2 His love for man - kind to show;

1 He gave His life, what more could He give:
2 What He did there brought hope from de - spair:

1 O how He loves you, O how He loves me,
2 O how He loves you, O how He loves me,

1 O how He loves you and me.
2 O how He loves you and me.

JESUS CHRIST: FRIENDSHIP AND LOVE

All That Thrills My Soul Is Jesus

229

"For to me, to live is Christ and to die is gain."—Philippians 1:21

Thoro Harris

ALL THAT THRILLS
Thoro Harris

1 Who can cheer the heart like Je - sus, By His pres-ence all di - vine?
2 Love of Christ so free - ly giv - en, Grace of God be - yond de - gree,
3 What a won-der-ful re - demp-tion! Nev - er can a mor-tal know
4 Ev - ery need His hand sup - ply - ing, Ev - ery good in Him I see;
5 By the crys - tal, flow-ing riv - er With the ran-somed I will sing,

1 True and ten - der, pure and pre - cious, O how blest to call Him mine!
2 Mer - cy high - er than the heav - en, Deep - er than the deep-est sea.
3 How my sin, tho' red like crim - son, Can be whit - er than the snow.
4 On His strength di-vine re - ly - ing, He is all in all to me.
5 And for - ev - er and for - ev - er Praise and glo - ri - fy the King.

All that thrills my soul is Je - sus; He is more than life to me; (to me;)

And the fair-est of ten thou - sand, In my bless-ed Lord I see.

JESUS CHRIST: FRIENDSHIP AND LOVE

230 Redeeming Love

"The Lord redeems his servants; no one who takes refuge in him will be condemned."—Psalm 34:22

Gloria Gaither

REDEEMING LOVE
William J. Gaither

1 From God's heav-en to a man-ger, From great rich-es to the
2 From a lov-ing heaven-ly Fa-ther, To a world that knew Him

1 poor, Came the Son of God to seek and save;
2 not, Came the "Man of Sor-rows," Christ the Lord;

1 From the a-zure halls of heav-en To a rough and rug-ged cross
2 In my wan-d'ring Je-sus found me, Bought my soul with His own blood,

1 Je-sus came and here His life for all He gave.
2 Gave to me a peace this world could not af-ford.

Re-deem-ing love, a love that knows no lim-it; Re-deem-ing

JESUS CHRIST: FRIENDSHIP AND LOVE

love, a love that shall not die; My soul shall sing through-out the

end-less a - ges With choirs ex-tol - ling this great love on high.

Jesus Loves the Little Children 231

" 'And whoever welcomes a little child like this in my name welcomes me.' "
—Matthew 18:5

8.7.7.7.7.11.
CHILDREN
George F. Root

Unknown

Je - sus loves the lit - tle chil - dren, All the chil-dren of the

world. Red and yel-low, black and white, They are pre - cious in His sight—

Je - sus loves the lit - tle chil - dren of the world.

JESUS CHRIST: FRIENDSHIP AND LOVE

232 Jesus Loves Me, This I Know

"And live a life of love, just as Christ loved us and gave himself up for us as a fragrant offering and sacrifice to God."—Ephesians 5:2

7.7.7.7.wR.

Anna B. Warner

JESUS LOVES ME
William B. Bradbury

1 Je - sus loves me! this I know, For the Bi - ble tells me so;
2 Je - sus loves me! He who died Heav-en's gate to o - pen wide;
3 Je - sus, take this heart of mine, Make it pure and whol-ly Thine;

1 Lit - tle ones to Him be - long, They are weak but He is strong.
2 He will wash a - way my sin, Let His lit - tle child come in.
3 On the cross You died for me, I will try to live for Thee.

Yes, Je - sus loves me! Yes, Je - sus loves me!

Yes, Je - sus loves me! The Bi - ble tells me so.

JESUS CHRIST: FRIENDSHIP AND LOVE

Jesus, Lover of My Soul

233

"You have been a refuge for the poor, a refuge for the needy in his distress, a shelter from the storm and a shade from the heat. For the breath of the ruthless is like a storm driving against a wall."—Isaiah 25:4

Charles Wesley

7.7.7.7.D.
ABERYSTWYTH
Joseph Parry

1 Je-sus, lov-er of my soul, Let me to Thy bos-om fly,
2 Oth-er ref-uge have I none, Hangs my help-less soul on Thee;
3 Plen-teous grace with Thee is found, Grace to cov-er all my sin;

1 While the near-er wa-ters roll, While the tem-pest still is high.
2 Leave, O leave me not a-lone, Still sup-port and com-fort me.
3 Let the heal-ing streams a-bound, Make and keep me pure with-in.

1 Hide me, O my Sav-ior, hide, 'Til the storm of life is past;
2 All my trust on Thee is stayed, All my help from Thee I bring;
3 Thou of life the foun-tain art, Free-ly let me take of Thee;

1 Safe in-to the ha-ven guide, O re-ceive my soul at last!
2 Cov-er my de-fense-less head With the shad-ow of Thy wing.
3 Spring Thou up with-in my heart, Rise to all e-ter-ni-ty. A-men.

JESUS CHRIST: FRIENDSHIP AND LOVE

234 And Can It Be That I Should Gain?

*" . . . in order that in the coming ages he might show the imcomparable riches
of his grace, expressed in his kindness to us in Christ Jesus."—Ephesians 2:7*

8.8.8.8.8.8.wR.

SAGINA

Charles Wesley

Thomas Campbell

1 And can it be that I should gain An in-terest
2 He left His Fa-ther's throne a-bove, So free, so
3 Long my im-pris-oned spir-it lay Fast bound in
4 No con-dem-na-tion now I dread: Je-sus, and

1 in the Sav-ior's blood? Died He for me, who caused His pain?
2 in-fi-nite His grace! Emp-tied Him-self of all but love,
3 sin and na-ture's night. Thine eye dif-fused a quick-ening ray;
4 all in Him, is mine! A-live in Him, my liv-ing Head,

1 For me, who Him to death pur-sued? A-maz-ing love! how
2 And bled for A-dam's help-less race! 'Tis mer-cy all, im-
3 I woke— the dun-geon flamed with light! My chains fell off, my
4 And clothed in right-eous-ness di-vine, Bold I ap-proach th'e-

1 can it be That Thou, my God, shouldst die for me?
2 mense and free, For, O my God, it found out me.
3 heart was free, I rose, went forth, and fol-lowed Thee.
4 ter-nal throne, And claim the crown, through Christ my own.

JESUS CHRIST: FRIENDSHIP AND LOVE

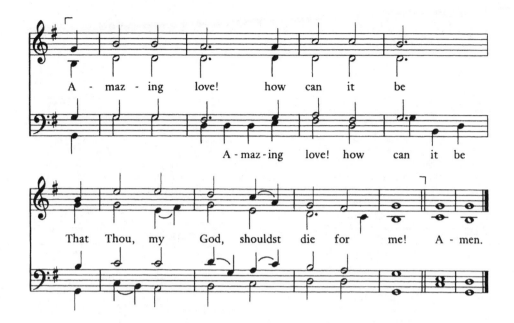

A - maz - ing love! how can it be

A - maz - ing love! how can it be

That Thou, my God, shouldst die for me! A - men.

No Greater Love **235**

As the Father has loved me, so have I loved you. Now remain in my love. If you obey my commands, you will remain in my love, just as I have obeyed my Father's commands and remain in his love. I have told you this so that my joy may be in you and that your joy may be complete.

My command is this:

Love each other as I have loved you. Greater love has no one than this, that one lay down his life for his friends. You are my friends if you do what I command. I no longer call you servants, because a servant does not know his master's business. Instead, I have called you friends, for everything that I learned from my Father I have made known to you.

John 15:9–15 (NIV)

236 What a Dear Friend Is Jesus

"Instead, I have called you friends, for everything that I have learned from my Father I have made known to you."—John 15:15b

Lizzie De Armond

DEAR FRIEND
Andrew L. Byers

1 He lift-ed my bur-den of sor-row and sin, The blood of His
2 He comes to my res-cue when-ev-er I call, I'm safe in His
3 My path may be thorn-y and dan-gers dis-may, His won-der-ful
4 With Je-sus be-side me I fear not the foe, His arm of pro-

1 cleans-ing has washed me with-in; He gave me the pow-er new life to be-gin,
2 keep-ing, no harm can be-fall; Tho fail-ures be man-y, in spite of them all,
3 prom-ise all fears will al-lay: "Lo, I will be with you by night and by day."
4 tec-tion a-round me He'll throw; His good-ness and mer-cy my cup o-ver-flow,

O what a dear friend is Je-sus! Such won-der-ful things He

does for me, Tho on-ly one step each day I see; The joy of my

JESUS CHRIST: FRIENDSHIP AND LOVE

life in-deed is He, O what a dear friend is Je - sus!

What Wondrous Love Is This 237

"But God demonstrates his own love for us in this: While we were still sinners,
Christ died for us."—Romans 5:8

American Folk Hymn

12.9.6.6.12.9.
WONDROUS LOVE
Southern Harmony

1 What won-drous love is this, O my soul, O my soul, What
2 To God and to the Lamb I will sing, I will sing, To
3 And when from death I'm free, I'll sing on, I'll sing on, And

1 won-drous love is this, O my soul! What won-drous love is
2 God and to the Lamb I will sing; To God and to the
3 when from death I'm free, I'll sing on; And when from death I'm

1 this that caused the Lord of bliss To bear the dread-ful curse for my
2 Lamb, who is the great "I Am," While mil - lions join the theme, I will
3 free, I'll sing and joy - ful be, And through e - ter - ni - ty I'll sing

1 soul, for my soul, To bear the dread-ful curse for my soul!
2 sing, I will sing, While mil - lions join the theme, I will sing!
3 on, I'll sing on, And through e - ter - ni - ty I'll sing on!

JESUS CHRIST: FRIENDSHIP AND LOVE

238 O the Deep, Deep Love of Jesus

" . . . and to know this love that surpasses knowledge—that you may be filled to the measure of all the fullness of God."—Ephesians 3:19

Samuel Trevor Francis

8.7.8.7.D.
NETTLETON
John Wyeth

1 O the deep, deep love of Je-sus, Vast, un-mea-sured, bound-less, free!
2 O the deep, deep love of Je-sus—Spread His praise from shore to shore!
3 O the deep, deep love of Je-sus, Love of ev-'ry love the best!

1 Roll-ing as a might-y o-cean In its full-ness o-ver me!
2 How He loves us, ev-er loves us, Changes nev-er, nev-er-more!
3 'Tis an o-cean full of bless-ing, 'Tis a ha-ven giv-ing rest!

1 Un-der-neath me, all a-round me, Is the cur-rent of Thy love—
2 How He watch-es o'er His loved ones, Died to call them all His own;
3 O the deep, deep love of Je-sus— 'Tis a heaven of heavens to me;

1 Lead-ing on-ward, lead-ing home-ward, To Thy glo-rious rest a-bove!
2 How for them He in-ter-ced-eth, Watch-ing o'er them from the throne!
3 And it lifts me up to glo-ry, For it lifts me up to Thee!

JESUS CHRIST: FRIENDSHIP AND LOVE

There Is Not a Friend Like Jesus

239

Mrs. H. A. Hendricks

8.7.8.7.wR.
NO FRIEND LIKE JESUS
D. Otis Teasley

1 There is not a friend like Je-sus In the try-ing scenes of life;
2 There is not a friend like Je-sus: Bid the scoff-ing world a-dieu;
3 There is not a friend like Je-sus: Trust him ev-'ry-where you go;
4 There is not a friend like Je-sus: What a bless-ed tho't to be

1 He can hear the heart's faint whis-per, Calm the tem-pest's rag-ing strife.
2 For if you're a-shamed of Je-sus, He will be a-shamed of you.
3 He has trod the way be-fore you, Suf-fered ev-ery pain and woe.
4 Fold-ed in His arms of pow-er, Ev-er in e-ter-ni-ty!

There is not a friend like Je-sus, Pa-tient, ten-der, kind and true;

There is not a friend like Je-sus, He will be a friend to you.

JESUS CHRIST: FRIENDSHIP AND LOVE

240 Jesus Is All the World to Me

"For to me, to live is Christ and to die is gain."—Philippians 1:21

Will L. Thompson

ELIZABETH
Will L. Thompson

1 Je-sus is all the world to me, My life, my joy, my all;
2 Je-sus is all the world to me, My Friend in tri-als sore;
3 Je-sus is all the world to me, And true to Him I'll be;
4 Je-sus is all the world to me, I want no bet-ter friend;

1 He is my strength from day to day, With-out Him I would fall.
2 I go to Him for bless-ings, and He gives them o'er and o'er.
3 O how could I this Friend de-ny, When He's so true to me?
4 I trust Him now, I'll trust Him when Life's fleet-ing days shall end.

1 When I am sad to Him I go, No oth-er one can cheer me so;
2 He sends the sun-shine and the rain, He sends the har-vest's gold-en grain;
3 Fol-low-ing Him I know I'm right, He watch-es o'er me day and night;
4 Beau-ti-ful life with such a Friend; Beau-ti-ful life that has no end;

1 When I am sad He makes me glad, He's my Friend.
2 Sun-shine and rain, har-vest of grain, He's my Friend.
3 Fol-low-ing Him by day and night, He's my Friend.
4 E-ter-nal life, e-ter-nal joy, He's my Friend.

JESUS CHRIST: FRIENDSHIP AND LOVE

I've Found a Friend, O Such a Friend

241

"Neither height nor depth, nor anything else in all creation, will be able to separate us from the love of God that is in Christ Jesus our Lord."
—Romans 8:39

James G. Small

8.7.8.7.D.
FRIEND
George C. Stebbins

1 I've found a Friend, O such a Friend! He loved me ere I knew Him;
2 I've found a Friend, O such a Friend! He bled, He died to save me:
3 I've found a Friend, O such a Friend! So kind, and true, and ten-der,

1 He drew me with the cords of love, And thus He bound me to Him.
2 And not a-lone the gift of life, But His own self He gave me.
3 So wise a Coun-se-lor and Guide, So might-y a De-fend-er!

1 And 'round my heart still close-ly twine Those ties which can't be sev-ered.
2 Naught that I have my own I call, I hold it for the giv-er;
3 From Him who loves me now so well, What power my soul can sev-er?

1 For I am His, and He is mine, For-ev-er and for-ev-er.
2 My heart, my strength, my life, my all Are His, and His for-ev-er.
3 Shall life or death, shall earth or hell? No! I am His for-ev-er.

JESUS CHRIST: FRIENDSHIP AND LOVE

242 We Shall Behold Him

*"Dear friends, now we are children of God, and what we will be has not yet
been made known. But we know that when he appears, we shall be like him,
for we shall see him as he is."—I John 3:2*

Dottie Rambo

WE SHALL BEHOLD HIM
Dottie Rambo

1 The sky shall un - fold, pre - par - ing His en - trance; The stars shall ap-
2 The an - gel shall sound the shout of His com - ing; The sleeping shall

1 plaud Him with thun-ders of praise. The sweet light in His eyes shall en-
2 rise from their slum-ber-ing place. And those who re - main shall be

1 hance those a - wait-ing; And we shall be - hold Him then face to face.
2 changed in a mo-ment; And we shall be - hold Him then face to face.

And we shall be - hold Him, We shall be - hold Him Face to

face in all of His glo - ry. O we shall be - hold Him, We shall be-

JESUS CHRIST: SECOND COMING

JESUS CHRIST: SECOND COMING

243 What a Day That Will Be

"... and I will raise him up at the last day."—John 6:40b

Jim Hill

WHAT A DAY
Jim Hill

1 There is com - ing a day when no heart - aches shall come,
2 There'll be no sor-row there, no more bur - dens to bear,

1 No more clouds in the sky, no more tears to dim the eye; All is
2 No more sick - ness, no pain, no more part - ing o - ver there; And for-

1 peace for ev - er - more on that hap - py gold-en shore—What a day,
2 ev - er I will be with the One who died for me— What a day,

1 glo - ri - ous day, that will be.
2 glo - ri - ous day, that will be.

What a day that will be when my

Je - sus I shall see, And I look up - on His face— the One who

JESUS CHRIST: SECOND COMING

saved me by His grace; When He takes me by the hand, and leads me

through the Prom-ised Land, What a day, glo-ri-ous day, that will be.

Hope 244

The sufferings of this present time are not worthy to be compared with the glory that is to be revealed to us.

For the anxious longing of the creation waits eagerly for the revealing of the sons of God.

For the creation was subjected to futility, not of its own will, but because of Him who subjected it, in hope that the creation itself also will be set free from its slavery to corruption into the freedom of the glory of the children of God.

For we know that the whole creation groans and suffers the pains of childbirth together until now.

And not only this, but also we ourselves, having the first fruits of the Spirit, even we ourselves groan within ourselves, waiting eagerly for our adoption as sons, the redemption of our body.

For in hope we have been saved, but hope that is seen is not hope; for why does one also hope for what he sees?

But if we hope for what we do not see, with perseverance we wait eagerly for it.

And in the same way the Spirit also helps our weakness; for we do not know how to pray as we should, but the Spirit Himself intercedes for us with groanings too deep for words.

And He who searches the hearts knows what the mind of the Spirit is, because He intercedes for the saints according to the will of God.

And we know that God causes all things to work together for good to those who love God, to those who are called according to His purpose.

For whom He foreknew, He also predestined to become conformed to the image of His Son, that He might be the firstborn among many brethren;

And whom He predestined, these He also called; and whom He called, these He also justified; and whom He justified, these He also glorified.

—Romans 8:18–30 (NASB)

JESUS CHRIST: SECOND COMING

245 *The Return of Christ*

Brothers and sisters, we want you to know the truth about those who have died, so that you will not be sad, as are those who have no hope.

We believe that Jesus died and rose again; so we believe that God will bring with Jesus those who have died believing in Him.

For this is the Lord's teaching we tell you: we who are alive on the day the Lord comes will not go ahead of those who have died.

There will be the shout of command, the archangel's voice, the sound of God's trumpet, and the Lord Himself will come down from heaven!

Those who have died believing in Christ will be raised to life first; then we who are living at that time will all be gathered up along with them in the clouds to meet the Lord in the air. And so we will always be with the Lord.

Therefore, cheer each other up with these words.

There is no need to write you about the times and occasions when these things will happen. For you yourselves know very well that the Day of the Lord will come like a thief comes at night.

When people say, "Everything is quiet and safe," then suddenly destruction will hit them! They will not escape.

But you are not in the darkness, and the Day should not take you by surprise like a thief.

All of you are people who belong to the light, who belong to the day.

God did not choose us to suffer His wrath, but to possess salvation through our Lord Jesus Christ.

Who died for us in order that we might live together with Him, whether we are alive or dead when He comes.

—*From I Thessalonians 4 and 5 (NKJV)*

246 *Expectation*

Lord Jesus Christ,

Help us to plan our lives as if You will never return; and help us live our lives as if Your coming is but a second away. So may our vision stretch into the future, seeing all the great things we can do on Your behalf. In our work we seek to extend the boundaries of Your kingdom. We long for our King to come. Amen.

—Bryan Jeffery Leech

Soon and Very Soon

247

"He who testifies to these things says, 'Yes, I am coming soon.' "
—Revelation 22:20

Andraé Crouch

SOON AND VERY SOON
Andraé Crouch

1, 4 Soon and ver - y soon, We are going to see the King;
2 No more cry-ing there, We are going to see the King;
3 No more dy-ing there, We are going to see the King;

1, 4 Soon and ver - y soon, We are going to see the King;
2 No more cry - ing there, We are going to see the King;
3 No more dy - ing there, We are going to see the King;

1, 4 Soon and ver - y soon, We are going to see the King;
2 No more cry - ing there, We are going to see the King; Hal-le -
3 No more dy - ing there, We are going to see the King;

lu - jah! Hal - le - lu - jah! We're going to see the King.

JESUS CHRIST: SECOND COMING

248 Come, Gracious Spirit, Heavenly Dove

"But when he, the Spirit of truth, comes, he will guide you into all truth."
—John 16:13a

L.M.
HAMBURG
Based on Gregorian Chant
Lowell Mason, alt.

Simon Browne

1 Come, gra-cious Spir - it, heav'n - ly Dove
2 The light of truth to us dis - play,
3 Lead us to Christ, the liv - ing Way,
4 Lead us to heav'n, that we may share

1 With light and com - fort from a - bove;
2 And make us know and choose Your way;
3 Nor let us from His pas - tures stray;
4 Full - ness of joy for - ev - er there;

1 Come, be our guard - ian and our guide,
2 Plant ho - ly fear in ev - 'ry heart,
3 Lead us to ho - li - ness, the road
4 Lead us to our e - ter - nal rest,

1 O'er ev - 'ry thought and step pre - side.
2 That we from God may ne'er de - part.
3 That we must take to dwell with God.
4 To be with God for - ev - er blest.

THE SPIRIT AT WORK IN THE CHURCH

O Day of Joy and Wonder! 249

*"Now, Lord, consider their threats and enable your servants to speak your word
with great boldness . . . After they prayed, the place where they were meeting
was shaken. And they were all filled with the Holy Spirit and spoke the word of
God boldly."—Acts 4:29,31*

Violet Buchanan

7.6.7.6.D.
LANCASHIRE
Henry T. Smart

1 O day of joy and won - der! Christ's prom-ise now ful - filled!
2 The world in sheer a - maze -ment, The truth must now de - clare—
3 We too may know Thy pow - er, Thy cour -age make us strong,

1 The com - ing of His Spir - it The Fa -ther's love has willed;
2 That those who once were cow - ards Are brave be - yond com - pare;
3 Thy love, Thy joy, Thy pa - tience, Can all to us be - long;

1 Our Lord in hu - man bod - y To mor - tal eye was lost,
2 And tongues which could not ut - ter Their faith in Je - sus' name
3 If Thou wilt dwell with - in us, O Com - fort-er di - vine

1 Yet He re - turned for - ev - er At bless - ed Pen - te - cost.
2 De - fy all per - se - cu - tion, His glo - ry to pro - claim!
3 Come to our hearts, we pray Thee, And keep them ev - er Thine.

THE SPIRIT AT WORK IN THE CHURCH

250 Thou, Whose Purpose Is to Kindle

"I have come to bring fire on the earth, and how I wish it were already kindled!"—Luke 12:49

8.7.8.7.D.

Based on Luke 12:49
David Elton Trueblood

HYFRYDOL
Rowland Hugh Prichard

1 Thou, whose pur - pose is to kin - dle, Now ig - nite us
2 Thou, who still a sword de - liv - ers Ra - ther than a
3 Thou, who in Thy ho - ly gos - pel Will that we should

1 with Thy fire; While the earth a - waits Thy burn - ing,
2 pla - cid peace, With Thy sharp - ened Word dis - turb us,
3 tru - ly live, Make us sense our share of fail - ure,

1 With Thy pas - sion us in - spire. O - ver - come our sin - ful
2 From com - pla - cen - cy re - lease! Save us now from sat - is -
3 Our tran - quil - li - ty for - give. Teach us cour - age as we

1 calm - ness, Rouse us with re - demp - tive shame; Bap - tize with Thy
2 fac - tion When we pri - vate - ly are free, Yet are un - dis -
3 strug - gle In all lib - er - a - ting strife; Lift the small - ness

THE SPIRIT AT WORK IN THE CHURCH

1 fi - ery Spir - it, Crown our lives with tongues of flame.
2 turbed in spir - it By our neigh - bor's mis - er - y.
3 of our vis - ion By Thine own a - bun - dant life.

Lord God, the Holy Ghost   **251**

"Suddenly a sound like the blowing of a violent wind came from heaven and filled the whole house where they were sitting. All of them were filled with the Holy Spirit . . . "—Acts 2:2,4a

S.M.

James Montgomery, Alt.

TRENTHAM
Robert Jackson

1 Lord God, the Ho - ly Ghost, In this ap -
2 We meet with one ac - cord In this ap -
3 Like might - y rush - ing wind Up - on the
4 The young, the old in - spire With wis - dom
5 O Light of light, ex - plore And chase our

1 point - ed hour, As on the day of Pen - te -
2 point - ed place, And wait the prom - ise of our
3 waves be - neath, With one con - vic - tion move each
4 from a - bove, And give us hearts and tongues of
5 gloom a - way, With lus - ter shin - ing more and

1 cost, De - scend with all your pow'r.
2 Lord, The Spir - it of all grace.
3 mind, One soul, one feel - ing breathe.
4 fire To pray and praise and love.
5 more Un - to the per - fect day. A - men.

THE SPIRIT AT WORK IN THE CHURCH

252 Love Divine, All Loves Excelling

"So I say, live by the Spirit, and you will not gratify the desires of the sinful nature."—Galatians 5:16

8.7.8.7.D.
BEECHER
John Zundel

Charles Wesley

1 Love di - vine, all loves ex - cel - ling, Joy of heaven to earth come down,
2 Breathe, O breathe, Thy lov - ing Spir - it In - to ev - ery trou - bled breast;
3 Come, Al - might - y, to de - liv - er, Let us all Thy life re - ceive;
4 Fin - ish then Thy new cre - a - tion, Pure and spot - less let us be;

1 Fix in us Thy hum - ble dwell - ing, All Thy faith - ful mer - cies crown.
2 Let us all in Thee in - her - it, Let us find Thy prom - ised rest.
3 Sud - den - ly re - turn, and nev - er, Nev - er - more Thy tem - ples leave.
4 Let us see Thy great sal - va - tion Per - fect - ly re - stored in Thee.

1 Je - sus, Thou art all com - pas - sion, Pure, un - bound - ed love Thou art;
2 Take a - way our bent to sin - ning, Al - pha and O - me - ga be;
3 Thee we would be al - ways bless - ing, Serve Thee as Thy hosts a - bove,
4 Changed from glo - ry in - to glo - ry, 'Til in heaven we take our place,

1 Vis - it us with Thy sal - va - tion, En - ter ev - ery trem - bling heart.
2 End of faith, as its be - gin - ning, Set our hearts at lib - er - ty.
3 Pray, and praise Thee with - out ceas - ing, Glo - ry in Thy per - fect love.
4 'Til we cast our crowns be - fore Thee, Lost in won - der, love, and praise. A - men.

THE SPIRIT AT WORK IN THE CHURCH

"Truly, truly, I say to you, he who believes in Me will also do the works that I do, and greater works than these will he do, because I go to the Father.

"Whatever you ask in My name, I will do it, that the Father may be glorified in the Son; if you ask anything in My name, I will do it.

"If you love me, you will keep My commandments. And I will pray the Father, and He will give you another Counselor, to be with you for ever,

"Peace I leave with you; My peace I give you; not as the world gives do I give to you. Let not your hearts be troubled, neither let them be afraid."

—From John 14:12-16, 27 (RSV)

O Breath of Life 254

"The Spirit gives life . . . "—John 6:63a

9.8.9.8.

DET AR ETT FAST ORD
Joel Blomquist

Besie Porter Head

1 O Breath of Life, come sweep-ing through us, Re-vive Your
2 O Wind of God, come bend us, break us, Till hum-bly
3 O Breath of Love, come breathe with-in us, Re-new-ing
4 O Heart of Christ, once bro-ken for us, 'Tis there we
5 Re-vive us, Lord! Is zeal a-bat-ing While har-vest

1 church with life and pow'r; O Breath of Life, come, cleanse, re-
2 we con-fess our need; Then in Your ten-der-ness re-
3 thought and will and heart; Come, Love of Christ, a-fresh to
4 find our strength and rest; Our bro-ken, con-trite hearts now
5 fields are vast and white? Re-vive us, Lord, the world is

1 new us, And fit Your church to meet this hour.
2 make us, Re-vive, re-store, for this we plead.
3 win us, Re-vive Your church in ev-'ry part.
4 sol-ace, And let Your wait-ing church be blest.
5 wait-ing, E-quip Your church to spread the light. A-men.

THE SPIRIT AT WORK IN THE CHURCH

255

The Comforter Has Come

"And I will ask the Father, and he will give you another Counselor to be with you forever—"—John 14:16

Frank Bottome

12.12.12.6.wR.
COMFORTER
William J. Kirkpatrick

1. O spread the ti - dings 'round wher - ev - er need is found, Wher -
2. The long, long night is past, the morn - ing breaks at last, And
3. Lo, the great King of kings, with heal - ing in His wings, To
4. O bound - less love di - vine! How shall this tongue of mine To

1. ev - er hu - man hearts and hu - man woes a - bound; Let ev - ery Chris - tian
2. hushed the dreadful sound and fu - ry of the blast, As o - ver gold - en
3. ev - ery cap - tive soul a full de - liv - erance brings; And through the vacant
4. won - dering mor - tals tell the match - less grace di - vine— That I, a child of

1. tongue pro - claim the joy - ful sound: The Com - fort - er has come!
2. hills the day ad - vanc - es fast! The Com - fort - er has come!
3. cells the song of tri - umph rings: The Com - fort - er has come!
4. hell, should in His im - age shine? The Com - fort - er has come!

The Com - fort - er has come, the Com - fort - er has come! The

THE SPIRIT AT WORK IN THE CHURCH

Ho - ly Ghost from heaven, the Fa-ther's prom-ise given; O spread the ti-dings
'round wher - ev - er need is found— The Com - fort - er has come!

Holy Spirit, Thou Art Welcome 256

"Do not put out the Spirit's fire."—I Thessalonians 5:19

Dottie Rambo
David Huntsinger

WELCOME
Dottie Rambo
David Huntsinger

Ho - ly Spir - it, Thou art wel - come in this place. Ho - ly
Spir - it, Thou art wel - come in this place. Om - ni - po-tent
Fa - ther of mer - cy and grace, Thou art wel - come in this place.

THE SPIRIT AT WORK IN THE CHURCH

257 Sweet, Sweet Spirit

"Now the Lord is the Spirit, and where the Spirit of the Lord is, there is freedom."—II Corinthians 3:17

SWEET, SWEET SPIRIT
Doris Akers

Doris Akers

1 There's a sweet, sweet Spir-it in this place, And I know that it's the
2 There are bless-ings you can-not re-ceive 'Til you know Him in His
3 If you say He saved you from your sin, Now you're weak, you're bound and

1 Spir-it of the Lord; There are sweet ex-pres-sions on each
2 full-ness and be-lieve; You're the one to prof-it when you
3 can-not en-ter in; You can make it right if you will

1 face, And I know they feel the pres-ence of the Lord.
2 say, "I am going to walk with Je-sus all the way."
3 yield— You'll en-joy the Ho-ly Spir-it that we feel.

Sweet Ho-ly Spir-it, Sweet heav-en-ly Dove, Stay right here

with us, Fill-ing us with Your love; And for these

THE SPIRIT AT WORK IN THE CHURCH

bless-ings We lift our hearts in praise: With-out a doubt we'll know

that we have been re-vived, When we shall leave this place.

The Indwelling Holy Spirit **258**

The indwelling of Jesus' Holy Spirit in our hearts
    Is something more important
        than the historical Incarnation.
Pentecost was a more earth-shaking event than Christmas.
        The Incarnation means that God became man,
whereas Pentecost means
        that man's been invited to become a child of God.
    Not only has God stooped down to us
    but He wants to lift us all the way up to Himself.
The Spirit's coming was far more resplendent than Christ's.
    The Incarnation took place at night
        in the seclusion of a cave,
    while Pentecost blazed forth in broad daylight
        with hundreds of people to witness
                the transformation.
    This was no longer God,
        submerged in anguish,
      becoming man;
  but a whole group of men,
      bathed in light and bliss,
        becoming children of God.
"You'll do greater things than I,"
    Jesus had promised, with His Church in mind.

—Louis Evely
From *That Man is You.*

259 Surely the Presence of the Lord Is in This Place

"For where two or three come together in my name, there am I with them."
—Matthew 18:20

Lanny Wolfe

SURELY THE PRESENCE
Lanny Wolfe

Sure-ly the pres-ence of the Lord is in this place; I can feel His might-y pow-er and His grace. I can hear the brush of an-gels' wings, I see glo-ry on each face; Sure-ly the pres-ence of the Lord is in this place.

THE SPIRIT AT WORK IN THE CHURCH

Holy Spirit, Truth Divine

260

"And I will ask the Father, and he will give you another Counselor to be with you forever—the Spirit of truth."—John 14:16,17a

7.7.7.7.
MERCY

Samuel Longfellow

Louis M. Gottshalk

1 Ho - ly Spir - it, Truth di - vine, Dawn up - on this
2 Ho - ly Spir - it, Love di - vine, Glow with - in this
3 Ho - ly Spir - it, Power di - vine, Fill and nerve this
4 Ho - ly Spir - it, Right di - vine, King with - in my

1 soul of mine; Word of God, an in - ward light,
2 heart of mine; Kin - dle ev - 'ry high de - sire;
3 will of mine; By Thee may I strong - ly live,
4 con - science reign; Be my law, and I shall be

1 Wake my spir - it, clear my sight.
2 Per - ish self in Thy pure fire.
3 Brave - ly bear, and no - bly strive.
4 Firm - ly bound, for - ev - er free. A - men.

THE SPIRIT AT WORK IN PERSONS

261 He Wants His Way in Thee

" . . . And this is how we know that He lives in us: We know it by the Spirit he gave us."—I John 3:24b,c

Charles W. Naylor

HIS WAY IN THEE
Henry C. Clausen

1 God has sent the Ho - ly Spir - it To our hearts an hon-ored guest,
2 Let the Spir - it do the plan - ning, Point the way thy feet shall go;
3 He doth some-times work in si - lence, When thou dost not know at all;
4 All thy - self to Him sur-ren - der, As He pleas - es let Him do;

1 To de - liv - er us from e - vil, And to bring us peace and rest.
2 Great-er than thine own His wis-dom, He the will of God doth know;
3 He doth some-times speak so soft-ly Thou must lis - ten for His call.
4 In the paths He lead-eth, fol-low, Wheth-er they be old or new.

1 He has come to work with -in us Heav-en's pur-pos - es so blest:
2 Bet - ter, wis - er than thy choos-ing Is the way that He will show:
3 But if thou wilt trust Him ful - ly, He will be thine all in all:
4 When the tasks seem hard be - fore thee, He with pow - er will en - due:

1 He wants His way in thee. Yield un - to the Ho - ly
2 He wants His way in thee.
3 He wants His way in thee.
4 He wants His way in thee.

THE SPIRIT AT WORK IN PERSONS

Breathe on Me, Breath of God 262

"We have not received the spirit of the world but the Spirit who is from God,
that we may understand what God has freely given us."—I Corinthians 2:12

Edwin Hatch

S.M.
TRENTHAM
Robert Jackson

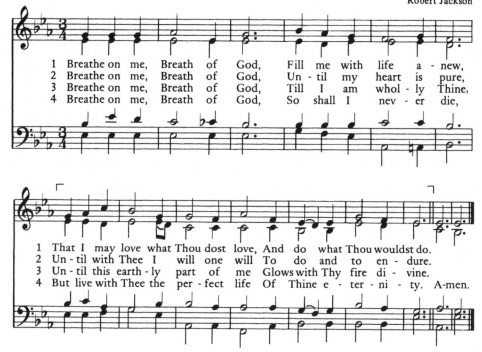

1 Breathe on me, Breath of God, Fill me with life a - new,
2 Breathe on me, Breath of God, Un - til my heart is pure,
3 Breathe on me, Breath of God, Till I am whol - ly Thine,
4 Breathe on me, Breath of God, So shall I nev - er die,

1 That I may love what Thou dost love, And do what Thou wouldst do.
2 Un - til with Thee I will one will To do and to en - dure.
3 Un - til this earth - ly part of me Glows with Thy fire di - vine.
4 But live with Thee the per - fect life Of Thine e - ter - ni - ty. A - men.

THE SPIRIT AT WORK IN PERSONS

263 Come, Holy Spirit

" . . . how much more will your Father in heaven give the Holy Spirit to those who ask Him!"—Luke 11:13b

Gloria Gaither
William J. Gaither

8.7.8.7.wR.
COME, HOLY SPIRIT
William J. Gaither

1 Come as a wis-dom to chil-dren, Come as new sight to the
2 Come as a rest to the wea-ry, Come as a balm for the
3 Come like a spring in the des-ert, Come to the with-ered of

1 blind, Come, Lord, as strength to my weak-ness, Take me: soul,
2 sore, Come as a dew to my dry-ness: Fill me with
3 soul; O let Your sweet heal-ing pow-er Touch me and

1 bod-y and mind.
2 joy ev-er-more. Come, Ho-ly Spir-it, I need You,
3 make me whole.

Come, sweet Spir-it, I pray; Come in Your strength and Your

pow-er, Come in Your own gen-tle way. A-men.

THE SPIRIT AT WORK IN PERSONS

There Is a Balm in Gilead 264

" . . . He has sent me to bind up the broken hearted, to proclaim freedom for the captives and release for the prisoners . . . "—Isaiah 61:1c

Jeremiah 8:22

BALM IN GILEAD
Traditional Spiritual

There is a balm in Gil-e-ad to make the wound-ed whole;

There is a balm in Gil-e-ad to heal the sin-sick soul.

1 Some - times I feel dis - cour-aged, And think my work's in vain,
2 If you can-not preach like Pe - ter, If you can -not pray like Paul,

1 But then the Ho - ly Spir - it Re - vives my soul a - gain.
2 You can tell the love of Je - sus, And say He died for all.

Fine

D.C. al Fine

THE SPIRIT AT WORK IN PERSONS

265 Spirit of the Living God

"And I will put my Spirit in you . . . "—Ezekiel 36:27a

Daniel Iverson

IVERSON
Daniel Iverson

Spir - it of the Liv - ing God, Fall fresh on me,

Spir - it of the Liv - ing God, Fall fresh on me.

Melt me, mold me, Fill me, use me.

Spir - it of the Liv - ing God, Fall fresh on me.

THE SPIRIT AT WORK IN PERSONS

Spirit of God, Descend Upon My Heart

266

"I am going to send you what my Father has promised; but stay in the city until you have been clothed with power from on high."—Luke 24:49

George Croly

10.10.10.10.
MORECAMBE
Frederick C. Atkinson

1 Spir - it of God, de - scend up - on my heart; Wean it from earth, through all its puls - es move; Stoop to my weak-ness, might-y as Thou art, And make me love Thee as I ought to love.

2 I ask no dream, no proph-et ec - sta - sies, No sud - den rend - ing of the veil of clay, No an - gel vis - i - tant, no o - pening skies: But take the dim-ness of my soul a - way.

3 Hast Thou not bid us love Thee, God and King? All, all Thine own— soul, heart and strength and mind! I see Thy cross—there teach my heart to cling: O let me seek Thee, and O let me find!

4 Teach me to feel that Thou art al - ways nigh; Teach me the strug - gles of the soul to bear, To check the ris - ing doubt, the reb - el sigh; Teach me the pa - tience of un - an - swered prayer.

5 Teach me to love Thee as Thine an - gels love, One ho - ly pas - sion fill - ing all my frame; The bap-tism of the heaven-de-scend-ed Dove: My heart an al - tar, and Thy love the flame. A-men.

THE SPIRIT AT WORK IN PERSONS

267

Spirit Holy

"Do not cast me from your presence or take your Holy Spirit from me."
—Psalm 51:11

8.7.8.7.wR.
SPIRIT HOLY

Charles W. Naylor

Andrew L. Byers

1 Spir-it ho-ly in me dwell-ing, Ev-er work as Thou shalt choose;
2 O how sweet is Thy a-bid-ing! O how ten-der is the love
3 Thou hast cleansed me for Thy tem-ple, Gar-nished with Thy grac-es rare;
4 In me now re-veal Thy glo-ry, Let Thy might be ev-er shown;

1 All my ran-somed pow'rs and tal-ents For Thy pur-pose Thou shalt use.
2 Thou dost shed a-broad with-in me From the Fa-ther-heart a-bove!
3 All my soul Thou art en-rich-ing By Thy full-ness dwell-ing there.
4 Keep me from the world's de-file-ment, Sa-cred for Thy-self a-lone.

Spir-it ho-ly, Spir-it ho-ly, All my
Spir-it ho-ly, Spir-it ho-ly,

be-ing now pos-sess; Lead me, rule me, work with-
All my be-ing now pos-sess; Lead me, rule me,

THE SPIRIT AT WORK IN PERSONS

in me, Through my life Thy will ex - press. A - men.
work with-in me, Through my life Thy will ex - press.

Come, Holy Spirit, Still My Heart   **268**

*"And the peace of God, which transcends all understanding, will guard your
hearts and your minds in Christ Jesus."—Philippians 4:7*

Anonymous

C.M.
ST. AGNES
John B. Dykes

1 Come, Ho - ly Spir - it! still my heart With gen - tle -
2 Give me a heart of calm re - pose A - mid the
3 A - bove these scenes of storm and strife There spreads a
4 Come, Ho - ly Spir - it! breathe that peace, That vic - t'ry

1 ness di - vine. In - dwell - ing peace You can im -
2 world's loud roar, A life that like a riv - er
3 re - gion fair; Help me to live that high - er
4 make me win; Then shall my soul its con - flict

1 part; O make that bless - ing mine!
2 flows A - long a peace - ful shore!
3 life, And breathe that heav'n - ly air.
4 cease, And find a heav'n with - in. A - men.

269 Fill Me with Thy Spirit, Lord

"... be filled with the Spirit."—Ephesians 5:18b

Daniel S. Warner

7.7.7.7.wR.
FILL ME
Andrew L. Byers

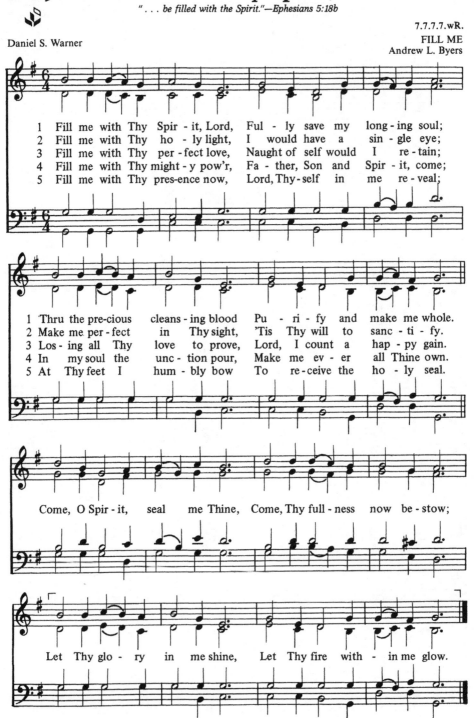

1 Fill me with Thy Spir - it, Lord, Ful - ly save my long - ing soul;
2 Fill me with Thy ho - ly light, I would have a sin - gle eye;
3 Fill me with Thy per - fect love, Naught of self would I re - tain;
4 Fill me with Thy might - y pow'r, Fa - ther, Son and Spir - it, come;
5 Fill me with Thy pres-ence now, Lord, Thy-self in me re - veal;

1 Thru the pre-cious cleans - ing blood Pu - ri - fy and make me whole.
2 Make me per - fect in Thy sight, 'Tis Thy will to sanc - ti - fy.
3 Los - ing all Thy love to prove, Lord, I count a hap - py gain.
4 In my soul the unc - tion pour, Make me ev - er all Thine own.
5 At Thy feet I hum - bly bow To re-ceive the ho - ly seal.

Come, O Spir - it, seal me Thine, Come, Thy full - ness now be - stow;

Let Thy glo - ry in me shine, Let Thy fire with - in me glow.

THE SPIRIT AT WORK IN PERSONS

With Thy Spirit Fill Me

270

"But you will receive power when the Holy Spirit comes on you; and you will be my witnesses in Jerusalem, and in all Judea and Samaria, and to the ends of the earth."—Acts 1:8

WITH THY SPIRIT FILL ME

Oswald J. Smith

B. D. Ackley

1 Lord, pos-sess me now, I pray, Make me whol-ly Thine to-day;
2 Lord, I yield my-self to Thee, All I am or hope to be,
3 Lord, com-mis-sion me, I pray! Souls are dy-ing ev-'ry day;

1 Glad-ly do I own Thy sway, With Thy Spir-it fill me.
2 Now and thru e-ter-ni-ty, With Thy Spir-it fill me.
3 Help me lead them in Thy way, With Thy Spir-it fill me.

With Thy Spir-it fill me, With Thy Spir-it fill me;

Make me whol-ly Thine, I pray, With Thy Spir-it fill me.

THE SPIRIT AT WORK IN PERSONS

271 Open My Eyes That I May See

"...but God has revealed it to us by his Spirit. The Spirit searches all things, even the deep things of God."—I Corinthians 2:10

Clara H. Scott

OPEN MY EYES
Clara H. Scott

1 O - pen my eyes, that I may see Glimp-ses of truth Thou hast for me;
2 O - pen my ears, that I may hear Voic - es of truth Thou send-est clear;
3 O - pen my mouth and let me bear Glad - ly the warm truth ev - 'ry-where;

1 Place in my hands the won-der-ful key That shall un-clasp and set me free.
2 And while the wave-notes fall on my ear, Ev - ery-thing false will dis - ap-pear.
3 O - pen my heart, and let me pre-pare Love with Thy chil-dren thus to share.

Si - lent-ly now I wait for Thee, Read-y, my God, Thy will to see;

1 O - pen my eyes, il - lu - mine me, Spir - it di - vine!
2 O - pen my ears, il - lu - mine me, Spir - it di - vine!
3 O - pen my heart, il - lu - mine me, Spir - it di - vine! A-men.

THE SPIRIT AT WORK IN PERSONS

Shine in Me

*"And we, who with unveiled faces all reflect the Lord's glory, are being
transformed into his likeness with ever-increasing glory, which comes from the
Lord, who is the Spirit."—II Corinthians 3:18*

Charles W. Naylor

SHINE IN ME
W. Dale Oldham

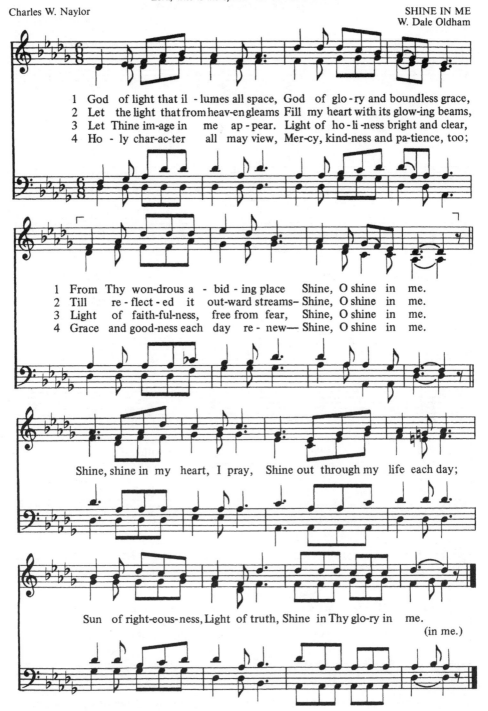

1 God of light that il-lumes all space, God of glo-ry and boundless grace,
2 Let the light that from heav-en gleams Fill my heart with its glow-ing beams,
3 Let Thine im-age in me ap-pear. Light of ho-li-ness bright and clear,
4 Ho-ly char-ac-ter all may view, Mer-cy, kind-ness and pa-tience, too;

1 From Thy won-drous a-bid-ing place Shine, O shine in me.
2 Till re-flect-ed it out-ward streams— Shine, O shine in me.
3 Light of faith-ful-ness, free from fear, Shine, O shine in me.
4 Grace and good-ness each day re-new— Shine, O shine in me.

Shine, shine in my heart, I pray, Shine out through my life each day;

Sun of right-eous-ness, Light of truth, Shine in Thy glo-ry in me.
(in me.)

THE SPIRIT AT WORK IN PERSONS

273 Though I May Speak with Bravest Fire

"If I give all I possess to the poor and surrender my body to the flames, but have not love, I gain nothing."—1 Corinthians 13:3

Based on I Corinthians 13
Hal Hopson

L.M.
GIFT OF LOVE
Hal Hopson
Based on an American Folk Tune

Unison

1 Though I may speak with brav-est fire,
2 Though I may give all I pos-sess,
3 Come Spir-it, come, our hearts con-trol,

1 And have the gift to all in-spire,
2 And striv-ing so my love pro-fess,
3 Our spir-its long to be made whole.

1 And have not love, my words are vain
2 But not be giv'n by love with-in,
3 Let in-ward love guide ev-'ry deed;

1 As sound-ing brass, and hope-less gain.
2 The prof-it soon turns strange-ly thin.
3 By this we wor - ship and are freed.

THE SPIRIT AT WORK IN PERSONS

Blessed Quietness

"There remains, then, a Sabbath-rest for the people of God."—Hebrews 4:9

Manie P. Ferguson

BLESSED QUIETNESS
W. S. Marshall

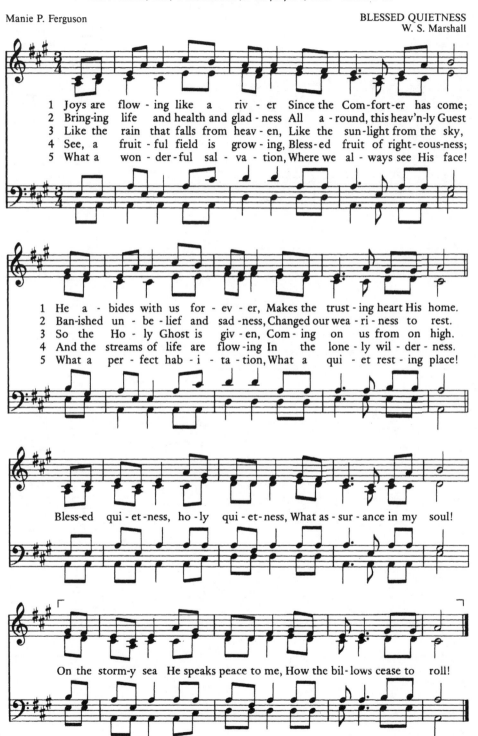

1 Joys are flow-ing like a riv-er Since the Com-fort-er has come;
2 Bring-ing life and health and glad-ness All a-round, this heav'n-ly Guest
3 Like the rain that falls from heav-en, Like the sun-light from the sky,
4 See, a fruit-ful field is grow-ing, Bless-ed fruit of right-eous-ness;
5 What a won-der-ful sal-va-tion, Where we al-ways see His face!

1 He a-bides with us for-ev-er, Makes the trust-ing heart His home.
2 Ban-ished un-be-lief and sad-ness, Changed our wea-ri-ness to rest.
3 So the Ho-ly Ghost is giv-en, Com-ing on us from on high.
4 And the streams of life are flow-ing In the lone-ly wil-der-ness.
5 What a per-fect hab-i-ta-tion, What a qui-et rest-ing place!

Bless-ed qui-et-ness, ho-ly qui-et-ness, What as-sur-ance in my soul!

On the storm-y sea He speaks peace to me, How the bil-lows cease to roll!

THE SPIRIT AT WORK IN PERSONS

275 Where the Spirit of the Lord Is

"Now the Lord is the Spirit, and where the Spirit of the Lord is, there is freedom."—II Corinthians 3:17

Stephen R. Adams

THERE IS PEACE
Stephen R. Adams

Where the Spir-it of the Lord is, there is peace;

Where the Spir-it of the Lord is, there is love.

There is com-fort in life's dark-est hour, There is light and life, there is

help and pow-er In the Spir-it, in the Spir-it of the Lord.

THE SPIRIT AT WORK IN PERSONS

Holy Spirit, Breathe on Me 276

"And with that he breathed on them and said, 'Receive the Holy Spirit.' "
—John 20:22

Based on John 20:22
Edwin Hatch

7.6.8.6.wR.
TRUETT
B. B. McKinney

1 Ho - ly Spir - it, breathe on me, Un - til my heart is clean;
2 Ho - ly Spir - it, breathe on me, My stub-born will sub - due;
3 Ho - ly Spir - it, breathe on me, Fill me with pow'r di - vine;
4 Ho - ly Spir - it, breathe on me, Till I am all Thine own,

1 Let sun-shine fill its in - most part With not a cloud be - tween.
2 Teach me in words of liv - ing flame What Christ would have me do.
3 Kin - dle a flame of love and zeal With - in this heart of mine.
4 Un - til my will is lost in Thine, To live for Thee a - lone.

Breathe on me, breathe on me, Ho - ly Spir - it, breathe on me;

Take Thou my heart, cleanse ev -'ry part, Ho - ly Spir - it, breathe on me.

THE SPIRIT AT WORK IN PERSONS

277 O Let the Son of God Enfold You

"And the disciples were filled with joy and with the Holy Spirit."—Acts 13:52

John Wimber

SPIRIT SONG
John Wimber

1. O let the Son of God en-fold you with His
2. O come and sing this song with glad-ness as your

1. Spir - it and His love; Let Him fill your heart and
2. hearts are filled with joy; Lift your hands in sweet sur -

1. sat - is - fy your soul. O let Him have the things that
2. ren - der to His name. O give Him all your tears and

1. hold you, and His Spir - it like a dove, Will de -
2. sad - ness, give Him all your years of pain, And you'll

1. scend up - on your life and make you whole.
2. en - ter in - to life in Je - sus' name.

THE SPIRIT AT WORK IN PERSONS

Je - sus, O Je - sus, come and

fill your lambs. Je - sus, O

Je - sus, come and fill your lambs.

Fully Alive 278

"In the same way, count yourselves dead to sin but alive to God in Christ Jesus."—Romans 6:11

Gloria Gaither

FULLY ALIVE
William J. Gaither

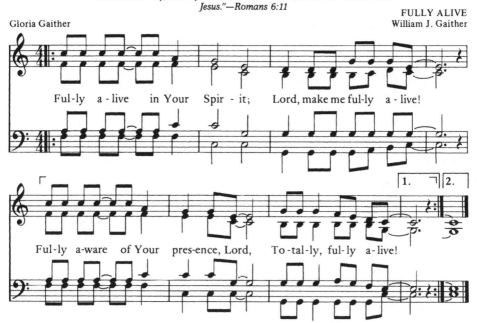

Ful-ly a - live in Your Spir - it; Lord, make me ful-ly a - live!

Ful-ly a-ware of Your pres-ence, Lord, To-tal-ly, ful-ly a-live!

THE SPIRIT AT WORK IN PERSONS

279 Gracious Spirit, Dwell with Me

"Do you not know that your body is a temple of the Holy Spirit, who is in you, whom you have received from God? You are not your own."—I Corinthians 6:19

7.7.7.7.7.7.
DIX

Thomas T. Lynch

Adapted from a chorale by Conrad Kocher

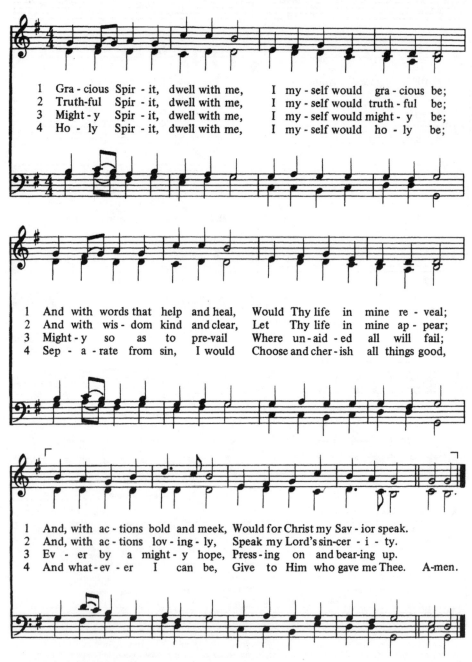

1 Gra - cious Spir - it, dwell with me, I my - self would gra - cious be;
2 Truth-ful Spir - it, dwell with me, I my - self would truth - ful be;
3 Might - y Spir - it, dwell with me, I my - self would might - y be;
4 Ho - ly Spir - it, dwell with me, I my - self would ho - ly be;

1 And with words that help and heal, Would Thy life in mine re - veal;
2 And with wis - dom kind and clear, Let Thy life in mine ap - pear;
3 Might - y so as to pre-vail Where un - aid - ed all will fail;
4 Sep - a - rate from sin, I would Choose and cher - ish all things good,

1 And, with ac - tions bold and meek, Would for Christ my Sav - ior speak.
2 And, with ac - tions lov - ing - ly, Speak my Lord's sin-cer - i - ty.
3 Ev - er by a might - y hope, Press-ing on and bear-ing up.
4 And what-ev - er I can be, Give to Him who gave me Thee. A-men.

THE SPIRIT AT WORK IN PERSONS

LEADER: Catch the Wind!

PEOPLE: *God, I'm so confused by all the noise, fragmentation, and busy bustle of my world.*

LEADER: Catch the Wind!

PEOPLE: *God, I'm scared. What if I can't cope with all that is demanded of me? Sometimes I feel as if everything is caving in on me.*

LEADER: Catch the Wind!

PEOPLE: *It's not easy to be loving—to forgive those who hurt me so badly.*

LEADER: Let the wind of My spirit blow across your life.

PEOPLE: *God, I want to be what You dream of my becoming.*

LEADER: Trust Me, My child, and yield to the wind of My spirit.

ALL: *He is the Spring Wind—I am the grass. Let Him blow.*

—Ann Smith

THE SPIRIT AT WORK IN PERSONS

281 Church of the Living God

"But in fact God has arranged the parts in the body, every one of them, just as he wanted them to be."—I Corinthians 12:18

D. Otis Teasley

S.M.D.
DIADEMATA
George J. Elvey

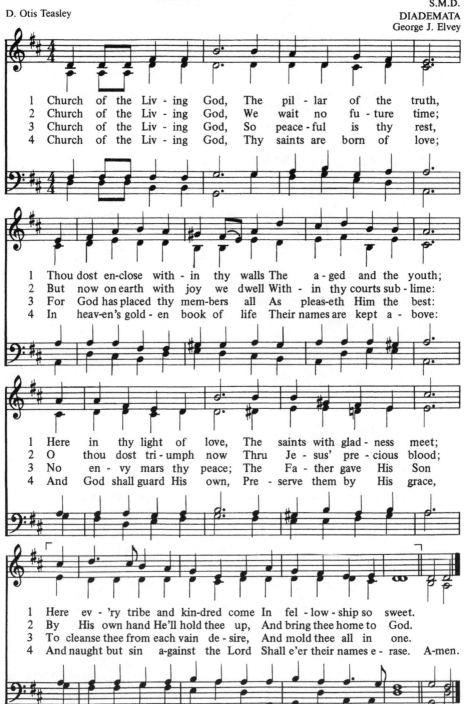

1 Church of the Liv-ing God, The pil-lar of the truth,
2 Church of the Liv-ing God, We wait no fu-ture time;
3 Church of the Liv-ing God, So peace-ful is thy rest,
4 Church of the Liv-ing God, Thy saints are born of love;

1 Thou dost en-close with-in thy walls The a-ged and the youth;
2 But now on earth with joy we dwell With-in thy courts sub-lime:
3 For God has placed thy mem-bers all As pleas-eth Him the best:
4 In heav-en's gold-en book of life Their names are kept a-bove:

1 Here in thy light of love, The saints with glad-ness meet;
2 O thou dost tri-umph now Thru Je-sus' pre-cious blood;
3 No en-vy mars thy peace; The Fa-ther gave His Son
4 And God shall guard His own, Pre-serve them by His grace,

1 Here ev-'ry tribe and kin-dred come In fel-low-ship so sweet.
2 By His own hand He'll hold thee up, And bring thee home to God.
3 To cleanse thee from each vain de-sire, And mold thee all in one.
4 And naught but sin a-gainst the Lord Shall e'er their names e-rase. A-men.

THE NATURE OF THE CHURCH

The Church's One Foundation 282

"So this is what the Sovereign Lord says: 'See, I lay a stone in Zion, a tested stone, a precious cornerstone for a sure foundation; the one who trusts will never be dismayed.' "—Isaiah 28:16

7.6.7.6.D.

Samuel J. Stone

AURELIA
Samuel S. Wesley

1 The Church-'s one foun - da - tion Is Je - sus Christ her Lord,
2 E - lect from ev - ery na - tion, Yet one o'er all the earth,
3 'Mid toil and trib - u - la - tion, And tu - mult of her war,
4 Yet she on earth hath un - ion With God, the Three in One,

1 She is His new cre - a - tion By wa - ter and the word;
2 Her char - ter of sal - va - tion, One Lord, one faith, one birth;
3 She waits the con - sum - ma - tion Of peace for ev - er - more;
4 And mys - tic sweet com - mun - ion With those whose rest is won;

1 From heaven He came and sought her To be His ho - ly bride;
2 One ho - ly name she bless - es, Par - takes one ho - ly food,
3 Till with the vi - sion glo - rious, Her long - ing eyes are blest,
4 O hap - py ones and ho - ly! Lord, give us grace that we

1 With His own blood He bought her, And for her life He died.
2 And to one hope she press - es, With ev - ery grace en - dued.
3 And the great Church vic - to - rious Shall be the Church at rest.
4 Like them, the meek and low - ly, On high may dwell with Thee. A-men.

THE NATURE OF THE CHURCH

283 A Glorious Church

"... and to present her to himself as a radiant church, without stain or wrinkle or any other blemish, but holy and blameless."—Ephesians 5:27

Ralph E. Hudson

GLORIOUS CHURCH
Ralph E. Hudson

1 Do you hear them com-ing clos - er, Throng-ing up the
2 Do you hear the stir-ring an - thems Fill - ing all the
3 Nev - er fear the clouds of sor - row; Nev - er fear the
4 Wave the ban - ner, shout His prais - es, For our vic - to -

1 steeps of light, Clad in glo - rious, shin - ing gar - ments—
2 earth and sky? 'Tis a grand, vic - to - rious ar - my.
3 storms of sin. We shall tri - umph on the mor - row;
4 ry is nigh! We shall join our con - qu'ring Sav - ior;

1 Blood-washed garments pure and white?
2 Lift its ban - ner up on high!
3 E - ven now our joys be - gin.   'Tis a glo - rious Church with-
4 We shall reign with Him on high!

out spot or wrin - kle, Washed in the blood of the Lamb. 'Tis a

glo-rious Church, with-out spot or wrin-kle, Washed in the blood of the Lamb.

I Love Your Kingdom, Lord 284

"I love the house where you live, O Lord, the place where your glory dwells."
—Psalm 26:8

S.M.

Based on Psalm 26:8
Timothy Dwight

ST. THOMAS
Williams' *New Universal Psalmodist*

1 I love Your king - dom, Lord, The house of Your a - bode,
2 I love Your Church, O God— Her walls be - fore You stand,
3 For her my tears shall fall, For her my prayers as - cend,
4 Sure as Your truth shall last, To Zi - on shall be given

1 The Church our blest Re - deem - er saved With His own pre - cious blood.
2 Dear as the ap - ple of Your eye, And held with - in Your hand.
3 To her my cares and toils be given 'Til all con - cerns shall end.
4 The bright-est glo - ries earth can yield, And bright - er joys of heaven. A-men.

285 Church of God, Beloved and Chosen

"to make her holy, cleansing her by the washing with water through the word, and to present her to himself as a radiant church, without stain or wrinkle or any other blemish, but holy and blameless."—Ephesians 5:26-27

Frances R. Havergal
D. S. Warner

8.7.8.7.D.

BEECHER
John Zundel

1 Church of God, be-loved and chos-en, Church of Christ for whom He died,
2 God Him-self has set the mem-bers, In His bod-y all com-plete,
3 God's own ho-li-ness with-in thee, His own beau-ty on thy brow,
4 Church of God, in heav-en writ-ten, Thine the ris-en life of Christ,

1 Claim thy gifts and praise the Giv-er, Ye are washed and sanc-ti-fied.
2 Or-gan-ized by Je-sus on-ly, O the un-ion pure and sweet!
3 Glo-ri-fied in His own im-age, This thy won-drous por-tion now.
4 And the treas-ures to thee giv-en, Nev-er, nev-er can be priced.

1 Sanc-ti-fied by God the Fa-ther, And by Je-sus Christ, His Son,
2 Church of God, the an-gels mar-vel At the mu-sic of thy song;
3 In thee dwells the Tri-une full-ness, Bless-ing all thy pil-grim days;
4 Far a-bove this world's con-fu-sion, Walk-ing close by Je-sus' side,

1 And by God the Ho-ly Spir-it, Ho-ly, ho-ly, Three in One.
2 Earth and heav'n re-sound in chor-us As thy ar-my moves a-long.
3 All a-round thee His sal-va-tion, And be-fore thee gates of praise.
4 Lean-ing on His lov-ing bo-som, Is the church, His chos-en bride. A-men.

THE NATURE OF THE CHURCH

The Church Has One Foundation

286

"For in Scripture it says: 'See, I lay a stone in Zion, a chosen and precious cornerstone, and the one who trusts in him will never be put to shame.'"
—I Peter 2:6

Charles W. Naylor
Samuel J. Stone, vs. 1 and 2

7.6.7.6.D.
ONE FOUNDATION
Andrew L. Byers

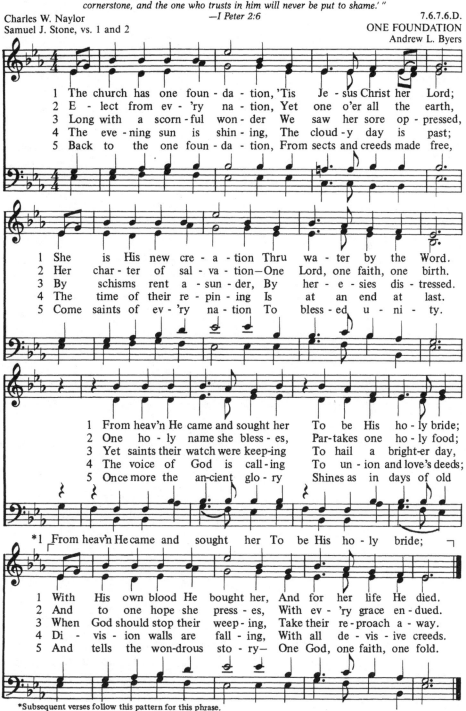

1 The church has one foun - da - tion, 'Tis Je - sus Christ her Lord;
2 E - lect from ev - 'ry na - tion, Yet one o'er all the earth,
3 Long with a scorn - ful won - der We saw her sore op - pressed,
4 The eve - ning sun is shin - ing, The cloud - y day is past;
5 Back to the one foun - da - tion, From sects and creeds made free,

1 She is His new cre - a - tion Thru wa - ter by the Word.
2 Her char - ter of sal - va - tion—One Lord, one faith, one birth.
3 By schisms rent a - sun - der, By her - e - sies dis - tressed.
4 The time of their re - pin - ing Is at an end at last.
5 Come saints of ev - 'ry na - tion To bless - ed u - ni - ty.

1 From heav'n He came and sought her To be His ho - ly bride;
2 One ho - ly name she bless - es, Par - takes one ho - ly food;
3 Yet saints their watch were keep - ing To hail a bright - er day,
4 The voice of God is call - ing To un - ion and love's deeds;
5 Once more the an - cient glo - ry Shines as in days of old

*1 From heav'n He came and sought her To be His ho - ly bride;

1 With His own blood He bought her, And for her life He died.
2 And to one hope she press - es, With ev - 'ry grace en - dued.
3 When God should stop their weep - ing, Take their re - proach a - way.
4 Di - vis - ion walls are fall - ing, With all de - vis - ive creeds.
5 And tells the won - drous sto - ry— One God, one faith, one fold.

*Subsequent verses follow this pattern for this phrase.

THE NATURE OF THE CHURCH

287

We Are God's People

"But you are a chosen people, a royal priesthood, a holy nation, a people belonging to God . . . "—I Peter 2:9a

11.11.14.8.9.
SYMPHONY
Johannes Brahms
Arranged by Fred Bock

Bryan Jeffery Leech

Unison

1 We are God's peo - ple, the cho - sen of the Lord,
2 We are God's loved ones, the Bride of Christ our Lord,
3 We are the Bod - y of which the Lord is Head,
4 We are a Tem - ple, the Spir - it's dwell - ing place,

1 Born of His Spir - it, es - tab - lished by His Word; Our
2 For we have known it, the love of God out - poured; Now
3 Called to o - bey Him, now ris - en from the dead; He
4 Formed in great weak - ness, a cup to hold God's grace; We

1 cor - ner-stone is Christ a - lone, And strong in Him we stand: O let us
2 let us learn how to re - turn The gift of love once given: O let us
3 wills us be a fam - i - ly, Di - verse yet tru - ly one: O let us
4 die a - lone, for on its own Each em - ber los - es fire: Yet joined in

1 live trans - par - ent - ly, And walk heart to heart and hand in hand.
2 share each joy and care, And live with a zeal that pleas - es Heaven.
3 give our gifts to God, And so shall His work on earth be done.
4 one the flame burns on To give warmth and light, and to in - spire.

THE NATURE OF THE CHURCH

Glorious Things of Thee Are Spoken

288

"Glorious things are said of you, O city of God."—Psalm 87:3

8.7.8.7.D.
AUSTRIAN HYMN
Franz Joseph Haydn

Based on Psalm 87:3; Isaiah 33:20, 21
John Newton

1 Glo - rious things of thee are spo - ken, Zi - on, cit - y of our God;
2 See, the streams of liv - ing wa - ters, Spring-ing from e - ter - nal Love,
3 Round each hab - i - ta - tion hov-ering, See the cloud and fire ap - pear

1 He whose word can - not be bro - ken Formed thee for His own a - bode.
2 Well sup - ply thy sons and daugh-ters, And all fear of want re - move.
3 For a glo - ry and a cov-ering, Show - ing that the Lord is near!

1 On the Rock of A - ges found-ed, What can shake thy sure re-pose?
2 Who can faint while such a riv - er Ev - er flows their thirst to assuage?
3 Thus de - riv - ing from their ban - ner Light by night and shade by day,

1 With sal - va - tion's walls sur-round-ed, Thou mayst smile at all thy foes.
2 Grace which, like the Lord, the Giv - er, Nev - er fails from age to age!
3 Safe they feed up - on the man-na Which He gives them when they pray. A-men.

THE NATURE OF THE CHURCH

289

O Church of God

"There is one body and one Spirit—just as you were called to one hope when
you were called—"—Ephesians 4:4

C.M.wR.

Charles W. Naylor

O CHURCH OF GOD
Andrew L. Byers

1 The church of God one bo-dy is, One Spir-it dwells with-in;
2 Di - vine-ly built, di - vine-ly ruled, To God she doth sub-mit;
3 God sets her mem-bers each in place, Ac - cord-ing to His will—
4 In beau - ty stand, O church of God, With right-eous-ness ar - rayed;

1 And all her mem-bers are re-deemed, And tri-umph o - ver sin.
2 His will her law, His truth her guide, Her path is glo-ry- lit.
3 A - pos-tles, proph-ets, teach-ers, all, His pur-pose to ful-fill.
4 Put on thy strength and face thy foes With cour-age un - dis-mayed.

O church of God! I love thy courts, Thou moth-er of the free;

Thou bless - ed home of all the saved, I dwell con-tent in thee.

THE NATURE OF THE CHURCH

Macedonia

290

"After Paul had seen the vision, we got ready at once to leave for Macedonia, concluding that God had called us to preach the gospel to them."—Acts 16:10

C.M.D.

Anne Ortlund

ALL SAINTS NEW
Henry S. Cutler

1 The vi-sion of a dy-ing world Is vast be-fore our eyes;
2 The sav-age hugs his god of stone And fears de-scent of night;
3 To-day, as un-der-stand-ing's bounds Are stretch'd on ev-'ry hand,
4 The warn-ing bell of judg-ment tolls, A-bove us looms the cross;

1 We feel the heart-beat of its need, We hear its fee-ble cries:
2 The cit-y dwell-er cring-es 'lone A-mid the gar-ish light:
3 O clothe Your Word in bright, new sounds, And speed it o'er the land;
4 A-round are ev-er-dy-ing souls— How great, how great the loss!

1 Lord Je-sus Christ, re-vive Your church In this, her cru-cial hour!
2 Lord Je-sus Christ, a-rouse Your church To see their mute dis-tress!
3 Lord Je-sus Christ, em-pow-er us To preach by ev-'ry means!
4 O Lord, con-strain and move Your church The glad news to im-part!

1 Lord Je-sus Christ, a-wake Your church With Spir-it-giv-en pow'r.
2 Lord Je-sus Christ, e-quip Your church With love and ten-der-ness.
3 Lord Je-sus Christ, em-bold-en us In near and dis-tant scenes.
4 And Lord, as You do stir Your church, Be-gin with-in my heart.

THE MISSION AND MINISTRY OF THE CHURCH

291 We Are Called to Be God's People

"To this you were called, because Christ suffered for you, leaving you an example, that you should follow in his steps."—I Peter 2:21

8.7.8.7.D.

Thomas A. Jackson

AUSTRIAN HYMN
Franz Joseph Haydn

1 We are called to be God's peo-ple, Show-ing by our lives His grace,
2 We are called to be God's ser-vants, Work-ing in His world to-day,
3 We are called to be God's proph-ets, Speak-ing for the truth and right,

1 One in heart and one in spir-it, Sign of hope for all the race.
2 Tak-ing His own task up-on us, All His sa-cred words o-bey.
3 Stand-ing firm for god-ly jus-tice, Bring-ing e-vil in-to light.

1 Let us show how He has changed us, And re-made us as His own,
2 Let us rise, then, to His sum-mons, Ded-i-cate to Him our all,
3 Let us seek the cour-age need-ed, Our high call-ing to ful-fill,

1 Let us share our life to-geth-er As we shall a-round His throne.
2 That we may be faith-ful ser-vants, Quick to an-swer now His call.
3 That all peo-ple know the bless-ing Of the do-ing of God's will.

THE MISSION AND MINISTRY OF THE CHURCH

O Church of God Triumphant 292

*"He went to him and bandaged his wounds, pouring on oil and wine. Then he
put the man on his own donkey, took him to an inn and took care of him."*
—Luke 10:34

7.6.7.6.D.

S. Ralph Harlow

LANCASHIRE
Henry T. Smart

1 O Church of God tri - um - phant a - bove the world's dark fears,
2 On Christ-mas eve her car - ols have set our hearts a - glow,
3 Her task on earth un - fin - ished till threats of war shall cease,
4 O Church of God tri - um - phant, we of - fer now in prayer

1 Where - in our souls find ref - uge through all these earth - ly years;
2 Her bells on Eas - ter morn - ing with faith still o - ver - flow;
3 Her voice must raise a pro - test where greed still robs our peace;
4 Our youth, our men, our wo - men, for Christ's great cause to dare,

1 Christ's stead-fast, ho - ly pur - pose, il - lum - ined by the cross,
2 Be - fore her hal-lowed al - tars we pledge our love in youth,
3 One fel - low-ship Christ called for, of ev - 'ry class and race,
4 That His re - deem - ing pur - pose may prove be - yond de - feat,

1 Guards us from e - vil's pow - er, re - veal - ing it but dross.
2 While in her sa - cred por - tals our minds have found God's truth.
3 The Church must live the vi - sion that shone in Je - sus' face.
4 Till in the Life Im - mor - tal with joy His chil - dren meet. A - men.

THE MISSION AND MINISTRY OF THE CHURCH

293 God of All, Whose Love Surrounds Us

"I thank Christ Jesus our Lord, who has given me strength, that he considered me faithful, appointing me to his service."—I Timothy 1:12

8.7.8.7.8.7.7.

Daniel B Merrick, Jr.

CWM RHONDDA
John Hughes

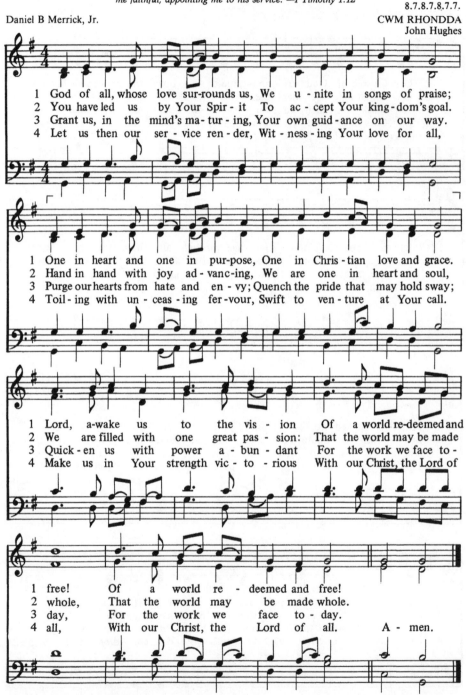

1 God of all, whose love sur-rounds us, We u-nite in songs of praise;
2 You have led us by Your Spir-it To ac-cept Your king-dom's goal.
3 Grant us, in the mind's ma-tur-ing, Your own guid-ance on our way.
4 Let us then our ser-vice ren-der, Wit-ness-ing Your love for all,

1 One in heart and one in pur-pose, One in Chris-tian love and grace.
2 Hand in hand with joy ad-vanc-ing, We are one in heart and soul,
3 Purge our hearts from hate and en-vy; Quench the pride that may hold sway;
4 Toil-ing with un-ceas-ing fer-vour, Swift to ven-ture at Your call.

1 Lord, a-wake us to the vis-ion Of a world re-deemed and
2 We are filled with one great pas-sion: That the world may be made
3 Quick-en us with power a-bun-dant For the work we face to-
4 Make us in Your strength vic-to-rious With our Christ, the Lord of

1 free! Of a world re-deemed and free!
2 whole, That the world may be made whole.
3 day, For the work we face to-day.
4 all, With our Christ, the Lord of all. A-men.

THE MISSION AND MINISTRY OF THE CHURCH

God Almighty, God Eternal 294

"Be imitators of God, therefore, as dearly beloved children and live a life of love, just as Christ loved us and gave himself up for us as a fragrant offering and sacrifice to God."—Ephesians 5:1,2

8.7.8.7.D.

Mary Jackson Cathey

HYMN TO JOY
Ludwig van Beethoven
Adapted by Edward Hodges

1 God al-might-y, God e-ter-nal, To Thy throne we bring our prayer,
2 God un-chang-ing, God for-ev-er, In these times of sky and space,
3 God the Sov-'reign our Cre-a-tor, Thou to whom all things be-long,

1 Ask-ing help and seek-ing guid-ance For Thy peo-ple ev-'ry-where;
2 When has come a new di-men-sion To our wide-spread hu-man race,
3 Thou who speak-est through the a-ges To the un-i-ver-sal throng,

1 In this age of chang-ing boun-d'ries, Wid-'ning spac-es, spread-ing spheres,
2 Lend to us Thine un-der-stand-ing, Lov-ing spir-it, fer-vent zeal
3 Speak a-gain to all Thy chil-dren, Voice Thy truth to us, we pray,

1 Give to us the strength to fol-low When Thy will for us ap-pears.
2 That our dai-ly, liv-ing wit-ness May be filled with Christ's ap-peal.
3 As the world of na-ture wid-ens, Teach us how to serve Christ's way. A-men.

THE MISSION AND MINISTRY OF THE CHURCH

295 Forward Through the Ages

*"Now to him who is able to do immeasurably more than all we ask or imagine,
according to his power that is at work within us, to him be glory in the church
and in Christ Jesus throughout all generations, for ever and ever! Amen."*
—Ephesians 3:20-21

6.5.6.5.D.wR.
ST. GERTRUDE
Arthur S. Sullivan

Frederick L. Hosmer

1 For-ward through the a - ges, In un - bro - ken line,
2 Wid - er grows the king - dom, Reign of love and light;
3 Not a - lone we con - quer, Not a - lone we fall;

1 Move the faith - ful spir - its At the call di - vine:
2 For it we must la - bor Till our faith is sight:
3 In each loss or tri - umph Lose or tri - umph all:

1 Gifts in dif - f'ring mea - sure, Hearts of one ac - cord,
2 Proph-ets have pro - claimed it, Mar - tyrs tes - ti - fied,
3 Bound by God's far pur - pose In one liv - ing whole,

1 Man - i - fold the ser - vice, One the sure re - ward.
2 Po - ets sung its glo - ry, He - roes for it died.
3 Move we on to - geth - er To the shin - ing goal.

THE MISSION AND MINISTRY OF THE CHURCH

For - ward through the a - ges, In un - bro - ken line,

Move the faith - ful spir - its At the call di - vine.

Eternity in the Moment **296**

The touch of the Master makes us *see*. When Jesus touched the blind man, scales fell from his eyes, and when He touches us, scales fall from our eyes, too. We see beauties we didn't know existed. We come alive in the world of the Spirit, the *real* world, and we see the hurts and pain, too, caused by the infection of evil and the facade of the temporary. It is that seeing which demands our energies and our moments.

If we are the body of Christ, we are the instruments of healing; we are Jesus to the world. We are the love and the warmth and the sunshine of His presence. Sensitized by His Spirit we begin to see and listen and touch. We begin to weigh the moments for the eternity in them.

Perhaps this is what the psalmist meant when he said, "So teach us to number our days, that we may apply our hearts unto wisdom" (Ps. 90:12). Wisdom—the ability to recognize the eternity in a moment. The habit of thinking "forever." In the middle of the noise of the traffic and clatter and voices calling for our attention, Jesus calls us to focus on the eternal—*in this moment.*

—Gloria Gaither
From *Fully Alive*

297
Together We Go to Make Disciples

"Therefore, go and make disciples of all nations, baptizing them in the name of the Father and of the Son and of the Holy Spirit, and teaching them to obey everything I have commanded you."—Matthew 28:19,20a

8.5.8.5.wR.

Based on Matthew 28:19-20
Frederick G. Shackleton

TOGETHER WE GO
Frederick G. Shackleton

1 Christ our might-y Lead-er calls us, "Go, make dis-ci-ples!"
2 Hear the Great Com-mis-sion sound-ing, "Go, make dis-ci-ples!"
3 Sow-ers shall re-joice with reap-ers— "Go, make dis-ci-ples!"

1 What a no-ble task be-falls us: "Go, make dis-ci-ples!"
2 Har-vest fields are now a-bound-ing. "Go, make dis-ci-ples!"
3 All who are each oth-er's keep-ers, "Go, make dis-ci-ples!"

To-geth-er we go to make dis-ci-ples for

Je-sus our Lord in ev-'ry land; We're reach-ing the lost for Christ, the

Sav - ior, On far - a - way shores and near at hand. To-

geth - er we go to tell our neigh - bors The

mes-sage of Christ, our tru-est Friend. All pow-er is His, pow'r in earth and

heav - en, And He will be with us to the end.

THE MISSION AND MINISTRY OF THE CHURCH

298

We've a Story to Tell
to the Nations

*" 'Therefore go and make disciples of all nations, baptizing them in the name of
the Father and of the Son and of the Holy spirit.' "—Matthew 28:19*

H. Ernest Nichol

10.8.8.7.7.wR.
MESSAGE
H. Ernest Nichol

1 We've a sto - ry to tell to the na - tions That shall turn their
2 We've a song to be sung to the na - tions That shall lift their
3 We've a mes - sage to give to the na - tions—That the Lord who
4 We've a Sav - ior to show to the na - tions Who the path of

1 hearts to the right, A sto - ry of truth and mer - cy, A
2 hearts to the Lord, A song that shall con - quer e - vil And
3 reign - eth a - bove has sent us His Son to save us And
4 sor - row has trod, That all of the world's great peo - ples Might

1 sto - ry of peace and light, A sto - ry of peace and light.
2 shat - ter the spear and sword, And shat - ter the spear and sword.
3 show us that God is love, And show us that God is love.
4 come to the truth of God, Might come to the truth of God.

For the dark-ness shall turn to dawn - ing, And the dawn-ing to noon-day bright,

THE MISSION AND MINISTRY OF THE CHURCH

And Christ's great king-dom shall come on earth, The king-dom of love and light.

Where Cross the Crowded Ways of Life

299

" 'Go to the street corners and invite to the banquet anyone you find.' "
—Matthew 22:9

L.M.

Frank Mason North

GERMANY
Gardiner's "Sacred Melodies"

1 Where cross the crowd-ed ways of life, Where sound the
2 In haunts of wretch-ed - ness and need, On shad-owed
3 The cup of wa - ter given for Thee Still holds the
4 O Mas-ter, from the moun-tain side, Make haste to
5 Till all the world shall learn Thy love And fol-low

1 cries of race and clan, A - bove the noise of self-ish
2 thresh-olds dark with fears, From paths where hide the lures of
3 fresh ness of Thy grace; Yet long these mul - ti - tudes to
4 heal these hearts of pain; A - mong these rest - less throngs a -
5 where Thy feet have trod; Till glo - rious from Thy heaven a -

1 strife We hear Thy voice, O Son of Man.
2 greed, We catch the vi - sion of Thy tears.
3 see The sweet com - pas - sion of Thy face.
4 bide, O tread the cit - y's streets a - gain,
5 bove Shall come the cit - y of our God. A - men.

THE MISSION AND MINISTRY OF THE CHURCH

300 God Through Christ at Work Within Us

"The Spirit of the Sovereign Lord is on me, because the Lord has anointed me to preach good news to the poor."—Isaiah 61:1a

F. Dale Bengtson

8.7.8.7.D.
NETTLETON
John Wyeth

1 God through Christ at work with-in us, In cre - a - tion will un - fold
2 How shall we be joined in spir - it? What of race and creed and age?
3 Rac - es joined with all cre - a - tion, Think-ing, feel-ing, mov-ing now,

1 Life and breath and work and strug-gle; In this part - ner-ship be bold!
2 Who can bridge the great di - vi - sions In a world where lives en - gage?
3 Are a cat - a - lyst for ac - tion, Mak-ing op - por-tune our vow:

1 How can we gain in per - spec-tive, When con - front-ed on all sides
2 God in Christ, the Man for oth - ers, We will fol - low, strive to be
3 We shall seek to give life mean-ing; Prompt-ed by de - sire to give,

1 By world is - sues, ten-sions, con-flicts? What de - sign will serve to guide?
2 Serv - ing in the hu - man con-flict, Know-ing truth can make us free.
3 Let our vis - ion of the fu - ture Mo - ti - vate us now to live.

Used by permission of F. Dale Bengtson, owner.

THE MISSION AND MINISTRY OF THE CHURCH

Rise Up, O Church of God 301

"Whoever serves me must follow me; and where I am, my servant also will be.
My Father will honor the one who serves me."—John 12:26

S.M.

William P. Merrill, alt.

ST. THOMAS
Aaron Williams

1 Rise up, O church of God! Have done with less-er things; Give
2 Rise up, O church of God! His king-dom tar-ries long; Bring
3 Rise up, O saints of God! The church for you doth wait, Her
4 Lift high the cross of Christ, Tread where His feet have trod; U-

1 heart and soul and mind and strength To serve the King of kings.
2 in the day of u-ni-ty And end the night of wrong.
3 strength un-e-qual to her task: Rise up, and make her great.
4 nit-ed by the Son of man, Rise up, O church of God! A-men.

Good News for All People 302

Mission is not an optional part of the Christian life. It is essential to it. Mission is inherent in a Christian view of God, the divine-human relationship, Christian experience, and the Church. The Church is under commission from its Lord to proclaim the whole gospel to the whole person in the whole world. Mission is woven into the basic task of the Church. It is the outreach of the Church in all areas of life.

How is the gospel "good news" in the ethnic minority communities of the United States? It is "good news" for the persons who hear the biblical message, because the message is that God loves all persons. God relates to people as Creator, Redeemer, and Judge. God wills fulfillment for the whole person physically, spiritually, emotionally, and intellectually. Through Christ, God offers redemption for the whole person. People find fulfillment through love of God and neighbor. God sees His creation as one of great worth, dignity, and potential. The gospel is "good news" for the Church because it explains that the Church is to proclaim God's message and to mediate His love to whole persons in the whole world. Further, it promises that God's Spirit will work in the world to empower the Church for its task.

—David Telfer

303 God Is Here

"But I, by your great mercy, will come into your house; in reverence will I bow down toward your holy temple."—Psalm 5:7

8.7.8.7.D.
HYFRYDOL

Fred Pratt Green

Rowland H. Prichard

1 God is here! As we His peo-ple meet to of-fer
2 Here are sym-bols to re-mind us of our life-long
3 Here our chil-dren find a wel-come in the Shep-herd's
4 Lord of all, of Church and King-dom, in an age of

1 praise and prayer, May we find in full-er meas-ure
2 need of grace; Here are ta-ble, pool and pul-pit;
3 flock and fold; Here, as bread and cup are tak-en,
4 change and doubt Keep us faith-ful to the gos-pel,

1 what it is in Christ we share. Here, as in the world a-
2 here the cross has cen-tral place. Here, in hon-es-ty of
3 Christ sus-tains us as of old. Here, the ser-vants of the
4 help us work your pur-pose out. Here, in this day's ded-i-

1 round us, all our var-ied skills and arts Wait the com-ing
2 preach-ing here in si-lence, as in speech, Here, in new-ness
3 Ser-vant seek in wor-ship to ex-plore What it means in
4 ca-tion, all we have to give, re-ceive; We, who can-not

THE MISSION AND MINISTRY OF THE CHURCH

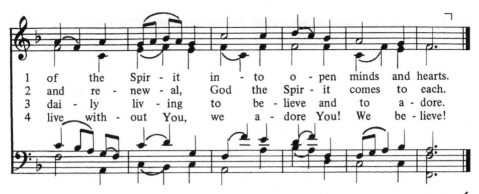

People Need the Lord 304

"How beautiful on the mountains are the feet of those who bring good news,
who proclaim peace, who bring good tidings, who proclaim salvation . . . "
—Isaiah 52:7a

Greg Nelson
Phill McHugh

PEOPLE NEED THE LORD
Greg Nelson
Phill McHugh

1 Peo-ple need the Lord, peo-ple need the
2 Peo-ple need the Lord, peo-ple need the

1 Lord; At the end of bro - ken dreams,
2 Lord; When will we re - al - ize

He's the o - pen door. peo-ple need the Lord.

THE MISSION AND MINISTRY OF THE CHURCH

305 Christ for the World We Sing

" 'Come to me, all you who are weary and burdened, and I will give you rest.' "
—Matthew 11:28

6.6.4.6.6.6.4.

Samuel Wolcott

ITALIAN HYMN
Felice de Giardini

1 Christ for the world we sing; The world to
2 Christ for the world we sing; The world to
3 Christ for the world we sing; The world to
4 Christ for the world we sing; The world to

1 Christ we bring With lov - ing zeal—
2 Christ we bring With fer - vent prayer—
3 Christ we bring With one ac - cord—
4 Christ we bring With joy - ful song—

1 The poor and them that mourn, The faint and o - ver-borne,
2 The way - ward and the lost, By rest - less pas - sions tossed,
3 With us the work to share, With us re - proach to dare,
4 The new - born souls whose days, Re - claimed from er - ror's ways,

1 Sin - sick and sor - row-worn, For Christ to heal.
2 Re - deemed at count-less cost From dark de - spair.
3 With us the cross to bear For Christ our Lord.
4 In - spired with hope and praise, To Christ be - long. A - men.

THE MISSION AND MINISTRY OF THE CHURCH

So Send I You

306

"Again Jesus said, 'Peace with you! As the Father has sent me, I am sending you.' "—John 20:21

Based on John 20:21
E. Margaret Clarkson

SO SEND I YOU
John W. Peterson

1 So send I you— by grace made strong to tri - umph O'er hosts of
2 So send I you— to take to souls in bond - age The word of
3 So send I you— My strength to know in weak - ness, My joy in
4 So send I you— to bear My cross with pa - tience, And then one

1 hell, o'er dark - ness, death and sin, My name to bear, and in that
2 truth that sets the cap - tive free, To break the bonds of sin, to
3 grief, My per - fect peace in pain, To prove My power, My grace, My
4 day with joy to lay it down, To hear My voice, "Well done, My

Sts. 1,2,3

1 name to con - quer— So send I you, my vic - to - ry to win.
2 loose death's fet - ters— So send I you, to bring the lost to me.
3 prom-ised pres - ence— So send I you, e - ter - nal fruit to gain.
4 faith - ful serv - ant— Come, share My throne, My king-dom and My

St. 4

crown!" "As the Fa - ther hath sent Me, So send I you."

THE MISSION AND MINISTRY OF THE CHURCH

307 The Voice of God Is Calling

"Then I heard the voice of the Lord saying, 'Whom shall I send? And who will go for us?' And I said, 'Here am I. Send me!' "—Isaiah 6:8

John Haynes Holmes

7.6.7.6.D.
WEBB
George J. Webb

1 The voice of God is call - ing Its sum-mons in our day;
2 "I hear My peo - ple cry - ing In slum and mine and mill;
3 We heed, O Lord, Your sum - mons And an - swer: Here are we!
4 From ease and plen - ty save us, From pride of place ab - solve;

1 As once He spoke in Zi - on, So now we hear Him say:
2 No field or mart is si - lent, No cit - y street is still.
3 Send us up - on Your er - rand, Let us Your ser - vants be.
4 Purge us of low de - sire, Lift us to high re - solve.

1 "Whom shall I send to res - cue My peo - ple in their need?
2 I see My peo - ple fall - ing In dark - ness and de - spair;
3 Our strength is dust and ash - es, Our years, a pass - ing hour;
4 Take us, and make us ho - ly, Teach us Your will and way;

1 Whom shall I send to loos - en The bonds of shame and greed?"
2 Whom shall I send to shat - ter The fet - ters which they bear?"
3 But You can use our weak-ness, To mag - ni - fy Your power.
4 Speak, and be-hold! we an - swer; Com-mand, and we o - bey! A-men.

THE MISSION AND MINISTRY OF THE CHURCH

Rescue the Perishing

308

"Snatch others from the fire and save them; to others show mercy, mixed with
fear—hating even the clothing stained by corrupt flesh."—Jude 23

11.10.11.10.wR.
RESCUE

Fanny J. Crosby

William H. Doane

1 Res - cue the per - ish - ing, Care for the dy - ing, Snatch them in pit - y from
2 Tho' they are slight-ing Him, Still He is wait - ing, Wait - ing the pen - i - tent
3 Down in the hu - man heart, Crushed by the tempt-er, Feel - ings lie bur -ied that
4 Res - cue the per - ish - ing— Du - ty de-mands it! Strength for thy la - bor the

1 sin and the grave; Weep o'er the err - ing one, Lift up the fall - en,
2 child to re - ceive; Plead with them ear-nest-ly, Plead with them gent - ly,
3 grace can re -store; Touched by a lov -ing heart, Wak - ened by kind - ness,
4 Lord will pro-vide; Back to the nar-row way Pa - tient - ly win them,

1 Tell them of Je - sus, the might-y to save.
2 He will for-give if they on - ly be - lieve.
3 Chords that are bro - ken will vi - brate once more.
4 Tell the poor wan-der-er a Sav - ior has died.

Res - cue the per - ish - ing,

Care for the dy - ing; Je - sus is mer - ci - ful, Je - sus will save.

THE MISSION AND MINISTRY OF THE CHURCH

309 Renew Thy Church, Her Ministries Restore

" 'In the same way, let your light shine before men, that they may see your good deeds and praise your Father in heaven.' "—Matthew 5:16

Kenneth Lorne Cober

10.6.10.6.8.8.8.6.

ALL IS WELL
J. T. White's Sacred Harp

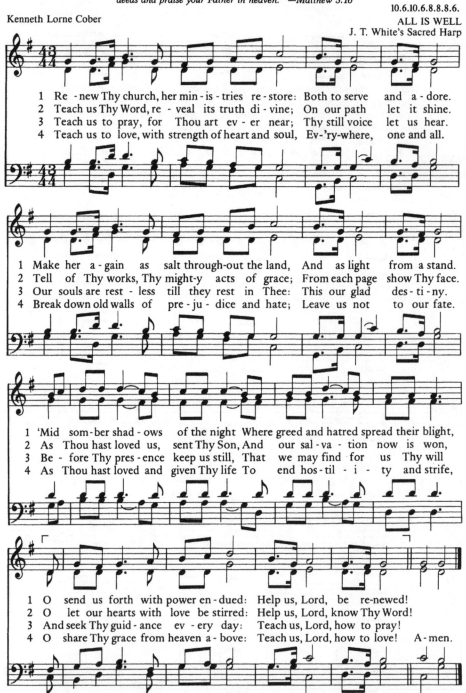

1 Re - new Thy church, her min - is - tries re - store: Both to serve and a - dore.
2 Teach us Thy Word, re - veal its truth di - vine; On our path let it shine.
3 Teach us to pray, for Thou art ev - er near; Thy still voice let us hear.
4 Teach us to love, with strength of heart and soul, Ev-'ry-where, one and all.

1 Make her a - gain as salt through-out the land, And as light from a stand.
2 Tell of Thy works, Thy might-y acts of grace; From each page show Thy face.
3 Our souls are rest - less till they rest in Thee: This our glad des - ti - ny.
4 Break down old walls of pre - ju - dice and hate; Leave us not to our fate.

1 'Mid som-ber shad - ows of the night Where greed and hatred spread their blight,
2 As Thou hast loved us, sent Thy Son, And our sal - va - tion now is won,
3 Be - fore Thy pres - ence keep us still, That we may find for us Thy will
4 As Thou hast loved and given Thy life To end hos - til - i - ty and strife,

1 O send us forth with power en - dued: Help us, Lord, be re-newed!
2 O let our hearts with love be stirred: Help us, Lord, know Thy Word!
3 And seek Thy guid - ance ev - ery day: Teach us, Lord, how to pray!
4 O share Thy grace from heaven a - bove: Teach us, Lord, how to love! A - men.

THE REFORMATION AND RENEWAL OF THE CHURCH

There Shall Be Showers of Blessing   310

" . . . there will be showers of blessing."—Ezekiel 34:26c

Daniel W. Whittle

SHOWERS OF BLESSING
James McGranahan

1 There shall be show-ers of bless - ing: This is the prom-ise of love;
2 There shall be show-ers of bless - ing— Pre - cious re - viv - ing a - gain;
3 There shall be show-ers of bless - ing: Send them up-on us, O Lord;
4 There shall be show-ers of bless - ing: O that to - day they might fall,

1 There shall be sea -sons re - fresh - ing, Sent from the Sav - ior a - bove.
2 O - ver the hills and the val - leys, Sound of a - bun-dance of rain.
3 Grant to us now a re - fresh - ing, Come, and now hon - or Thy Word.
4 Now as to God we're con - fess - ing, Now, as on Je - sus we call!

Show - ers of bless - ing, Show-ers of bless-ing we need:

Mer - cy-drops 'round us are fall - ing, But for the show-ers we plead.

THE REFORMATION AND RENEWAL OF THE CHURCH

311

The Reformation Glory

*"There is one body and one Spirit—just as you were called—one Lord, one faith,
one baptism; one God and Father of all, who is over all and through all and in
all."—Ephesians 4:4-6*

Charles W. Naylor

REFORMATION GLORY
Andrew L. Byers

1 There's a might-y ref-or-ma-tion sweep-ing o'er the land, God is
2 When the voice from heav-en sound-ed, warn-ing all to flee From the
3 Zi-on's walls a-gain are build-ing as in days of yore, And the
4 Chris-tians all should dwell to-geth-er in the bonds of peace, All the

1 gath-er-ing His peo-ple by His might-y hand; For the cloud-y day is
2 dark-some courts of Ba-bel back to Zi-on free; Glad my heart to hear the
3 scat-tered hosts re-turn-ing to their land once more Are re-joic-ing in their
4 clash-ing of o-pin-ion, all the strife should cease; Let di-vi-sions be for-

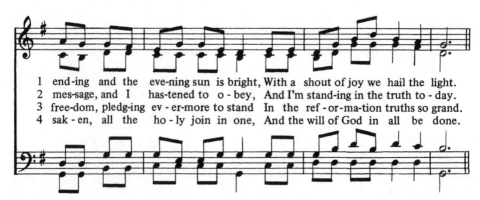

1 end-ing and the eve-ning sun is bright, With a shout of joy we hail the light.
2 mes-sage, and I has-tened to o-bey, And I'm stand-ing in the truth to-day.
3 free-dom, pledg-ing ev-er-more to stand In the ref-or-ma-tion truths so grand.
4 sak-en, all the ho-ly join in one, And the will of God in all be done.

THE REFORMATION AND RENEWAL OF THE CHURCH

O the ref - or - ma - tion glo - ry! Let it
O the ref - or - ma - tion glo - ry, O the glo - ry!

shine to ev - 'ry land. We will tell the
Let it shine to ev - 'ry land. We will tell the

bless - ed sto - ry; In its truth we e'er shall stand.
bless - ed sto - ry, bless-ed sto - ry;

THE REFORMATION AND RENEWAL OF THE CHURCH

312 The Church's Jubilee

" . . . May they be brought to complete unity to let the world know that you sent me and have loved them even as you have loved me."—John 17:23b

Charles W. Naylor

JUBILEE
Andrew L. Byers

1 The light of e-ven-tide now shines the dark-ness to dis-pel,
2 The Bi-ble is our rule of faith and Christ a-lone is Lord,
3 The day of sects and creeds for us for-ev-er-more is past,
4 O bless-ed truth that broke our bonds! In it we now re-joice,

1 The glo-ries of fair Zi-on's state ten thou-sand voic-es tell;
2 All we are e-qual in His sight when we o-bey His Word;
3 God's u-ni-ty joins all the saints up-on the world so vast;
4 While in the ho-ly church of God we hear our Sav-ior's voice;

1 For out of Ba-bel God doth call His scat-tered saints in one,
2 No earth-ly mas-ter do we know, to Christ a-lone we bow,
3 We reach our hands in fel-low-ship to ev-'ry blood-washed one,
4 And glad-ly to His bless-ed will sub-mis-sive we shall be,

1 To-geth-er all one church com-pose, the bod-y of His Son.
2 And to each oth-er and to God e-ter-nal true-ness vow.
3 While love en-twines a-bout each heart in which God's will is done.
4 And from the yokes of Ba-bel's lords from hence-forth we are free.

THE REFORMATION AND RENEWAL OF THE CHURCH

O church of God, the day of ju - bi - lee
O bless - ed church of God, the day of ju - bi - lee

Has dawned so bright and glo - ri - ous for thee;
Has dawned so fair and bright and glo - ri - ous for thee;

Re - joice, be glad! the Shep-herd has be - gun
Re - joice, and e'er be glad! the Shep - herd has be - gun

His long di - vid - ed flock a - gain to gath - er in - to one.

THE REFORMATION AND RENEWAL OF THE CHURCH

313 We're Building a Circle of Love

"We know that we have passed from death to life, because we love our brothers. Anyone who does not love remains in death."—I John 3:14

Ray McCutcheon

CIRCLE OF LOVE
Lloyd Larson

We're build-ing a cir - cle of love; We'll start with you and me. We're build-ing a cir - cle of love; Come join God's fam - i - ly! We'll

THE FELLOWSHIP AND UNITY OF THE CHURCH

reach out to our neigh-bor-hood, and then to all the

world.   We're build-ing a cir - cle of love, my friend. We're

build-ing a cir - cle *(clap clap)* of God's love.

1.

2.

We're   love.

THE FELLOWSHIP AND UNITY OF THE CHURCH

314 The Family of God

"Yet to all who received him, to those who believed in his name, he gave the right to become children of God."—John 1:12

Gloria Gaither
William J. Gaither

FAMILY OF GOD
William J. Gaither

I'm so glad I'm a part of the fam-ily of God— I've been washed in the foun-tain, cleansed by His blood! Joint heirs with Je-sus as we trav-el this sod, For I'm part of the fam-ily, the fam-ily of God.

Fine

1 You will no-tice we say "broth-er" and "sis-ter" 'round here— It's be-cause we're a fam-ily and these folks are so near;

2 From the door of an or-phanage to the house of the King— No long-er an out-cast, a new song I sing;

THE FELLOWSHIP AND UNITY OF THE CHURCH

1 When one has a heart-ache we all share the tears,
2 From rags un-to rich-es, from the weak to the strong;

D.C.

1 And re-joice in each vic-tory In this fam-ily so dear.
2 I'm not wor-thy to be here, But praise God, I be-long!

Come Sit with Me

315

Come sit with me . . .
I am Indian, Black, Hispanic, White and others
    not like yourself—

I have dreams, hopes, fears, frustrations
    but few seem to care.
Sometimes I am included in conversation
    on the fringe of things;
Seldom included at the heart of things.

Come sit with me . . .
I hear you say God loves me, God cares.
In quiet tones you speak to me high sounding phrases
    of security—peace—purpose—and an eternal destiny.
How can these things be?

Come sit with me . . .
I am Indian, Black, Hispanic, White and others
    not like yourself.
Perhaps, together, we could find God's eternal destiny.

—Joyce D. Foggs

THE FELLOWSHIP AND UNITY OF THE CHURCH

316 Because You Belong to Christ

"So in Christ we who are many form one body, and each member belongs to all the others."—Romans 12:5

Based on Romans 12:5, Eph. 5:21
Stanza 1, anonymous
Duane Blakley

MCDONALD
Duane Blakley

1 Be - cause you be-long to Christ, You are a - kin to me;
2 Be - cause I be-long to Christ, I will sub-mit to you;
3 Be - cause we be-long to Christ, We must ex-alt His Name;

1 One in the bonds un - break-a - ble, Made for e - ter - ni - ty.
2 Serv-ing in love and u - ni - ty, We can be-gin a - new.
3 Let - ting the world see Christ in us, His love for all pro - claim.

1 Spir - it with spir - it joined, Who can the ties un - do?
2 Leav - ing the past be - hind, Look - ing to Christ our Head,
3 Lift up the cross of Christ, His res - ur - rec - tion show,

1 Bind - ing the Christ in my heart, With the Christ in you.
2 Let us be one in His Name, And by Him be led.
3 Un - til we all shall see Him, And His full - ness know!

THE FELLOWSHIP AND UNITY OF THE CHURCH

As a prisoner for the Lord, then, I urge you to live a life worthy of the calling you have received.

Be completely humble and gentle; be patient, bearing with one another in love.

Make every effort to keep the unity of the Spirit through the bond of peace.

There is one body and one Spirit—just as you were called to one hope when you were called—

One Lord, one faith, one baptism;

One God and Father of all, who is over all and through all and in all.

If you have any encouragement from being united with Christ, if any comfort from His love, if any fellowship with the Spirit, if any tenderness and compassion,

Then make my joy complete by being likeminded, having the same love, being one in spirit and purpose.

Do nothing out of selfish ambition or vain conceit, but in humility consider others better than yourselves.

Each of you should look not only to your own interests, but also to the interests of others.

—Eph. 4:1–6, Phil. 2:1–4 (NIV)

THE FELLOWSHIP AND UNITY OF THE CHURCH

318 Bind Us Together

*" . . . May they be brought to complete unity to let the world know that you
sent me and have loved them even as you have loved me."—John 17:23b*

Bob Gillman

BIND US
Bob Gillman

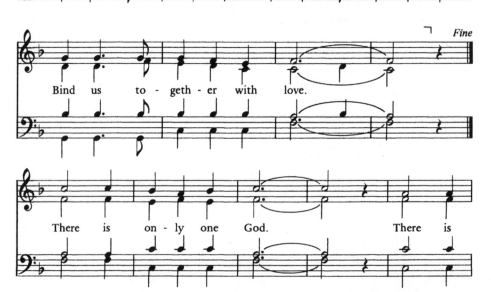

Bind us to - geth - er, Lord; Bind us to - geth - er with
cords that can - not be bro - ken.
Bind us to - geth - er, Lord; Bind us to - geth - er, Lord,
Bind us to - geth - er with love. *Fine*
There is on - ly one God. There is

THE FELLOWSHIP AND UNITY OF THE CHURCH

on - ly one King.   There is on - ly one

D.C. al Fine

bod - y,   That is why we can sing:

God's Love 319

LEADER: Dear Friends, let us love one another, for love comes from God. Everyone who loves has been born of God and knows God.

PEOPLE: *Whoever does not love does not know God, because God is love.*

LEADER: This is how God showed his love among us: He sent his one and only Son into the world that we might live through him.

PEOPLE: *This is love; not that we loved God, but that he loves us and sent his Son as an atoning sacrifice for our sins.*

LEADER: Dear friends, since God so loved us, we also ought to love one another.

PEOPLE: *No one has ever seen God;*

LEADER: But if we love each other, God lives in us and his love is made complete in us.

PEOPLE: *We know that we live in him and he in us, because he has given us of His Spirit.*

LEADER: And we have seen and testify that the Father has sent his Son to be the Savior of the world. God is love. Whoever lives in love lives in God, and God in him.

PEOPLE: *Love is made complete among us so that we will have confidence on the day of judgment, because in this world we are like him.*

LEADER: If anyone says, "I love God," yet hates his brother, he is a liar. For anyone who does not love his brother, whom he has seen, cannot love God, whom he has not seen.

PEOPLE: *And he has given us this command: Whoever loves God must also love his brother.*

—I John 4:7–14, 16–17, 20–21 (NIV)

THE FELLOWSHIP AND UNITY OF THE CHURCH

320 Blest Be the Tie That Binds

" . . . And this is my prayer: that your love may abound more and more . . . "
—Philippians 1:9a

S.M.
DENNIS
Johann G. Naegeli

John Fawcett

1 Blest be the tie that binds Our hearts in Chris - tian love;
2 Be - fore our Fa - ther's throne We pour our ar - dent prayers;
3 We share each oth - er's woes, Each oth - er's bur - dens bear;
4 From sor - row, toil, and pain, And sin we shall be free;

1 The fel - low-ship of kin - dred minds Is like to that a - bove.
2 Our fears, our hopes, our aims are one, Our com - forts and our cares.
3 And of - ten for each oth - er flows The sym - pa - thiz - ing tear.
4 And per - fect love and joy shall reign Through all e - ter - ni - ty.

321 One Flock, One Shepherd

"He is before all things, and in him all things hold together."—Colossians 1:17

ONE FLOCK
Stephen R. Adams

Stephen R. Adams

We are one flock, led by one Shep-herd, The sweet-est

THE FELLOWSHIP AND UNITY OF THE CHURCH

sto - ry that has ev - er been told! We are one flock led by one

Shep - herd; And some - day He will lead us to one fold.

Let Love Be Genuine **322**

Love must be sincere. Hate what is evil; cling to what is good. Be devoted to one another in brotherly love. Honor one another above yourselves. Never be lacking in zeal, but keep your spiritual fervor, serving the Lord. Be joyful in hope, patient in affliction, faithful in prayer. Share with God's people who are in need. Practice hospitality.

Bless those who persecute you; bless and do not curse. Rejoice with those who rejoice; mourn with those who mourn. Live in harmony with one another. Do not be proud, but be willing to associate with people of low position. Do not be conceited. Do not repay anyone evil for evil. Be careful to do what is right in the eyes of everybody. If it is possible, as far as it depends on you, live at peace with everyone.

—Romans 12:9–18 (NIV)

323

The Bond of Love

"We know that we have passed from death to life, because we love our brothers. Anyone who does not love remains in death."—I John 3:14

Otis Skillings

BOND OF LOVE
Otis Skillings

1 We are one in the bond of love, We are one in the
2 Let us sing now, ev-ery-one, Let us feel His

1 bond of love; We have joined our spir-it with the
2 love be-gun; Let us join our hands that the

1 Spir-it of God, We are one in the bond of love.
2 world will know We are one in the bond of love.

©1971 by Lillenas Publishing Company. All Rights Reserved. Used By Permission.

324

We Will Stand

"Stand firm then, with the belt of truth buckled around your waist, with the breastplate of righteousness in place."—Ephesians 6:14

Russ Taff
Tori Taff

WE WILL STAND
James Hollihan

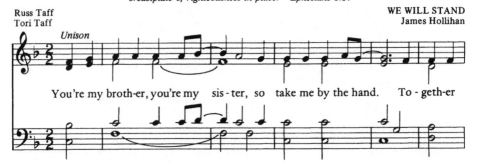

Unison

You're my broth-er, you're my sis-ter, so take me by the hand. To-geth-er

©Copyright 1983 by Word Music. All Rights Reserved. International Copyright Secured. Used By Permission.

THE FELLOWSHIP AND UNITY OF THE CHURCH

we will work un-til He comes. There's no foe that can de-feat us when we're

walk-ing side by side; As long as there is love, we will stand.

By One Spirit 325

LEADER: There are different kinds of gifts, but the same Spirit. There are different kinds of service, but the same Lord. There are different kinds of working, but the same God works all of them in all men.

PEOPLE: *Now to each one the manifestation of the Spirit is given for the common good.*

LEADER: To one there is given through the Spirit the message of wisdom, to another the message of knowledge by means of the same Spirit, to another faith by the same Spirit, to another gifts of healing by that one Spirit, to another miraculous powers, to another prophecy, to another the ability to distinguish between spirits, to another the ability to speak in different kinds of tongues, and to still another the interpretation of tongues.

PEOPLE: *All these are the work of one and the same Spirit, and he gives them to each one, just as he determines.*

LEADER: The body is a unit, though it is made up of many parts; and though all its parts are many, they form one body. So it is with Christ.

PEOPLE: *For we were all baptized by one Spirit into one body—whether Jews or Greeks, slave or free—and we were all given the one Spirit to drink.*

—*I Corinthians 12:4–13 (NIV)*

326 I Am Loved

" . . . because through Christ Jesus the law of the Spirit of life set me free from the law of sin and death."—Romans 8:2

Gloria Gaither
William J. Gaither

I AM LOVED
William J. Gaither

1 I am loved, I am loved, I can risk lov-ing you
2 You are loved, you are loved, you can risk lov-ing, too,

1 For the One who knows me best loves me most.
2 For the One who knows you best loves you most.

1 I am loved, you are loved— Won't you please take my hand?
2 I am loved, we are loved— Won't you please take our hand?

1 We are free to love each oth-er— we are loved.
2 We are free to love each oth-er— we are loved.

THE FELLOWSHIP AND UNITY OF THE CHURCH

I believe in one God the Father Almighty, Maker of heaven and earth, and of all things visible and invisible.

And in one Lord Jesus Christ, the only-begotten Son of God, begotten of His Father before all worlds, God of God, Light of Light, very God of very God, begotten, not made, being of one substance with the Father, by Whom all things were made; Who for us and for our salvation came down from heaven, and was incarnate by the Holy Spirit of the Virgin Mary, and was made man, and crucified also for us under Pontius Pilate; He suffered and was buried, and the third day He rose again according to the Scriptures, and ascended into heaven, and sitteth on the right hand of the Father; And He shall come again with glory to judge both the quick and the dead; Whose kingdom shall have no end.

And I believe in the Holy Spirit, the Lord and Giver of life, who proceedeth from the Father and the Son, who with the Father and the Son together is worshiped and glorified; who spoke by the prophets.

And I believe in one universal and apostolic church; I acknowledge one baptism, the remission of sins, and I look for the resurrection of the dead, and the life of the world to come. Amen.

—Statement of Faith at Nicea

In Christ There Is No East or West **328**

"There is neither Jew nor Greek, slave nor free, male nor female, for you are all one in Christ Jesus."—Galatians 3:28

C.M.

John Oxenham

ST. PETER
Alexander R. Reinagle

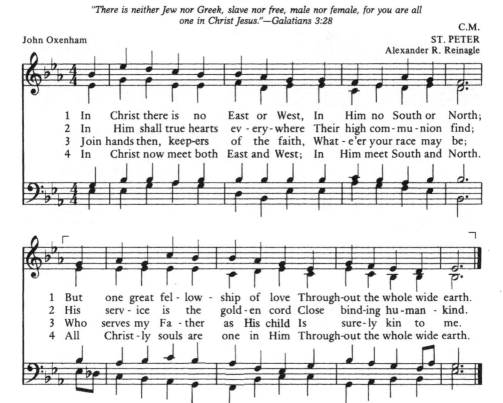

1 In Christ there is no East or West, In Him no South or North;
2 In Him shall true hearts ev-ery-where Their high com-mu-nion find;
3 Join hands then, keep-ers of the faith, What-e'er your race may be;
4 In Christ now meet both East and West; In Him meet South and North.

1 But one great fel-low-ship of love Through-out the whole wide earth.
2 His serv-ice is the gold-en cord Close bind-ing hu-man-kind.
3 Who serves my Fa-ther as His child Is sure-ly kin to me.
4 All Christ-ly souls are one in Him Through-out the whole wide earth.

THE FELLOWSHIP AND UNITY OF THE CHURCH

329 O Church of God, United

*"There is one body and one Spirit—just as you were called—one Lord, one faith,
one baptism; one God and Father of all, who is over all and through all and in
all."—Ephesians 4:4-6*

Based on Acts 2:5-11
Frederick B. Morley

7.6.7.6.D.
AURELIA
Samuel S. Wesley

1 O church of God, u - nit - ed To serve one com-mon Lord,
2 From ev - 'ry land and na - tion The or-dered ranks ap - pear;
3 Though creeds and tongues may dif - fer, They speak, O Christ, of Thee;
4 May Thy great prayer be an-swered That we may all be one,

1 Pro - claim to all one mes - sage With hearts in glad ac - cord.
2 To serve one val - iant lead - er They come from far and near.
3 And in Thy lov - ing Spir - it We shall one peo - ple be.
4 Close-bound, by love u - nit - ed In Thee, God's bless-ed Son.

1 Christ ev - er goes be - fore us; We fol - low day by day
2 They chant their one con - fes - sion, They praise one liv - ing Lord,
3 Lord, may our faith - ful ser - vice And sin - gle-ness of aim
4 To bring a sin - gle wit - ness, To make the path-way bright,

1 With strong and ea - ger foot-steps A - long the up - ward way.
2 And place their sure de - pen-dence Up - on His sav - ing Word.
3 Pro - claim to all the pow - er Of Thy re - deem-ing name.
4 That souls who grope in dark-ness May find the one true Light. A-men.

THE FELLOWSHIP AND UNITY OF THE CHURCH

The Bond of Perfectness

"And over all these virtues put on love, which binds them all together in perfect unity."—Colossians 3:14

Daniel S. Warner

8.7.8.7. wR.
PERFECTNESS
Barney E. Warren

1 How sweet this bond of per-fect-ness, The won-drous love of Je-sus!
2 O praise the Lord for love di-vine That binds us all to-geth-er!
3 "God o-ver all and in us all," Thru sis-ter and thru bro-ther,
4 O mys-ter-y of heav-en's peace! O bond of heav-en's un-ion!

1 A pure fore-taste of heav-en's bliss, O fel-low-ship so pre-cious!
2 A thou-sand cords our hearts en-twine For-ev-er and for-ev-er.
3 No pow'r of earth or hell, with-al, Can rend us from each oth-er.
4 Our souls in fel-low-ship em-brace, And live in sweet com-mun-ion.

Be-lov-ed, how this per-fect love U-nites us all in Je-sus! One

heart, and soul, and mind: we prove The un-ion heav-en gave us.

THE FELLOWSHIP AND UNITY OF THE CHURCH

331 Teach Me to Pray

"This is how you should pray . . . "—Matthew 6:9a

Albert S. Reitz

TEACH ME TO PRAY
Albert S. Reitz

1 Teach me to pray, Lord, teach me to pray; This is my
2 Pow-er in prayer, Lord, pow-er in prayer, Here 'mid earth's
3 My weak-ened will, Lord, Thou canst re-new; My sin-ful
4 Teach me to pray, Lord, teach me to pray; Thou art my

1 heart-cry, day un-to day; I long to know Thy will and Thy
2 sin and sor-row and care; Souls lost and dy-ing, souls in des-
3 na-ture Thou canst sub-due; Fill me just now with pow-er a-
4 pat-tern, day un-to day; Thou art my sure-ty, now and for

1 way; Teach me to pray, Lord, teach me to pray.
2 pair; O give me pow-er, pow-er in prayer!
3 new, Pow-er to pray and pow-er to do!
4 aye; Teach me to pray, Lord, teach me to pray.

Liv-ing in Thee, Lord, and Thou in me, Con-stant a-

bid - ing, this is my plea; Grant me Thy pow - er,

bound-less and free: Pow - er with - in and pow-er with Thee.

Prayer: An Expression of the Heart

332

Prayer is a devotional expression of the heart, and like the rising of incense, ascends to the throne of grace, imploring mercy, seeking help, or giving vent to the praise and thanksgiving of the soul. It may be spoken in audible tones, or may be a whisper, a gentle breathing of the desire of the heart, or but a fervent thought, sent out in petition to Him who is "able to do exceedingly abundantly above all that we ask or think."

Prayer, mingled with faith, brings salvation to the sinner, healing to the sick, joy to the sorrowful and hope to the discouraged. It causes the enemy to flee, unlocks the great treasurehouse of the Lord, opens the windows of heaven and brings down showers of blessings upon the humble Christian.

—Enoch E. Byrum
from *The Secret of Prayer*

333 'Tis the Blessed Hour of Prayer

"Morning by morning, O Lord, you hear my voice; morning by morning I lay my requests before you and wait in expectation."—Psalm 5:3

7.6.7.6.D.wR.

Fanny J. Crosby

DOANE
William H. Doane

1 'Tis the bless-ed hour of prayer, when our hearts low-ly bend,
2 'Tis the bless-ed hour of prayer, when the Sav-ior draws near
3 'Tis the bless-ed hour of prayer, when the tempt-ed and tried
4 At the bless-ed hour of prayer, trust-ing Him, we be-lieve

1 And we gath-er to Je-sus our Sav-ior and Friend;
2 With a ten-der com-pas-sion His chil-dren to hear;
3 To the Sav-ior who loves them their sor-row con-fide;
4 That the bless-ing we're need-ing we'll sure-ly re-ceive;

1 If we come to Him in faith, His pro-tec-tion to share,
2 When He tells us we may cast at His feet ev-ery care,
3 With a sym-pa-thiz-ing heart He re-moves ev-ery care;
4 In the full-ness of this trust we shall lose ev-ery care;

1 What a balm for the wea-ry! O how sweet to be there!
2 What a balm for the wea-ry! O how sweet to be there!
3 What a balm for the wea-ry! O how sweet to be there!
4 What a balm for the wea-ry! O how sweet to be there!

THE CHURCH AT PRAYER

Bless-ed hour of prayer, bless-ed hour of prayer, What a balm for the wea-ry! O how sweet to be there! A - men.

A Prayer to Live the Abundant Life 334

Gracious Lord, You have created us for
Yourself and made our hearts restless until they
find their rest in You. Set us free from all that
keeps us up-tight, tied-down, and bound up.
Then we will be free to live by Christ's Spirit,
walk in His Spirit, and be filled by His Spirit.
We claim our freedom in Him to live the
abundant life now and eternal life forever.
Hallelujah, and Amen!

—Lloyd John Ogilvie

335 Near to the Heart of God

"But as for me, it is good to be near God. I have made the Sovereign Lord my refuge; I will tell of all your deeds."—Psalm 73:28

C.M.wR.

Cleland B. McAfee

McAFEE
Cleland B. McAfee

1 There is a place of qui - et rest, Near to the heart of God;
2 There is a place of com-fort sweet, Near to the heart of God;
3 There is a place of full re - lease, Near to the heart of God;

1 A place where sin can - not mo-lest, Near to the heart of God.
2 A place where we our Sav - ior meet, Near to the heart of God.
3 A place where all is joy and peace, Near to the heart of God.

O Je - sus, blest Re - deem - er, Sent from the heart of God,

Hold us, who wait be - fore Thee, Near to the heart of God.

I Must Tell Jesus

336

"Because he himself suffered when he was tempted, he is able to help those who are being tempted."—Hebrews 2:18

Elisha A. Hoffman

ORWIGSBURG
Elisha A. Hoffman

1 I must tell Je-sus all of my tri-als, I can-not bear these
2 I must tell Je-sus all of my trou-bles, He is a kind, com-
3 Tempt-ed and tried, I need a great Sav-ior, One who can help my
4 O how the world of e-vil al-lures me! O how my heart is

1 bur-dens a-lone; In my dis-tress He kind-ly will help me,
2 pas-sion-ate friend; If I but ask Him, He will de-liv-er,
3 bur-dens to bear; I must tell Je-sus, I must tell Je-sus,
4 tempt-ed to sin! I must tell Je-sus, and He will help me

1 He al-ways loves and cares for His own.
2 Make of my trou-bles quick-ly an end.
3 He all my cares and sor-rows will share.
4 O-ver the world the vic-tory to win.

I must tell Je-sus!

I must tell Je-sus! I can-not bear my bur-dens a-lone; I must tell

Je-sus! I must tell Je-sus! Je-sus can help me, Je-sus a-lone.

THE CHURCH AT PRAYER

337 Alone with God

"He will call upon me, and I will answer him; I will be with him in trouble, I will deliver him and honor him."—Psalm 91:15

Johnson Oatman, Jr.

ALONE WITH GOD
William J. Kirkpatrick

1 When storms of life are 'round me beat - ing, When
2 What tho' the clouds have gath - ered o'er me? What
3 'Tis there I find new strength for du - ty, As
4 And when I see the mo - ment near - ing When

1 rough the path that I have trod, With - in my clos - et
2 tho I've passed be - neath the rod? God's per - fect will there
3 o'er the sands of time I plod; I see the King in
4 I shall sleep be - neath the sod, When time with me is

1 door re - treat - ing, I love to be a - lone with God.
2 lies be - fore me, When I am thus a - lone with God.
3 all His beau - ty, While rest - ing there a - lone with God.
4 dis - ap - pear - ing, I want to be a - lone with God.

A - lone with God, the world for - bid - en, A - lone with
A - lone with God,

THE CHURCH AT PRAYER

God, O blest re - treat! A - lone with God, and
A - lone with God,

in Him hid - den, To hold with Him com-mun-ion sweet.
To hold with Him

Lord, Listen to Your Children 338
Praying

"Listen to my prayer, O God, do not ignore my plea."—Psalm 55:1

Ken Medema

CHILDREN PRAYING
Ken Medema

Lord, lis - ten to Your chil-dren pray - ing, Lord, send Your

Spir-it in this place; Lord, lis - ten to Your chil-dren pray - ing,

1 (optional) D.C. | Final

Send us love, send us pow'r, send us grace. grace.

THE CHURCH AT PRAYER

339 Standin' in the Need of Prayer

"Brothers, pray for us."—I Thessalonians 5:25

Traditional

NEED OF PRAYER
Traditional

Leader

1 Not my broth-er, nor my sis-ter, but it's me, O Lord,
2 Not the preach-er, nor the dea-con, but it's me, O Lord,
3 Not my fa-ther, nor my moth-er, but it's me, O Lord
4 Not the strang-er, nor my neigh-bor, but it's me, O Lord,

Response ... **Leader**

1 Stand-in' in the need of prayer: Not my broth-er, nor my sis-ter,
2 Stand-in' in the need of prayer: Not the preach-er, nor the dea-con,
3 Stand-in' in the need of prayer: Not my fa-ther, nor my moth-er,
4 Stand-in' in the need of prayer: Not the stran-ger, nor my neigh-bor,

Response

1 but it's me, O Lord, Stand-in' in the need of prayer.
2 but it's me, O Lord, Stand-in' in the need of prayer.
3 but it's me, O Lord, Stand-in' in the need of prayer.
4 but it's me, O Lord, Stand-in' in the need of prayer.

All

It's me, it's me, O Lord, Stand-in' in the need of prayer.
It's me,

THE CHURCH AT PRAYER

It's me, it's me, O Lord, Stand-in' in the need of prayer.
It's me,

Where Could I Go?

340

"Simon Peter answered him, 'Lord, to whom shall we go? You have the words of eternal life.' "—John 6:68

James B. Coats

WHERE COULD I GO
James B. Coats

1 Liv - ing be - low in this old sin - ful world, Hard - ly a
2 Neigh - bors are kind, I love them ev - ery one, We get a -
3 Life here is grand with friends I love so dear, Com - fort I
Chorus: Where could I go, O where could I go, Seek - ing a

1 com - fort can af - ford; Striv - ing a - lone to
2 long in sweet ac - cord; But when my soul needs
3 get from God's own Word; Yet when I face the
Chorus: ref - uge for my soul? Need - ing a friend to

D.C. for Chorus

1 face temp - ta - tions sore, Where could I go but to the Lord?
2 man - na from a - bove, Where could I go but to the Lord?
3 chill - ing hand of death, Where could I go but to the Lord?
Chorus: help me in the end, Where could I go but to the Lord?

341 All Your Anxiety

"Humble yourselves, therefore, under God's mighty hand, that he may lift you
up in due time. Cast all your anxiety on him because he cares for you."
—I Peter 5:6-7

Edward Henry Joy

ALL YOUR ANXIETY
Edward Henry Joy

1 Is there a heart o'er-bound by sor-row? Is there a life weighed
2 No oth-er friend so keen to help you, No oth-er friend so
3 Come then at once—de-lay no long-er! Heed His en-treat-y

1 down by care? Come to the cross—each bur-den bear-ing,
2 quick to hear; No oth-er place to leave your bur-den,
3 kind and sweet; You need not fear a dis-ap-point-ment—

1 All your anx-i-e-ty— leave it there.
2 No oth-er one to hear your prayer. All your anx-i-e-ty,
3 You shall find peace at the mer-cy seat.

all your care, Bring to the mer-cy seat— leave it there; Nev-er a

bur-den He can-not bear, Nev-er a friend like Je-sus!

I Need Thee Every Hour

342

"Hear, O Lord, and answer me, for I am poor and needy."—Psalm 86:1

6.4.6.4.wR.
NEED
Robert Lowry

Annie S. Hawks
Robert Lowry

1 I need Thee ev-ery hour, Most gra - cious Lord;
2 I need Thee ev-ery hour, Stay Thou near by;
3 I need Thee ev-ery hour, In joy or pain;
4 I need Thee ev-ery hour, Teach me Thy will,

1 No ten - der voice like Thine Can peace af - ford.
2 Temp - ta - tions lose their power When Thou art nigh.
3 Come quick - ly, and a - bide, Or life is vain.
4 And Thy rich prom-is - es In me ful - fill.

I need Thee, O I need Thee; Ev - ery hour I need Thee!

O bless me now, my Sav - ior— I come to Thee.

343 Sweet Hour of Prayer

"One day Peter and John were going up to the temple at the time of prayer."
—Acts 3:1

William W. Walford

L.M.D.
SWEET HOUR
William B. Bradbury

1 Sweet hour of prayer, sweet hour of prayer, That calls me from a world of care,
2 Sweet hour of prayer, sweet hour of prayer, Thy wings shall my pe - ti - tion bear

1 And bids me at my Fa-ther's throne Make all my wants and wish-es known:
2 To Him whose truth and faith - ful-ness En - gage the wait - ing soul to bless:

1 In sea - sons of dis - tress and grief My soul has of - ten found re - lief,
2 And since He bids me seek His face, Be - lieve His Word, and trust His grace,

1 And oft es-caped the tempt-er's snare By thy re-turn, sweet hour of prayer.
2 I'll cast on Him my ev - ery care, And wait for thee, sweet hour of prayer.

No One Understands Like Jesus

"For we do not have a high priest who is unable to sympathize with our weaknesses, but we have one who has been tempted in every way, just as we are—yet was without sin."—Hebrews 4:15

John W. Peterson

ARIZONA
John W. Peterson

1 No one un-der-stands like Je - sus, He's a friend be-yond com - pare;
2 No one un-der-stands like Je - sus, Ev - ery woe He sees and feels;
3 No one un-der-stands like Je - sus, When the foes of life as - sail;
4 No one un-der-stands like Je - sus, When you fal - ter on the way,

1 Meet Him at the throne of mer - cy, He is wait-ing for you there.
2 Ten - der - ly He whis - pers com-fort, And the bro-ken heart He heals.
3 You should nev-er be dis - cour-aged, Je - sus cares and will not fail.
4 Tho' you fail Him, sad - ly fail Him, He will par - don you to - day.

No one un-der-stands like Je - sus, When the days are dark and grim;

No one is so near, so dear as Je-sus— Cast your ev-ery care on Him.

THE CHURCH AT PRAYER

345 The Lord's Prayer

"This is how you should pray . . . "—Matthew 6:9a

Matthew 6:9-13

MALOTTE
Albert Hay Malotte
Arranged by Donald P. Hustad

Our Fa - ther, which art in heav-en,

Hal - low - ed be Thy name.

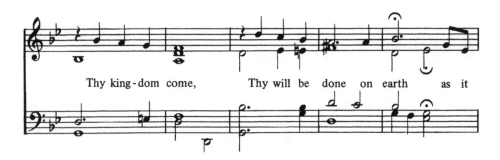

Thy king - dom come, Thy will be done on earth as it

is in heav - en. Give us this day our dai - ly

THE CHURCH AT PRAYER

346 What a Friend We Have in Jesus

"Do not be anxious about anything, but in everything, by prayer and petition, with thanksgiving, present your requests to God."—Philippians 4:6

8.7.8.7.D.
CONVERSE

Joseph M. Scriven

Charles C. Converse

1 What a friend we have in Je - sus, All our sins and griefs to bear!
2 Have we tri - als and temp - ta - tions? Is there trou-ble an - y - where?
3 Are we weak and heav - y - lad - en, Cum-bered with a load of care?

1 What a priv - i - lege to car - ry Ev - ery-thing to God in prayer!
2 We should nev-er be dis - cour-aged— Take it to the Lord in prayer!
3 Pre - cious Sav - ior, still our ref - uge— Take it to the Lord in prayer!

1 O what peace we of - ten for - feit, O what need-less pain we bear,
2 Can we find a friend so faith - ful, Who will all our sor - rows share?
3 Do thy friends de-spise, for - sake thee? Take it to the Lord in prayer!

1 All be-cause we do not car - ry Ev - ery-thing to God in prayer.
2 Je - sus knows our ev - ery weak - ness— Take it to the Lord in prayer!
3 In His arms He'll take and shield thee— Thou wilt find a sol - ace there.

LEADER: All Scripture is God-breathed and is useful for teaching, rebuking, correcting and training in righteousness,

PEOPLE: *So that the man of God may be thoroughly equipped for every good work.*

LEADER: Do your best to present yourself to God as one approved, a workman who does not need to be ashamed and who correctly handles the word of truth.

PEOPLE: *For the word of God is living and active. Sharper than any double-edged sword, it penetrates even to dividing soul and spirit, joints and marrow; it judges the thoughts and attitudes of the heart.*

LEADER: Oh, how I love your law! I meditate on it all day long.

PEOPLE: *How sweet are your promises to my taste, sweeter than honey to my mouth!*

LEADER: I gain understanding from your precepts; therefore I hate every wrong path.

PEOPLE: *Your word is a lamp to my feet and a light for my path.*

LEADER: I have taken an oath and confirmed it, that I will follow your righteous laws.

PEOPLE: *Your statutes are wonderful; therefore I obey them.*

LEADER: The entrance of your words gives light; it gives understanding to the simple.

—II Timothy 3:16–17, 2:15, Hebrews 4:12, Psalm 119:97, 103–106, 129–130 (NIV)

348 By Your Blessed Word Obeying

" . . . My Father will love him, and we will come to him and make our home with him."—John 14:23b

Based on John 14:23-24
Daniel S. Warner

C.M.wR.
OBEYING YOUR WORD
Andrew L. Byers

1 By Your bless-ed Word o-bey-ing, Lord, we prove our love sin-cere;
2 Ev-'ry pre-cept You have spo-ken Is es-sen-tial to our life;
3 In Your wis-dom, Lord, con-fid-ing We will fol-low in Your way;
4 Each com-mand-ment You have giv-en Is a way-mark on the road

1 For we hear You gen-tly say-ing, "Love will do as well as hear."
2 All Your man-dates are love's tok-en, To op-pose them is but strife.
3 With Your love in us a-bid-ing 'Tis de-light-ful to o-bey.
4 Lead-ing up from earth to heav-en To the bless-ed throne of God.

Dear Re-deem-er, we would hal-low All Your Word, so firm and true,

In Your foot-steps meek-ly fol-low; Your com-mands we love to do. A-men.

THE HOLY SCRIPTURES

Blessed is the man who does not walk in the counsel of the wicked or stand in the way of sinners or sit in the seat of mockers.

But his delight is in the law of the Lord, and on his law he meditates day and night.

He is like a tree planted by streams of water, which yields its fruit in season and whose leaf does not wither. Whatever he does prospers.

Not so the wicked! They are like chaff that the wind blows away.

Therefore the wicked will not stand in the judgment nor sinners in the assembly of the righteous.

The Lord watches over the way of the righteous, but the way of the wicked will perish.

—Psalm I:1–6 (NIV)

350 Wonderful Words of Life

" 'The Spirit gives life; the flesh counts for nothing. The words I have spoken to
you are spirit and they are life.' "—John 6:63

Philip P. Bliss, alt.

8.6.8.6.6.6.wR.
WORDS OF LIFE
Philip P. Bliss

1 Sing them o-ver a-gain to me, Won-der-ful words of life;
2 Christ, the bless-ed One, gives to all Won-der-ful words of life;
3 Sweet-ly ech-o the gos-pel call, Won-der-ful words of life;

1 Let me more of their beau-ty see, Won-der-ful words of life.
2 Lis-ten well to the lov-ing call, Won-der-ful words of life.
3 Of-fer par-don and peace to all, Won-der-ful words of life.

1 Words of life and beau-ty, Teach me faith and du-ty:
2 All the won-drous sto-ry, Show-ing us His glo-ry:
3 Je-sus, on-ly Sav-ior, Sanc-ti-fy for-ev-er:

Beau-ti-ful words, won-der-ful words, Won-der-ful words of life. life.

THE HOLY SCRIPTURES

Thanks to God Whose Word Was Spoken   351

"For the word of God is living and active. Sharper than any double-edged sword, it penetrates even to dividing soul and spirit, joints and marrow; it judges the thoughts and attitudes of the heart."—Hebrews 4:12

R. T. Brooks

8.7.8.7.8.7.
REGENT SQUARE
Henry T. Smart

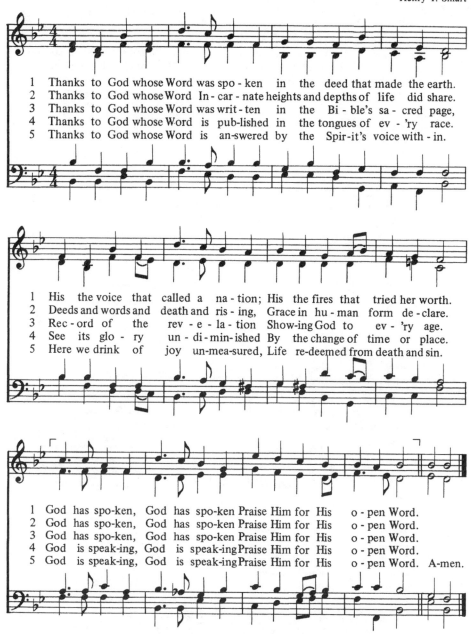

1 Thanks to God whose Word was spo-ken in the deed that made the earth.
2 Thanks to God whose Word In-car-nate heights and depths of life did share.
3 Thanks to God whose Word was writ-ten in the Bi-ble's sa-cred page,
4 Thanks to God whose Word is pub-lished in the tongues of ev-'ry race.
5 Thanks to God whose Word is an-swered by the Spir-it's voice with-in.

1 His the voice that called a na-tion; His the fires that tried her worth.
2 Deeds and words and death and ris-ing, Grace in hu-man form de-clare.
3 Rec-ord of the rev-e-la-tion Show-ing God to ev-'ry age.
4 See its glo-ry un-di-min-ished By the change of time or place.
5 Here we drink of joy un-mea-sured, Life re-deemed from death and sin.

1 God has spo-ken, God has spo-ken Praise Him for His o-pen Word.
2 God has spo-ken, God has spo-ken Praise Him for His o-pen Word.
3 God has spo-ken, God has spo-ken Praise Him for His o-pen Word.
4 God is speak-ing, God is speak-ing Praise Him for His o-pen Word.
5 God is speak-ing, God is speak-ing Praise Him for His o-pen Word. A-men.

THE HOLY SCRIPTURES

352 Standing on the Promises

"Through these he has given us his very great and precious promises, so that through them you may participate in the divine nature and escape the corruption in the world caused by evil desires."—II Peter 1:4

R. Kelso Carter

11.11.11.9.wR.
PROMISES
R. Kelso Carter

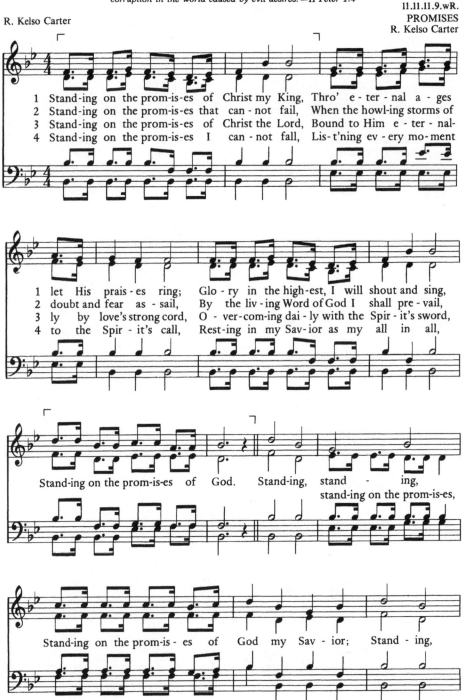

1 Stand-ing on the prom-is-es of Christ my King, Thro' e-ter-nal a-ges
2 Stand-ing on the prom-is-es that can-not fail, When the howl-ing storms of
3 Stand-ing on the prom-is-es of Christ the Lord, Bound to Him e-ter-nal-
4 Stand-ing on the prom-is-es I can-not fall, Lis-t'ning ev-ery mo-ment

1 let His prais-es ring; Glo-ry in the high-est, I will shout and sing,
2 doubt and fear as-sail, By the liv-ing Word of God I shall pre-vail,
3 ly by love's strong cord, O-ver-com-ing dai-ly with the Spir-it's sword,
4 to the Spir-it's call, Rest-ing in my Sav-ior as my all in all,

Stand-ing on the prom-is-es of God. Stand-ing, stand - ing,
stand-ing on the prom-is-es,

Stand-ing on the prom-is-es of God my Sav-ior; Stand-ing,

THE HOLY SCRIPTURES

stand - ing, I'm stand-ing on the prom-is - es of God.
stand-ing on the prom-is - es,

Thy Word

353

"Your word is a lamp to my feet and a light for my path."—Psalm 119:105

Amy Grant
Based on Psalm 119:105

THY WORD
Michael W. Smith

3rd time, Fine

Thy Word is a lamp un-to my feet And a light un-to my path.

1 When I feel a - fraid, I think I've lost my way,
2 I will not for - get Your love for me and yet,

1 Still You're there right be - side me, Noth-ing will I fear as
2 I'll for - ev - er be wand - 'ring. Je - sus, be my guide,..

D.C.

1 long as You are near, Please be near me to the end.
2 hold me to Your side; I will love You to the end.

THE HOLY SCRIPTURES

354 Back to the Blessed Old Bible

"And we also thank God continually because, when you received the word of God, which you heard from us, you accepted it not as the word of men, but as it actually is, the word of God, which is at work in you who believe."
—I Thessalonians 2:13

D. Otis Teasley

BLESSED BIBLE
D. Otis Teasley

1. Back to the bless-ed old Bi - ble, Back to the cit - y of God,
2. Back to the bless-ed old Bi - ble, Saints of Je - ho - vah, re - joice;
3. Back to the bless-ed old Bi - ble, Leav-ing con - fu - sion and strife,
4. Back to the bless-ed old Bi - ble, Back at the Mas - ter's call,

1. Back to the one - ness of heav - en, Back where the faith - ful have trod,
2. Je - sus is call - ing His chil - dren Back to the land of their choice;
3. Flee-ing from Ba - bel to Zi - on Back to the joy of our life.
4. Back to the words of our Sav - ior, Lov - ing, o - bey - ing them all.

1. Back from the land of con - fu - sion, Free from the bond-age of creeds,
2. Oft - en the peo-ple had sought it While they in Ba - bel a - bode,
3. O - ver the moun-tains we wan-dered, Look-ing in vain for the right;
4. Nev - er in sects to be scat-tered, Nev - er a - gain to do wrong:

1 Back to the light of the morn - ing, Je - sus our Cap - tain leads.
2 Now we have found the fair cit - y, Church of the liv - ing God.
3 Now in the eve - ning we've found it: Truth of the gos - pel light.
4 U - ni - ty, ho - li - ness, heav - en, Ev - er shall be our song.

Back to the bless-ed old Bi - ble, Back to the light of its word;

Be on our ban - ners for - ev - er, "Ho - li - ness un-to the Lord."

THE HOLY SCRIPTURES

355 Praise God for His Word

"The grass withers and the flowers fall, but the word of our God stands forever."—Isaiah 40:8

George O. Webster

PRAISE GOD FOR HIS WORD
James H. Fillmore

1 Praise God for His Word! from its pag - es di - vine
2 Praise God for His Word! for the heav - en - ly light
3 Praise God for His Word! not a prom - ise shall fail;

1 Came the light of His love to this poor heart of mine:
2 It is send - ing a - far in - to sin's dark - some night;
3 What - so - e'er may op - pose, still its truth will pre - vail:

1 I had wan - dered a - far in the by - ways of sin,
2 For the hope which it gives, where be - fore was de - spair,
3 'Tis the word of our God and for - e'er must en - dure;

1 When the light of His truth to my heart en - tered in.
2 For the heav - en re - vealed and the way lead - ing there!
3 Earth and heav - en may pass, but it stand - eth se - cure.

THE HOLY SCRIPTURES

Praise God for His grace which its pa-ges un-fold! For the sto-ry of love which will nev-er grow old! For the light on life's path-way which streams from its pa-ges! Praise God for His Word, bless-ed Book of the A-ges!

Go Forth, Strong Word of God 356

"Your word, O Lord, is eternal; it stands firm in the heavens."—Psalm 119:89

S.M.

Frank Cross

ST. THOMAS
Aaron Williams

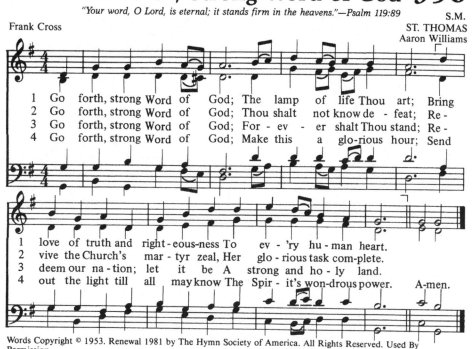

1 Go forth, strong Word of God; The lamp of life Thou art; Bring
2 Go forth, strong Word of God; Thou shalt not know de - feat; Re -
3 Go forth, strong Word of God; For - ev - er shalt Thou stand; Re -
4 Go forth, strong Word of God; Make this a glo-rious hour; Send

1 love of truth and right-eous-ness To ev-'ry hu-man heart.
2 vive the Church's mar-tyr zeal, Her glo-rious task com-plete.
3 deem our na-tion; let it be A strong and ho-ly land.
4 out the light till all may know The Spir-it's won-drous power. A-men.

THE HOLY SCRIPTURES

357 Break Thou the Bread of Life

"But here is the bread that comes down from heaven, which a man may eat and not die."—John 6:50

Based on Matthew 14:19
Mary A. Lathbury, stanzas 1, 2
Alexander Groves, stanzas 3, 4

6.4.6.4.D.
BREAD OF LIFE
William F. Sherwin

1 Break Thou the bread of life, Dear Lord, to me, As Thou didst
2 Bless Thou the truth, dear Lord, To me, to me, As Thou didst
3 Thou art the bread of life, O Lord, to me, Thy ho - ly
4 O send Thy Spir - it, Lord, Now un - to me, That He may

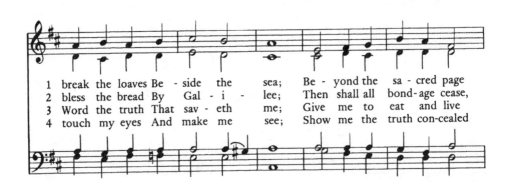

1 break the loaves Be - side the sea; Be - yond the sa - cred page
2 bless the bread By Gal - i - lee; Then shall all bond-age cease,
3 Word the truth That sav - eth me; Give me to eat and live
4 touch my eyes And make me see; Show me the truth con-cealed

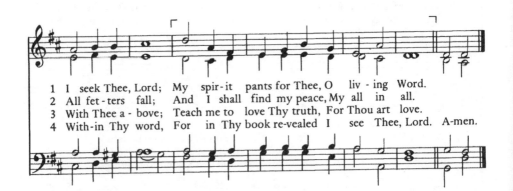

1 I seek Thee, Lord; My spir-it pants for Thee, O liv-ing Word.
2 All fet-ters fall; And I shall find my peace, My all in all.
3 With Thee a - bove; Teach me to love Thy truth, For Thou art love.
4 With-in Thy word, For in Thy book re-vealed I see Thee, Lord. A-men.

Send the Light

358

" . . . that God was reconciling the world to himself in Christ, not counting men's sins against them. And he has committed to us the message of reconciliation."—II Corinthians 5:19

11.6.11.6.wR.
McCABE
Charles H. Gabriel

Charles H. Gabriel

1 There's a call comes ring-ing o'er the rest-less wave, "Send the light!
2 We have heard the chal-lenge of the call to-day, "Send the light!
3 Let us pray that grace may ev-ery-where a-bound, Send the light!
4 Let us not grow wea-ry in the work of love, Send the light!

1 Send the light!" There are souls to res-cue, there are souls to save,
2 Send the light!" And a gold-en of-fering at the cross we lay,
3 Send the light! And a Christ-like spir-it ev-ery-where be found,
4 Send the light! Let us gath-er jew-els for a crown a-bove,

Send the light! Send the light! Send the light, the bless-ed gos-pel light;

1 Let it shine from shore to shore! Send the
2 shine from shore to shore!

PROCLAMATION OF THE GOSPEL

359 Jesus Saves!

"And everyone who calls on the name of the Lord will be saved."—Acts 2:21

7.6.7.6.7.7.7.6.
JESUS SAVES

Priscilla J. Owens

William J. Kirkpatrick

1 We have heard the joy - ful sound: Je - sus saves! Je - sus saves!
2 Send it on the roll - ing tide: Je - sus saves! Je - sus saves!
3 Sing a - bove the bat - tle strife: Je - sus saves! Je - sus saves!
4 Give the winds a might - y voice: Je - sus saves! Je - sus saves!

1 Spread the ti - dings all a - round: Je - sus saves! Je - sus saves!
2 Tell to sin - ners far and wide: Je - sus saves! Je - sus saves!
3 By His death and end - less life: Je - sus saves! Je - sus saves!
4 Let the na - tions now re - joice: Je - sus saves! Je - sus saves!

1 Bear the news to ev - ery land, Climb the steeps and cross the waves;
2 Sing, ye is - lands of the sea; Ech - o back, ye o - cean caves;
3 Sing it soft - ly through the gloom, When the heart for mer - cy craves;
4 Shout sal - va - tion full and free, High - est hills and deep - est caves;

1 On - ward! 'tis our Lord's com - mand; Je - sus saves! Je - sus saves!
2 Earth shall keep her ju - bi - lee: Je - sus saves! Je - sus saves!
3 Sing in tri - umph o'er the tomb: Je - sus saves! Je - sus saves!
4 This our song of vic - to - ry: Je - sus saves! Je - sus saves!

PROCLAMATION OF THE GOSPEL

Tell Me the Old, Old Story   360

"We love because he first loved us."—1 John 4:19

7.6.7.6.D.wR.
EVANGEL
William H. Doane

Katherine Hankey

1 Tell me the old, old story Of un-seen things a - bove, Of Je - sus
2 Tell me the sto - ry slow - ly, That I may take it in— That won-der-
3 Tell me the same old sto - ry When you have cause to fear That this world's

1 and His glo - ry, Of Je - sus and His love. Tell me the sto - ry
2 ful re - demp - tion, God's rem-e - dy for sin. Tell me the sto - ry
3 emp - ty glo - ry Is cost-ing me too dear. Yes, and when that world's

1 sim - ply, As to a lit - tle child; For I am weak and wea - ry,
2 of - ten, For I for -get so soon; The ear-ly dew of morn - ing
3 glo - ry Is dawn-ing on my soul, Tell me the old, old sto - ry:

1 And help-less and de - filed.
2 Has passed a - way at noon. Tell me the old, old sto-ry. Tell me the
3 "Christ Je - sus makes thee whole."

old, old sto-ry. Tell me the old, old sto - ry, Of Je-sus and His love.

PROCLAMATION OF THE GOSPEL

361   I Love to Tell the Story

"He said to them 'Go into all the world and preach the good news to all creation.' "—Mark 16:15

Katherine Hankey
Refrain by William G. Fischer

7.6.7.6.D.wR.
HANKEY
William G. Fischer

1 I love to tell the sto - ry Of un - seen things a - bove,
2 I love to tell the sto - ry— More won - der - ful it seems
3 I love to tell the sto - ry— 'Tis pleas - ant to re - peat
4 I love to tell the sto - ry— For those who know it best

1 Of Je - sus and His glo - ry, Of Je - sus and His love;
2 Than all the gold - en fan - cies Of all our gold - en dreams;
3 When seems, each time I tell it, More won - der - ful - ly sweet;
4 Seem hun - ger - ing and thirst - ing To hear it like the rest;

1 I love to tell the sto - ry— Be - cause I know 'tis true,
2 I love to tell the sto - ry— It did so much for me,
3 I love to tell the sto - ry— For some have nev - er heard
3 And when in scenes of glo - ry I sing the new, new song,

1 It sat - is - fies my long - ings As noth - ing else can do.
2 And that is just the rea - son I tell it now to thee.
3 The mes - sage of sal - va - tion From God's own ho - ly word.
4 'Twill be the old, old sto - ry That I have loved so long.

PROCLAMATION OF THE GOSPEL

The Challenge Comes, the Trumpet Sounds

362

" 'Ask the Lord of the harvest, therefore, to send out workers into his harvest field.' "—Matthew 9:38

Carlton C. Buck

L.M.
CANONBURY
Robert Schumann

1 The chal - lenge comes, the trum - pet sounds The ur - gent call: His truth pro - claim! The need for wit - ness - es a - bounds, Cour - ag - eous saints with stead - fast aim.

2 Pre - pare, train well, the cause is great, The work of Christ makes large de - mands; Sal - va - tion's press - ing tasks a - wait Skilled minds and con - se - crat - ed hands.

3 For - sake the less - er for the best, God's best for all the world in need; From north to south and east to west, Con - vey His love by word and deed.

4 As proph - ets in the days of old Pro - claimed the mes - sage for their day, Preach now the love of God; be bold And turn all hearts to Christ, the Way. A-men.

PROCLAMATION OF THE GOSPEL

363   **Whosoever Will**

" . . . Whoever is thirsty, let him come; and whoever wishes, let him take the
free gift of the water of life."—Revelation 22:17c,d

Based on Revelation 22:17
Philip P. Bliss

WHOSOEVER WILL
Philip P. Bliss

1 "Who-so-ev-er hear-eth," shout, shout the sound! Spread the bless-ed ti-dings
2 Who-so-ev-er com-eth need not de-lay, Now the door is o-pen,
3 "Who-so-ev-er will," the prom-ise is se-cure; "Who-so-ev-er will" for-

1 all the world a-round; Tell the joy-ful news wher-ev-er sin is found,
2 en-ter while you may; Je-sus is the true, the on-ly Liv-ing Way:
3 ev-er must en-dure; "Who-so-ev-er will," 'tis life for-ev-er-more;

"Who-so-ev-er will may come." "Who-so-ev-er will, who-so-ev-er will!"

Send the proc-la-ma-tion o-ver vale and hill; 'Tis a lov-ing Fa-ther

calls the wan-d'rer home: "Who-so-ev-er will may come."

Tell Me the Story of Jesus

"Then Philip began with that very passage of Scripture and told him the good news about Jesus."—Acts 8:35

8.7.8.7.D.wR.
STORY OF JESUS

Fanny J. Crosby

John R. Sweney

1 Tell me the sto - ry of Je - sus, Write on my heart ev - ery word;
2 Fast - ing a - lone in the des - ert, Tell of the days that are past,
3 Tell of the cross where they nailed Him, Writh - ing in an - guish and pain;

Refrain: Tell me the sto - ry of Je - sus, Write on my heart ev - ery word;

Fine

1 Tell me the sto - ry most pre - cious, Sweet - est that ev - er was heard.
2 How for our sins He was tempt - ed, Yet was tri - um - phant at last.
3 Tell of the grave where they laid Him, Tell how He liv - eth a - gain.

Refrain: Tell me the sto - ry most pre - cious, Sweet - est that ev - er was heard.

1 Tell how the an - gels in cho - rus Sang as they wel - comed His birth,
2 Tell of the years of His la - bor, Tell of the sor - row He bore,
3 Love in that sto - ry so ten - der Clear - er than ev - er I see:

D.C. for Refrain

1 "Glo - ry to God in the high - est! Peace and good ti - dings to earth."
2 He was de - spised and af - flict - ed, Home - less, re - ject - ed and poor.
3 Lord, may I al - ways re - mem - ber Love paid the ran - som for me.

PROCLAMATION OF THE GOSPEL

365 I'll Tell the World That I'm a Christian

"I am not ashamed of the gospel, because it is the power of God for the salvation of everyone who believes . . . "—Romans 1:16a

Baynard L. Fox

TUCKER
Baynard L. Fox

1 I'll tell the world that I'm a Chris-tian— I'm not a-shamed His name to
2 I'll tell the world that He is com-ing— It may be near or far a-

1 bear; I'll tell the world that I'm a Chris-tian— I'll take Him with me
2 way; But we must live as if His com-ing Would be to-mor-row

1 an-y-where. I'll tell the world how Je-sus saved me, And how He
2 or to-day. For when He comes and life is o-ver, For those who

PROCLAMATION OF THE GOSPEL

1 gave me a life brand-new; And I know that if you trust Him
2 love Him there's more to be; Eyes have nev-er seen the won-ders

1 That all He gave me He'll give to you. I'll tell the world
2 That He's pre-par-ing for you and me. O tell the world

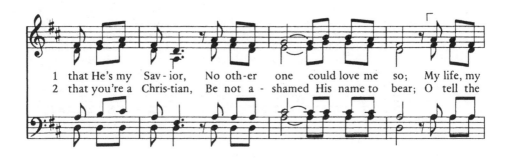

1 that He's my Sav-ior, No oth-er one could love me so; My life, my
2 that you're a Chris-tian, Be not a-shamed His name to bear; O tell the

1 all is His for-ev-er, And where He leads me I will go.
2 world that you're a Chris-tian, And take Him with you ev-ery-where.

PROCLAMATION OF THE GOSPEL

366 Look and Live

*"So Moses made a bronze snake and put it up on a pole. Then when anyone
was bitten by a snake and looked at the bronze snake, he lived."*
—Numbers 21:9

W. A. Ogden

LOOK AND LIVE
W. A. Ogden

1 I've a mes-sage from the Lord, Hal - le - lu - jah! The
2 I've a mes-sage full of love, Hal - le - lu - jah! A
3 Life is of-fered un - to you, Hal - le - lu - jah! E -
4 I will tell you how I came, Hal - le - lu - jah! To

1 mes-sage un - to you I'll give; 'Tis re - cord-ed in His Word,
2 mes-sage, O my friend, for you; 'Tis a mes-sage from a - bove,
3 ter - nal life your soul shall have, If you'll on - ly look to Him.
4 Je - sus when He made me whole: 'Twas be - liev-ing on His name,

1 Hal - le - lu - jah! It is on - ly that you "look and live."
2 Hal - le - lu - jah! Je - sus said it, and I know 'tis true.
3 Hal - le - lu - jah! Look to Je - sus, who a - lone can save.
4 Hal - le - lu - jah! I trust-ed, and He saved my soul.

PROCLAMATION OF THE GOSPEL

"Look and live," look now and live,
"Look and live," look now and live, "Look and live,"

Look to Je - sus now and live; 'Tis re - cord - ed in His Word,

Hal - le - lu - jah! It is on - ly that you "look and live."

367 Tell It Out with Gladness

"You will be his witness to all men of what you have seen and heard."
—Acts 22:15

8.7.8.7.D.
HYMN TO JOY
Ludwig van Beethoven

Georgia Harkness

1 Tell it! Tell it out with glad-ness, God's good news to ev-'ry one:
2 Lord, we thank Thee for the trea-sure Hid with-in the sa-cred page.
3 "Go and teach!" thus spoke the Mas-ter, Ris-en vic-tor from the grave.

1 Sin for-giv-en, lives trans-fig-ured, All through God's be-lov-ed Son.
2 We would be Thy faith-ful her-alds To our deep-ly trou-bled age:
3 Still He gives this great com-mis-sion To His faith-ful ones and brave.

1 In the Book is found the wit-ness To His might-y acts of yore:
2 We would pub-lish Thy sal-va-tion, Ev-er on Thy side to stand,
3 Let all know the gos-pel sto-ry Of what we through Christ can be.

1 Lis-ten heed, o - bey and serve Him, Kneel be-fore Him and a-dore.
2 Liv-ing, serv-ing, giv-ing, send-ing Life to quick-en ev-'ry land.
3 Send it! Send it to the na-tions That God's love may set us free. A-men.

PROCLAMATION OF THE GOSPEL

What shall we say, then? Shall we go on sinning so that grace may increase?

By no means! We died to sin; how can we live in it any longer?

Or don't you know that all of us who were baptized into Christ Jesus were baptized into his death? We were therefore buried with him through baptism into death in order that, just as Christ was raised from the dead through the glory of the Father, we too may live a new life.

If we have been united with him in his death, we will certainly also be united with him in his resurrection.

For we know that our old self was crucified with him so that the body of sin might be rendered powerless, that we should no longer be slaves to sin—because anyone who has died has been freed from sin.

Now if we died with Christ, we believe that we will also live with him.

For we know that since Christ was raised from the dead, he cannot die again; death no longer has mastery over him. The death he died, he died to sin once for all; but the life he lives, he lives to God.

In the same way, count yourselves dead to sin but alive to God in Christ Jesus.

Therefore do not let sin reign in your mortal body so that you obey its evil desires. Do not offer the parts of your body to sin, as instruments of wickedness, but rather offer yourselves to God, as those who have been brought from death to life; and offer the parts of your body to him as instruments of righteousness.

For sin shall not be your master, because you are not under law, but under grace.

—Romans 6:1–14 (NIV)

BAPTISM

369   Come, Holy Spirit, Dove Divine

"We were therefore buried with him through baptism unto death in order that,
just as Christ was raised from the dead through the glory of the Father, we too
may live a new life."—Romans 6:4

L.M.

Adoniram Judson

MARYTON
H. Percy Smith

1 Come, Ho-ly Spir-it, Dove di-vine, On these bap-tis-mal wa-ters shine,
2 We love Thy name, we love Thy laws, And joy-ful-ly em-brace Thy cause;
3 We sink be-neath the wa-ter's face, And thank Thee for Thy sav-ing grace;
4 And as we rise with Thee to live, O let the Ho-ly Spir-it give

1 And teach our hearts, in high-est strain, To praise the Lamb for sin-ners slain.
2 We love Thy cross, the shame, the pain, O Lamb of God for sin-ners slain.
3 We die to sin and seek a grave With Thee, be-neath the yield-ing wave.
4 The seal-ing unc-tion from a-bove, The joy of life, the fire of love. A-men.

370   We Were Baptized in Christ Jesus

"Having been buried with him in baptism and raised with him through your
faith in the power of God, who raised him from the dead."—Colossians 2:12

John Ylvisaker

QUIMETTE
John Ylvisaker

1 We were bap-tized in Christ Je-sus, We were bap-tized in His
2 In the wa-ter and the wit-ness, In the break-ing of the
3 Glo-ry be to our Cre-a-tor, Glo-ry be to Christ the

BAPTISM

1 death; For as Christ was raised vic - to-rious, We might live a brand new
2 bread, In the wait - ing arms of Je - sus Who is ris - en from the
3 Son, Glo - ry to the Ho - ly Spir - it, Ev - er three and ev - er

1 life. And if we have been u - nit-ed In a dread - ful death like
2 dead, We have found a new be - gin-ning In the ash - es of our
3 one. As it was in the be - gin-ning, It will be as it was

1 His, We will all be re - u - nit-ed, for He lives.
2 past; In the los - ing and the win-ning we hold fast.
3 planned, In a world that has no end-ing. A - men.

BAPTISM

I received from the Lord that which I also delivered to you:

that the Lord Jesus on the same night in which He was betrayed took bread: and when He had given thanks, He broke it and said,

"Take, eat; this is My body which is broken for you; do this in remembrance of Me."

In the same manner He also took the cup after supper, saying,

"This cup is the new covenant in My blood.

This do, as often as you drink it, in remembrance of Me."

For as often as you eat this bread and drink this cup, you proclaim the Lord's death till He comes.

Therefore whoever eats this bread or drinks this cup of the Lord in an unworthy manner

will be guilty of the body and blood of the Lord.

But let a man examine himself, and so let him eat of that bread and drink of that cup.

—*From I Corinthians 11 (NKJV)*

372 Do This, and Remember Me

"This is my body given for you; do this in remembrance."—Luke 22:19b

Based on Mark 14:22-24
Ernest H. Gross, Jr.

REMEMBER ME
Ernest H. Gross, Jr.

1 The Lord as He sat at the ta-ble, Took bread and gave
2 The same way He took the cup, And when He had
3 As oft as we eat the bread, As oft as we

1 thanks and broke it, Say - ing, "Take,
2 giv-en thanks passed it, Say - ing, "Take,
3 drink the cup, He says to you, to

1 eat, this is my bod-y bro-ken for you, Do this
2 drink, this is my blood shed for you, Do this
3 me, "You show my death un-til I re-turn, Do this

and re-mem-ber me, Do this and re-mem-ber me."

ORDINANCE OF THE LORD'S SUPPER

We Meet, As in That Upper Room

373

"When the hour came, Jesus and his apostles reclined at the table."—Luke 22:14

10.10.10.10.
MORECAMBE
Frederick C. Atkinson

Based on Luke 22:14-20
George W. Briggs

1 We meet, as in that up-per room they met;
2 One bod-y we, one bod-y who par-take,
3 One with each oth-er, Lord, for one in Thee,

1 Thou at the ta - ble, bless-ing, yet dost stand:
2 One church u - nit - ed in com-mun-ion blest;
3 Who art our Sav - ior and our liv-ing Head;

1 "This is My bod - y:" so Thou giv-est yet:
2 One name we bear, one bread of life we break
3 Then o - pen Thou our eyes, that we may see;

1 Faith still re - ceives the cup as from Thy hand.
2 With all Thy saints on earth and saints at rest.
3 Be known to us in break-ing of the bread. A - men.

ORDINANCE OF THE LORD'S SUPPER

374 Let Us Break Bread Together

"They devoted themselves . . . to the breaking of bread . . . "—Acts 2:42

American Folk Hymn

LET US BREAK BREAD
American Folk Melody

1 Let us break bread to - geth - er on our knees;
2 Let us drink wine to - geth - er on our knees;
3 Let us praise God to - geth - er on our knees;

1 Let us break bread to - geth - er on our knees;
2 Let us drink wine to - geth - er on our knees;
3 Let us praise God to - geth - er on our knees;

When I fall on my knees, With my face to the ris - ing sun,

O Lord, have mer - cy on me.

ORDINANCE OF THE LORD'S SUPPER

Here in Our Upper Room

375

"Therefore, as we have opportunity, let us do good to all people, especially to those who belong to the family of believers."—Galatians 6:10

Paul M. Robinson

L.M.
MARYTON
H. Percy Smith

1 Here in our up - per room with Thee, A - round Thy
2 As Thou, our blest Ex - am - ple, taught, We kneel to
3 We share with Thee the feast of love As hearts are
4 With heart, and not with hands a - lone, We keep the

1 hal - lowed ta - ble, Lord, May we with deep hu - mil - i -
2 serve each o - ther's need, The cleans - ing of Thy Spir - it
3 knit in u - ni - ty; O may Thy Spir - it in us
4 or - di - nance di - vine, And through these sa - cred sym - bols

1 ty Ful - fill the pre - cepts of Thy word.
2 sought In heart and mind, in thought and deed.
3 move Our wills to serve and hon - or Thee.
4 own The grace that makes our serv - ice Thine. A - men.

ORDINANCE OF THE LORD'S SUPPER

376 In Remembrance

"And he took bread, gave thanks and broke it, and gave it to them, saying,
'This is my body given for you; do this in remembrance of me.'"—Luke 22:19

Ragan Courtney

RED
Buryl Red
Arr. by Robert F. Douglas

In re - mem-brance of Me,
(In re -) mem-brance of Me,

1 eat this bread. In re - mem-brance of Me, drink this wine. In re -
2 heal the sick. In re - mem-brance of Me, feed the poor. In re -

1 mem-brance of Me, pray for the time when God's own will is
2 mem-brance of Me, o - pen the door and let your neigh-bor

done. In re -
in, Let them in.

Take, eat, and be com - fort - ed; drink and re - mem - ber

ORDINANCE OF THE LORD'S SUPPER

too, That this is My bod-y and pre-cious blood shed for

you, shed for you. In re-mem-brance of Me,

search for truth. In re-mem-brance of Me, al-ways love. In re-

mem-brance of Me, don't look a-bove, but in your heart

Optional ending (Choir or congregation)

look for God. Do this in re-mem-brance of Me.

ORDINANCE OF THE LORD'S SUPPER

Therefore having been justified by faith, we have peace with God through our Lord Jesus Christ,

Through whom also we have obtained our introduction by faith into this grace in which we stand; and we exult in hope of the glory of God.

And not only this, but we also exult in our tribulations, knowing that tribulation brings about perseverance;

And perseverance, proven character; and proven character, hope;

And hope does not disappoint, because the love of God has been poured out within our hearts through the Holy Spirit who was given to us.

For while we were still helpless, at the right time Christ died for the ungodly.

For one will hardly die for a righteous man; though perhaps for the good man someone would dare even to die.

But God demonstrates His own love toward us, in that while we were yet sinners, Christ died for us.

Much more then, having now been justified by His blood, we shall be saved from the wrath of God through Him.

For if while we were enemies, we were reconciled to God through the death of His Son, much more, having been reconciled, we shall be saved by His life.

And not only this, but we also exult in God through our Lord Jesus Christ, through whom we have now received the reconciliation.

So then as through one transgression there resulted condemnation to all men, even so through one act of righteousness there resulted justification of life to all men.

—Rom. 5:1–11, 18 (NASB)

Christ Is Here with His People 378

"Is not the cup of thanksgiving for which we give thanks a participation in the blood of Christ? And is not the bread that we break a participation in the body of Christ?"—I Corinthians 10:16

Deborah Govenor
Fred Shively, stanza 3

14.14.14.13.
CHRIST IS HERE
Deborah Govenor

1 Christ is here with His peo-ple in the break-ing of the bread.
2 Christ is here with His peo-ple in the preach-ing of the Word.
3 Christ is here with His peo-ple in the ba-sin and the towel.
4 Through His blood and His bod-y, through the Spir-it and the Word,

1 For His pres-ence we hun-ger, with His bod-y we are fed.
2 Now the Spir-it is giv-en, now the sav-ing prom-ise heard.
3 By ex-am-ple He teach-es us to seek and hum-bly bow.
4 We shall all be u-nit-ed in the pres-ence of the Lord.

1 We are one with each oth-er through His ho-ly blood out-poured.
2 Now for-give-ness is spok-en, with the shar-ing of the Word.
3 As we fol-low His bid-ding, love and bless-ing gent-ly meet.
4 Now on earth, then in heav-en we will share these gifts di-vine;

1 Come and eat, come and drink at the ta-ble of the Lord.
2 Come be cleansed, be re-newed in the wor-ship of the Lord.
3 Let us serve one an-oth-er in the wash-ing of the feet.
4 Fount of life, meal of love, Word and Spir-it, bread and wine.

ORDINANCE OF THE LORD'S SUPPER

379 Come, Share the Lord

"If you have any encouragement from being united with Christ, if any comfort from his love, if any fellowship with the Spirit, if any tenderness and compassion, then make my joy complete by being like-minded, having the same love, being one in spirit and purpose."—Philippians 2:1-2

Bryan Jeffery Leech

DIVERNON
Bryan Jeffery Leech

1 We gath-er here in Je-sus' name, His love is
2 He joins us here, He breaks the bread. The Lord who
3 We'll gath-er soon where an-gels sing, We'll see the

1 burn-ing in our hearts like liv-ing flame. For through the lov-ing Son the Fa-ther
2 pours the cup is ris-en from the dead. The One we love the most is now our
3 glo-ry of our Lord and com-ing King. Now we an-ti-ci-pate the feast for

1 makes us one.
2 gra-cious host. Come take the bread, come drink the wine, come share the Lord.
3 which we wait.

1 No one is a stran-ger here, ev-'ry-one be-longs.
2 We are now a fam-i-ly of which the Lord is head.

ORDINANCE OF THE LORD'S SUPPER

D.C. al Fine

1 Find-ing our for-give-ness here, we in turn for-give all wrongs.
2 Though un-seen He meets us here in the break-ing of the bread.

A Hymn of Joy We Sing 380

"Make vows to the Lord your God and fulfill them; let all the neighboring lands bring gifts to the One to be feared."—Psalm 76:11

Based on Matthew 26:30
Aaron R. Wolfe

S.M.
SCHUMANN
Mason and Webb's *Cantus Laudis*

1 A hymn of joy we sing A - round Thy ta - ble, Lord;
2 Here have we seen Thy face And felt Thy pres-ence near;
3 In self - for - get - ting love Be our com-mun-ion shown,

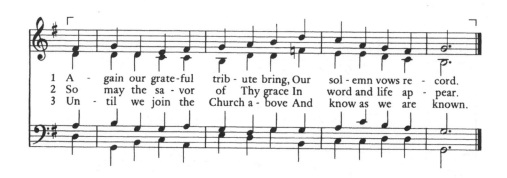

1 A - gain our grate-ful trib - ute bring, Our sol - emn vows re - cord.
2 So may the sa - vor of Thy grace In word and life ap - pear.
3 Un - til we join the Church a - bove And know as we are known.

ORDINANCE OF THE LORD'S SUPPER

381 Sent Forth by God's Blessing

"They devoted themselves to the apostles' teaching and to the fellowship, to the breaking of bread and to prayer. Everyone was filled with awe, and many wonders and miraculous signs were done by the apostles."—Acts 2:42-43

Omer Westendorf

6.6.11.6.6.11.D.
ASH GROVE
Welsh Folk Tune

1 Sent forth by God's bless-ing, our true faith con-fess-ing, The
2 With praise and thanks-giv-ing to God ev-er-liv-ing, The

1 peo-ple of God from his dwell-ing take leave.
2 tasks of our ev-ery-day life we will face.

1 The *sup-per is end-ed. O now be ex-tend-ed The
2 Our faith ev-er shar-ing, in love ev-er car-ing, Em-

1 fruits of this ser-vice in all who be-lieve: The
2 brac-ing His chil-dren of each tribe and race. With

*Optional text "worship"

©Copyright 1964 World Library Publications, Inc. All Rights Reserved. Used With Permission.

ORDINANCE OF THE LORD'S SUPPER

1 seed of His teach-ing, re-cep-tive souls reach-ing, Shall
2 Your feast You feed us, with Your light now lead us; U-

1 blos-som in ac-tion for God and for all. His
2 nite us as one in this life that we share. Then

1 grace did in-vite us, His love shall u-nite us To
2 may all the liv-ing with praise and thanks-giv-ing Give

1 work for God's king-dom and an-swer His call.
2 hon-or to Christ and His name that we bear.

ORDINANCE OF THE LORD'S SUPPER

382 He Washed His Servants' Feet

"So after He washed their feet . . . "—John 13:12

C.M.
AMAZING GRACE
American Melody
Carrell and Clayton's *Virginia Harmony*
Harmonized by Edwin O. Excell

Zion's Hymns

1 Dis - robed of all His heav'n - ly dress, The Sav - ior came to earth; Clothed in a veil of mor - tal flesh, And bowed His head in death.

2 That aw - ful night in which be - trayed, He in - tro - duced the feast, Which we, my friends, have seen dis - played, Where each has been a guest.

3 The sol - emn scene a - bout to close, To make the whole com - plete, He meek - ly from com - mun - ion rose And washed His ser - vants' feet.

4 "To each," He said, "let oth - ers do As I your Lord, have done: The heav'n - ly pat - tern still pur - sue, In form as I have shown."

5 Since Christ has the ex - am - ple set, Re - cord - ed in His Word; We'll hum - bly wash each oth - er's feet, O - bed - ient to our Lord. A - men.

FEETWASHING

Love Consecrates the Humblest Act

383

"I have set you an example that you should do as I have done for you."
—John 13:15

C.M.
AZMON
Carl G. Gläser

Based on John 13:1-20
S. B. McManus

1 Love con - se - crates the hum - blest act, And
2 When in the shad - ow of the cross, Christ
3 "As I have done this un - to you, As
4 Love serves, yet will - ing, stoops to serve, What

1 sanc - ti - fies each deed; It sheds a ben - e -
2 bowed and washed the feet Of His dis - ci - ples,
3 you have seen this night, Thus would I have you
4 Christ in love so true Hath free - ly done for

1 dic - tion sweet, And hal - lows ev - 'ry need.
2 'twas a sign Of His great love com - plete.
3 do to each When I have passed from sight."
4 one and all, Shall we not glad - ly do? A - men.

FEETWASHING

384 Be Ready When He Comes

"So you also must be ready, because the Son of Man will come at an hour when you do not expect him."—Matthew 24:44

D. Otis Teasley

BE READY
D. Otis Teasley

1 Would you flee from sin and serve the Lord? Be read-y when He comes;
2 It is not His will that you be lost, Be read-y when He comes;
3 Do you know the end of time is near? Be read-y when He comes;
4 There is aw-ful dan-ger in de-lay, Be read-y when He comes;

1 He will soon ap-pear with His re-ward, Be read-y when He comes.
2 Would you save your soul at an-y cost? Be read-y when He comes.
3 Soon the Lord to judge us shall ap-pear; Be read-y when He comes.
4 Will you cast your on-ly hope a-way? Be read-y when He comes.

Be read-y, Be read-y, Be read-y when He comes;
when He comes, when He comes,

Be read-y, Be read-y, Be read-y when He comes.
when He comes, when He comes,

INVITATION AND RESPONSE

Give Me Thy Heart

385

"Here I am! I stand at the door and knock. If anyone hears my voice and opens the door, I will come in and eat with him, and he with me."—Revelation 3:20

Eliza E. Hewitt

GIVE ME THY HEART
William J. Kirkpatrick

1 "Give Me thy heart," says the Fa-ther a-bove, No gift so
2 "Give Me thy heart," says the Sav-ior our Lord, Call-ing in
3 "Give Me thy heart," says the Spir-it di-vine, "All that thou

1 pre-cious to Him as our love; Soft-ly he whis-pers, wher-
2 mer-cy a-gain thru His Word; "Turn now from sin, and from
3 hast, to my keep-ing re-sign; Grace more a-bound-ing is

1 ev-er thou art, "Grate-ful-ly trust Me, and give Me thy heart."
2 e-vil de-part, Have I not died for Thee? Give Me thy heart."
3 Mine to im-part, Make full sur-ren-der and give Me thy heart."

"Give Me Thy heart, give Me Thy heart," Hear the soft whis-per, wher-

ev-er Thou art: From this dark world He would draw Thee a-

part; Speak-ing so ten-der-ly, "Give Me Thy heart."

386   **Only Trust Him**

"They replied, 'Believe in the Lord Jesus, and you will be saved—you and your household.' "—Acts 16:31

C.M.wR.
MINERVA
John H. Stockton

John H. Stockton

1 Come, ev-ery soul by sin op-pressed, There's mer-cy with the Lord;
2 For Je-sus shed His pre-cious blood, Rich bless-ings to be-stow;
3 Yes, Je-sus is the Truth, the Way, That leads you in-to rest:

1 And He will sure-ly give you rest By trust-ing in His word.
2 He of-fers now the crim-son flood To wash us white as snow.
3 Be-lieve in Him with-out de-lay, And you are ful-ly blest.

On-ly trust Him, on-ly trust Him, On-ly trust Him now;

He will save you, He will save you, He will save you now.

INVITATION AND RESPONSE

Speak to My Heart, Lord Jesus 387

"Draw near to God and He will draw near to you."—James 4:8a

Baylus B. McKinney

7.6.7.6.wR.
HOLCOMB
Baylus B. McKinney

1 Speak to my heart, Lord Je-sus, Speak that my soul may hear;
2 Speak to my heart, Lord Je-sus, Purge me from ev-'ry sin;
3 Speak to my heart, Lord Je-sus, It is no long-er mine:

1 Speak to my heart, Lord Je-sus, Calm ev-'ry doubt and fear.
2 Speak to my heart, Lord Je-sus, Help me the lost to win.
3 Speak to my heart, Lord Je-sus, I would be whol-ly thine.

Speak to my heart, oh, speak to my heart, Speak to my heart, I pray;

Yield-ed and still, seek-ing Thy will, Oh, speak to my heart to-day.

INVITATION AND RESPONSE

388 Speak Lord, for Thy Servant Heareth

" . . . Then Samuel said, 'Speak, for your servant is listening.' "
—I Samuel 3:10b

Based on I Samuel 3:1-10
William J. Gaither

SPEAK, LORD
William J. Gaither

1 Here am I, dear Lord, please use me; I am thine, O Lord, for
2 Show Thy will to me, I pray, Lord, Show the way my feet should

1 aye; Take my life, my all, I'll serve Thee, Be my
2 trod; Speak, dear Lord, for Thy ser - vant hear - eth, Thou art

1 Mas-ter, O Lord, I pray. Speak, Lord, for Thy ser - vant
2 now and for - ev - er my God.

hear - eth, Speak, Lord, I will do Thy will; Take me, I will

ev - er serve Thee, Use me, with Thy Spir - it fill.

INVITATION AND RESPONSE

Into My Heart

389

"If anyone hears My voice and opens the door, I will come in to him and eat with him, and he with Me."—Revelation 3:20b

Harry D. Clarke

CLARKE
Harry D. Clarke

In-to my heart, in-to my heart, Come in-to my heart, Lord Je - sus:

Come in to-day, Come in to stay, Come in-to my heart, Lord Je - sus.

I'll Live for Him

390

"I have been crucified with Christ and I no longer live, but Christ lives in me. The life I live in the body, I live by faith in the Son of God, who loved me and gave himself for me."—Galations 2:20

Ralph E. Hudson

8.8.8.6.wR.
DUNBAR
C. R. Dunbar

1 My life, my love I give to Thee, Thou Lamb of God who died for me;
2 I now be-lieve Thou dost re-ceive, For Thou hast died that I might live;
3 O Thou who died on Cal - va - ry, To save my soul and make me free,
Refrain: I'll live for Him who died for me, How hap-py then my life shall be!

D.C. for Refrain

1 O may I ev - er faith-ful be, My Sav - ior and my God!
2 And now hence-forth I'll trust in Thee, My Sav - ior and my God!
3 I'll con - se - crate my life for Thee, My Sav - ior and my God!
Ref.: I'll live for Him who died for me, My Sav - ior and my God!

INVITATION AND RESPONSE

391 I Am Praying for You

"For this reason, since the day we heard about you, we have not stopped praying for you . . . "—Colossians 1:9a

S. O'Maley Cluff

INTERCESSION
Ira D. Sankey

1 I have a Sav - ior—He's plead - ing in glo - ry, A dear, lov - ing
2 I have a Fa - ther—to me He has giv - en A hope for e -
3 I have a robe; 'tis re - splen - dent in white-ness, A - wait - ing in
4 When He has found you—tell oth - ers the sto - ry, That my lov - ing

1 Sav - ior, though earth - friends be few; And now He is watch - ing in
2 ter - ni - ty, bless - ed and true; And soon He will call me to
3 glo - ry my won - der - ing view; O when I re - ceive it all
4 Sav - ior is your Sav - ior, too; Then pray that your Sav - ior will

1 ten - der-ness o'er me, But O that my Sav - ior were your Sav-ior, too.
2 meet Him in heav - en, But O that He'd let me bring you with me, too!
3 shin - ing in bright-ness, Dear friend, could I see you re - ceiv - ing one, too!
4 bring them to glo - ry, And prayer will be an-swered-'twas an-swered for you!

For you I am pray - ing, For you I am pray - ing, For

you I am pray - ing, I'm pray - ing for you.

INVITATION AND RESPONSE

The Savior Is Waiting

392

"Here I am! I stand at the door and knock. If anyone hears my voice and opens the door, I will come in and eat with him, and he with me."—Revelation 3:20

11.7.11.7.wR.
CARMICHAEL
Ralph Carmichael

Ralph Carmichael

1 The Sav - ior is wait - ing to en - ter your heart, Why don't you
2 If you'll take one step toward the Sav - ior, my friend, You'll find His

1 let Him come in? There's noth-ing in this world to keep you a -
2 arms o - pen wide; Re - ceive Him, and all of your dark-ness will

1 part, What is your an - swer to Him?
2 end, With-in your heart He'll a - bide.

Time af - ter time He has

wait - ed be - fore, And now He is wait-ing a - gain To see

if you're will-ing to o - pen the door: O how He wants to come in.

INVITATION AND RESPONSE

393 Turn Your Eyes Upon Jesus

" . . . His face shone like the sun, and his clothes became as white as the light."
—Matthew 17:2b

Helen H. Lemmel

9.8.9.8.wR.
LEMMEL
Helen H. Lemmel

1 O soul, are you wea-ry and trou - bled? No light in the
2 Through death in - to life ev - er - last - ing He passed, and we
3 His word shall not fail you—He prom - ised; Be - lieve Him, and

1 dark-ness you see? There's light for a look at the Sav - ior, And
2 fol - low Him there; O - ver us sin no more hath do - min - ion—For
3 all will be well: Then go to a world that is dy - ing, His

1 life more a - bun-dant and free!
2 more than con-querors we are!
3 per - fect sal - va - tion to tell!

Turn your eyes up-on Je - sus,

Look full in His won - der - ful face, And the things of

earth will grow strange - ly dim In the light of His glo - ry and grace.

INVITATION AND RESPONSE

Have You Any Room for Jesus? 394

"For he says, 'In the time of my favor I heard you, in the day of salvation I helped you.' I tell you, now is the time of God's favor, now is the day of salvation."—II Corinthians 6:2

Unknown

8.7.8.7.wR.
ANY ROOM
C. C. Williams

1 Have you an - y room for Je - sus, He who bore your load of sin?
2 Room for pleas-ure, room for busi - ness— But, for Christ the cru - ci - fied,
3 Have you an - y room for Je - sus, As in grace He calls a - gain?
4 Room and time now give to Je - sus, Soon will pass God's day of grace;

1 As He knocks and asks ad - mis - sion, Will you ev - er let Him in?
2 Not a place that He can en - ter, In the heart for which He died?
3 Here to - day is time ac - cept - ed, To - mor - row you may call in vain.
4 Soon thy heart left cold and si - lent, And thy Sav - ior's plead-ing cease.

Room for Je - sus, King of glo - ry! Has - ten now, His word o - bey;

Swing your heart's door wide-ly o - pen, Bid Him en-ter while you may.

395

Jesus Is Calling

"Today, if you hear his voice, do not harden your hearts as in the rebellion . . . "—Hebrews 3:7b,8a

Fanny J. Crosby

10.8.10.7.wR.
CALLING TODAY
George C. Stebbins

1 Je - sus is ten - der - ly call - ing you home— Call - ing to - day,
2 Je - sus is call - ing the wea - ry to rest— Call - ing to - day,
3 Je - sus is wait - ing, O come to Him now— Wait - ing to - day,
4 Je - sus is plead - ing, O hear now His voice— Hear Him to - day,

1 call - ing to - day; Why from the sun - shine of love will you roam
2 call - ing to - day; Bring Him your bur - den and you shall be blest—
3 wait - ing to - day; Come with your sins, at His feet low - ly bow—
4 hear Him to - day; They who be - lieve on His name shall re - joice—

1 Far - ther and far - ther a - way?
2 He will not turn you a - way.
3 Come, and no long - er de - lay.
4 Quick - ly a - rise and a - way.

Call - ing to - day,

Call - ing to - day, Je - sus is

call - ing, Is ten - der - ly call - ing to - day.

INVITATION AND RESPONSE

Lord, Here Am I

396

" 'Come, follow me,' Jesus said, 'and I will make you fishers of men.' At once
they left their nets and followed him."—Mark 1:17-18

Fanny J. Crosby

10.10.10.10.wR.
HERE AM I
John Ness Beck

1 Mas - ter, Thou call - est, I glad - ly o - bey; On - ly di -
2 Will - ing, my Sav - ior, to take up the cross; Will - ing to
3 Liv - ing or dy - ing, I still would be Thine, Yet I am

1 rect me, and I'll find Thy way. Teach me the mis - sion ap -
2 suf - fer re - proach - es and loss; Will - ing to fol - low, if
3 mor - tal, while Thou art di - vine. Par - don, when - ev - er I

1 point - ed for me, What is my la - bor, and where it shall
2 Thou wilt but lead; On - ly sup - port me with grace in my
3 turn from the right; Pi - ty and bring me a - gain to the

1 be. Mas - ter, Thou call - est, and this I re - ply:
2 need.
3 light.

"Read - y and will - ing, Lord, here am I."

Music © Copyright 1984 Beckenhorst Press Inc. Used By Permission.

INVITATION AND RESPONSE

397 Lord, Take the First Place

"That if you confess with your mouth, 'Jesus is Lord,' and believe in your heart that God raised him from the dead, you will be saved."—Romans 10:9

Barney E. Warren

11.8.11.8.wR.
THE FIRST PLACE
Barney E. Warren

1. I yield to Thee, Sav - ior, for - sak - ing my all, From sin - ful things now I will part, To Thee I sur - ren - der, for mer - cy I call; Come, take the first place in my heart.

2. O come, gen - tle Spir - it, don't leave me, I pray, From Thee I will nev - er de - part; I come to Thee now, for I can - not de - lay, Lord, take the first place in my heart.

3. I can - not be lost, Lord, for Thee I will live, For - give -ness, O Sav - ior, im - part; If I will con -fess Thou wilt free - ly for - give, And take the first place in my heart.

4. The joy -bells of heav - en will ring in my soul, My Sav - ior, Re - deem -er, Thou art; To Thee I sur - ren - der, wilt Thou make me whole? Take now the first place in my heart.

INVITATION AND RESPONSE

O take the first place in my heart, (my heart,) O
take the first place in my heart; (my heart;) I o - pen the door, come
in, I im - plore, Lord, take the first place in my heart. (my heart.)

Reconciliation 398

If when we were enemies we were reconciled to God through the death of His Son, much more, having been reconciled, we shall be saved by His life.

And not only that, but we also rejoice in God through our Lord Jesus Christ, through whom we have now received the reconciliation.

Now all things are of God, who has reconciled us to Himself through Jesus Christ, and has given us the ministry of reconciliation.

That is, that God was in Christ reconciling the world to Himself, not imputing their trespasses to them, and has committed to us the word of reconciliation.

Therefore we are ambassadors for Christ, as though God were pleading through us; we implore you on Christ's behalf, be reconciled to God.

Now in Christ Jesus you who once were far off have been made near by the blood of Christ.

For He Himself is our peace, who has made both one, and has broken down the middle wall of division between us, having abolished in His flesh the enmity, that is, the law of commandments contained in ordinances, so as to create in Himself one new man from the two, thus making peace.

And that He might reconcile them both to God in one body through the cross, thereby putting to death the enmity.

And He came and preached peace to you who were afar off and to those who were near.

For through Him we both have access by one Spirit to the Father.

—Rom. 5:10–11; II Cor. 5:18–20;
Eph. 2:13–18 (NKJV)

INVITATION AND RESPONSE

399 Will You Come?

*"For he says, 'In the time of my favor I heard you, and in the day of salvation I
helped you.' I tell you, now is the time of God's favor, now is the day of
salvation."—II Corinthians 6:2*

WILL YOU COME
Barney E. Warren

Barney E. Warren

1 Will you come to Je - sus? He is call - ing; Will you come to
2 Will you come to Je - sus, full of mer - cy? Will you give Him
3 Will you come to Je - sus? Do not grieve Him, He has paid the
4 Will you come to Je - sus? Time is fly - ing; Do not wait a

1 Him with - out de - lay? He is full of love, so kind and gra - cious,
2 time, and tal - ents, too? Will you not pre-pare to reign in glo - ry?
3 ran - som for your soul; Tar - ry then no long-er, just re - ceive Him,
4 mo - ment, come just now; Man - y souls in sin each day are dy - ing;

1 He will sure - ly save your soul to - day.
2 Sin - ner, to your pre-cious soul be true.
3 And in mer - cy He will make you whole.
4 Come, and at His feet re - pent-ing bow.

Will you come to Him, the

Lord of all? Will you come to Him, for mer - cy call?

INVITATION AND RESPONSE

Will you come to Him, and pros-trate fall? Will you come?

Take My Life, Lead Me, Lord 400

"...he will be an instrument for noble purposes, made holy, useful to the Master and prepared to do any good work."—II Timothy 2:21b

R. Maines Rawls

6.6.7.D.
LANGLEY
R. Maines Rawls

1 Take my life, lead me, Lord, Take my life, lead me, Lord,
2 Take my life, teach me, Lord, Take my life, teach me, Lord,
3 Here am I, send me, Lord, Here am I, send me, Lord,

1 Make my life use-ful to Thee; Take my life, lead me, Lord,
2 Make my life use-ful to Thee; Take my life, teach me, Lord,
3 Make my life use-ful to Thee; Here am I, send me, Lord,

1 Take my life, lead me, Lord, Make my life use-ful to Thee.
2 Take my life, teach me, Lord, Make my life use-ful to Thee.
3 Here am I, send me, Lord, Make my life use-ful to Thee.

INVITATION AND RESPONSE

401 Jesus Is Lord of All

"Therefore let all Israel be assured of this: God has made this Jesus, whom you crucified, both Lord and Christ."—Acts 2:36

LeRoy McClard

LORDSHIP OF CHRIST
LeRoy McClard

1 Je - sus is Sav - ior and Lord of my life,
2 Bless - ed Re - deem - er, all glo - ri - ous King,
3 Will you sur - ren - der your all to Him now?

1 My hope, my glo - ry, my all; Won - der - ful Mas - ter in
2 Wor - thy of rev - 'rence I pay; Trib - ute and prais - es I
3 Fol - low His will and o - bey, Crown Him as Sov - 'reign, be -

1 joy and in strife, On Him you, too, may call.
2 joy - ful - ly bring To You, the Life, the Way.
3 fore His throne bow; Give Him your heart to - day.

Je - sus is Lord of all, Je - sus is Lord of all,

INVITATION AND RESPONSE

Lord of my thoughts and my ser-vice each day, Je-sus is Lord of all.

Just As I Am, Without One Plea 402

"All that the Father gives me will come to me, and whoever comes to me I will never drive away."—John 6:37

L.M.
WOODWORTH
William B. Bradbury

Charlotte Elliott

1 Just as I am, with-out one plea, But
2 Just as I am, and wait-ing not To
3 Just as I am, Thou wilt re-ceive, Wilt
4 Just as I am, Thy love un-known Hath

1 that Thy blood was shed for me, And that Thou bid'st me
2 rid my soul of one dark blot; To Thee, whose blood can
3 wel-come, par-don, cleanse, re-lieve; Be-cause Thy prom-ise
4 bro-ken ev-ery bar-rier down; Now, to be Thine, yes,

1 come to Thee— O Lamb of God, I come, I come!
2 cleanse each spot, O Lamb of God, I come, I come!
3 I be-lieve, O Lamb of God, I come, I come!
4 Thine a-lone, O Lamb of God, I come, I come!

403 I Surrender All

"... offer yourselves to God ..."—Romans 6:13b

Judson W. Van de Venter

8.7.8.7.wR.
SURRENDER
Winfield S. Weeden

1 All to Je-sus I sur-ren-der, All to Him I free-ly give;
2 All to Je-sus I sur-ren-der, Hum-bly at His feet I bow,
3 All to Je-sus I sur-ren-der, Make me, Sav-ior, whol-ly Thine.
4 All to Je-sus I sur-ren-der, Lord, I give my-self to Thee;

1 I will ev-er love and trust Him, In His pres-ence dai-ly live.
2 World-ly pleas-ures all for-sak-en, Take me, Je-sus, take me now.
3 Let me feel the Ho-ly Spir-it, Tru-ly know that Thou art mine.
4 Fill me with Thy love and pow-er, Let Thy bless-ing fall on me.

I sur-ren-der all,
I sur-ren-der all,
I sur-ren-der all,
I sur-ren-der all,

All to Thee, my bless-ed Sav-ior, I sur-ren-der all.

INVITATION AND RESPONSE

Softly and Tenderly

404

"Come to me, all you who are weary and burdened, and I will give you rest."
—Matthew 11:28

Will L. Thompson

11.7.11.7.wR.
THOMPSON
Will L. Thompson

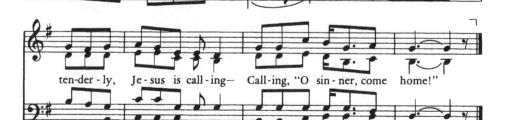

1 Soft - ly and ten - der - ly Je - sus is call - ing, Call - ing for
2 Why should we lin - ger when Je - sus is plead-ing, Plead-ing for
3 O for the won - der - ful love He has prom-ised, Prom-ised for

1 you and for me; Pa - tient and lov - ing, He's wait-ing and watch-ing,
2 you and for me? Why should we wait, then, and heed not His mer-cies,
3 you and for me; Tho' we have sinned, He has mer - cy and par - don,

1 Watch-ing for you and for me. Come home, come home,
2 Mer - cies for you and for me? Come home, come home,
3 Par - don for you and for me.

You who are wea - ry, come home; Ear - nest - ly,

ten-der - ly, Je - sus is call-ing— Call-ing, "O sin - ner, come home!"

INVITATION AND RESPONSE

405 Jesus, I Come

"The Spirit of the Sovereign Lord is on me, because the Lord has anointed me to preach good news to the poor. He has sent me to bind up the brokenhearted, to proclaim freedom for the captives and release for the prisoners."—Isaiah 61:1

William T. Sleeper
Jeff Redd, alt.

JESUS, I COME
George C. Stebbins

1 Out of my bond-age, sor - row and night, Je - sus, I come, Je - sus, I come;
2 Out of my shame-ful fail - ure and loss, Je - sus, I come, Je - sus, I come;
3 Out of un - rest and ar - ro-gant pride, Je - sus, I come, Je - sus, I come;
4 Out of the fear and dread of the tomb, Je - sus, I come, Je - sus, I come;

1 In - to Thy free - dom, glad - ness and light, Je - sus, I come to Thee.
2 In - to the glo - rious gain of Thy cross, Je - sus, I come to Thee.
3 In - to Thy bless - ed will to a - bide, Je - sus, I come to Thee.
4 In - to the joy and light of Thy home, Je - sus, I come to Thee.

1 Out of my sick - ness in - to Thy health, Out of my need and in -to Thy wealth,
2 Out of earth's sor-rows in - to Thy balm, Out of life's storms and in-to Thy calm,
3 Out of my-self to dwell in Thy love, Out of de-spair to rap-tures a-bove,
4 Out of the depths of ru - in un-told, In - to Thy peace-ful, shel-ter-ing fold,

1 Out of my sin and in - to Thy-self, Je - sus, I come to Thee.
2 Out of dis-tress to ju - bi-lant psalm, Je - sus, I come to Thee.
3 Up - ward I rise on wings like a dove, Je - sus, I come to Thee.
4 Ev - er Thy glo - rious face to be-hold, Je - sus, I come to Thee.

INVITATION AND RESPONSE

There's Room at the Cross for You 406

"And let him who hears say, 'Come!' Whoever is thirsty, let him come; and whoever wishes, let him take the free gift of the water of life."
—Revelation 22:17b

Ira F. Stanphill

STANPHILL
Ira F. Stanphill

1 The cross up-on which Je-sus died Is a shel-ter in
2 Though mil-lions have found Him a friend And have turned from the
3 The hand of my Sav-ior is strong, And the love of my

1 which we can hide; And its grace so free is suf-
2 sins they have sinned, The Sav-ior still waits to
3 Sav-ior is long; Through sun-shine or rain, through

1 fi-cient for me, And deep is its foun-tain— as wide as the sea.
2 o-pen the gates And wel-come a sin-ner be-fore it's too late.
3 loss or in gain, The blood flows from Cal-vary to cleanse ev-ery stain.

There's room at the cross for you, There's room at the cross for you; Though

millions have come, There's still room for one—Yes, there's room at the cross for you.

INVITATION AND RESPONSE

407   Are You Washed in the Blood?

"I answered, 'Sir, you know.' And he said, 'These are they who have come out of the great tribulation; they have washed their robes and made them white in the blood of the Lamb.' "—Revelation 7:14

11.9.11.9.wR.

WASHED IN THE BLOOD
Elisha A. Hoffman

Elisha A. Hoffman

1 Have you been to Je-sus for the cleans-ing power? Are you
2 Are you walk-ing dai-ly by the Sav-ior's side? Are you
3 When the Bride-groom com-eth, will your robes be white, Pure and
4 Lay a-side the gar-ments that are stained with sin And be

1 washed in the blood of the Lamb? Are you ful-ly trust-ing in His
2 washed in the blood of the Lamb? Do you rest each mo-ment in the
3 white in the blood of the Lamb? Will your souls be read-y for the
4 washed in the blood of the Lamb. There's a foun-tain flow-ing for the

1 grace this hour? Are you washed in the blood of the Lamb?
2 Cru-ci-fied? Are you washed in the blood of the Lamb?
3 man-sions bright And be washed in the blood of the Lamb?
4 soul un-clean; O be washed in the blood of the Lamb.

Are you

washed in the blood, In the soul-cleans-ing blood of the Lamb? Are your

REPENTANCE AND FORGIVENESS

gar-ments spotless? Are they white as snow? Are you washed in the blood of the Lamb?

Cleanse Me

408

"Search me, O God, and know my heart; test me and know my anxious thoughts."—Psalm 139:23

J. Edwin Orr

10.10.10.10.
MAORI
Maori Melody

1 Search me, O God, and know my heart to-day; Try me, O
2 I praise Thee, Lord, for cleans-ing me from sin; Ful-fill Thy
3 Lord, take my life, and make it whol-ly Thine; Fill my poor
4 O Ho-ly Ghost, re-viv-al comes from Thee; Send a re-

1 Sav-ior, know my thoughts, I pray. See if there be some wick-ed
2 Word and make me pure with-in. Fill me with fire, where once I
3 heart with Thy great love di-vine. Take all my will, my pas-sion,
4 viv-al, start the work in me. Thy Word de-clares Thou wilt sup-

1 way in me; Cleanse me from ev-ery sin, and set me free.
2 burned with shame; Grant my de-sire to mag-ni-fy Thy name.
3 self, and pride; I now sur-ren-der, Lord—in me a-bide.
4 ply our need; For bless-ing now, O Lord, I hum-bly plead.

409 Lord, I'm Coming Home

"I will set out and go back to my father and say to him: 'Father, I have sinned against heaven and against you.' "—Luke 15:18

8.5.8.5.wR.
COMING HOME
William J. Kirkpatrick

William J. Kirkpatrick

1 I've wan-dered far a - way from God, Now I'm com-ing home;
2 I've wast - ed man - y pre - cious years, Now I'm com-ing home;
3 I've tired of sin and stray - ing Lord, Now I'm com-ing home;
4 My soul is sick, my heart is sore, Now I'm com-ing home;

1 The paths of sin too long I've trod, Lord, I'm com-ing home.
2 I now re-pent with bit - ter tears, Lord, I'm com-ing home.
3 I'll trust Thy love, be - lieve Thy word, Lord, I'm com-ing home.
4 My strength re-new, my hope re - store, Lord, I'm com-ing home.

Com- ing home, com - ing home, Nev - er - more to roam.

O - pen wide Thine arms of love, Lord, I'm com-ing home.

REPENTANCE AND FORGIVENESS

Jesus Paid It All

"Do you not know that your body is a temple of the Holy Spirit, who is in you,
whom you have received from God? You are not your own; you were bought at
a price. Therefore honor God with your body." —I Corinthians 6:19–20

Elvina M. Hall

6.6.7.7.wR.
ALL TO CHRIST
John T. Grape

1 I hear the Sav-ior say, "Thy strength in-deed is small!
2 For noth-ing good have I Where-by Thy grace to claim—
3 And when be-fore the throne I stand in Him com-plete,

1 Child of weak-ness watch and pray, Find in me thine all in all."
2 I will wash my gar-ments white In the blood of Cal-vary's Lamb.
3 "Je-sus died my soul to save," My lips shall still re-peat.

Je - sus paid it all, All to Him I owe;

Sin had left a crim-son stain— He washed it white as snow.

©1986 by Rocksmith Music. All Rights Reserved. Used By Permission.

REPENTANCE AND FORGIVENESS

411 Lord, I Want to Be a Christian

*"Don't let anyone look down on you because you are young, but set an example
for the believers in speech, in life, in love, in faith and in purity."*
—I Timothy 4:12

Spiritual

IN MY HEART
Traditional Spiritual

1 Lord, I want to be a Chris-tian In my heart, in my heart;
2 Lord, I want to be more lov-ing In my heart, in my heart;
3 Lord, I want to be more ho-ly In my heart, in my heart;
4 Lord, I want to be like Je-sus In my heart, in my heart;

1 Lord, I want to be a Chris - tian In my heart.
2 Lord, I want to be more lov - ing In my heart.
3 Lord, I want to be more ho - ly In my heart.
4 Lord, I want to be like Je - sus In my heart.

In my heart, In my heart,
In my heart, In my heart,

1 Lord, I want to be a Chris - tian In my heart.
2 Lord, I want to be more lov - ing In my heart.
3 Lord, I want to be more ho - ly In my heart.
4 Lord, I want to be like Je - sus In my heart.

REPENTANCE AND FORGIVENESS

Transformed

412

"Take my yoke upon you and learn from me, for I am gentle and humble in heart, and you will find rest for your souls."—Matthew 11:29

Mrs. F. G. Burroughs

C.M.wR.
TRANSFORMED
Bentley D. Ackley

1 Dear Lord, take up the tan-gled strands, Where we have wrought in vain,
2 Touch Thou the sad, dis-cord-ant keys Of ev-'ry troub-led breast,
3 Where bro-ken vows in frag-ments lie— The toll of wast-ed years—
4 Take all the fail-ures, each mis-take Of our poor, hu-man ways,

1 That by the skill of Thy dear hands Some beau-ty may re-main.
2 And change to peace-ful har-mo-nies The sigh-ings of un-rest.
3 Do Thou make whole a-gain, we cry, And give a song for tears.
4 Then, Sav-ior, for Thine own dear sake, Make them show forth Thy praise.

Trans-formed by grace di-vine, The glo-ry shall be Thine;
Trans-formed The glo-ry

To Thy most ho-ly will, O Lord, We now our all re-sign.

REPENTANCE AND FORGIVENESS

413

It Is No Secret

"But now in Christ Jesus you who once were far away have been brought near through the blood of Christ."—Ephesians 2:13

IT IS NO SECRET
Stuart Hamblen

Stuart Hamblen

It is no se - cret what God can do.

What He's done for oth - ers, He'll do for you.

With arms wide o - pen, He'll par - don you.

It is no se - cret what God can do.

REPENTANCE AND FORGIVENESS

I Believe in Miracles

414

"Therefore, if anyone is in Christ, he is a new creation; the old has gone, the new has come!"—II Corinthians 5:17

Carlton C. Buck

MIRACLES
John W. Peterson

1 Cre - a - tion shows the power of God—There's glo - ry all a - round, And
2 I can-not doubt the work of God— It's plain for all to see; The
3 The love of God! O power di-vine! 'Tis won-der-ful to see The

1 those who see must stand in awe, For mir - a - cles a - bound.
2 mir - a - cles that He has wrought Should lead to Cal - va - ry.
3 mir - a - cle of grace per-formed With - in the heart of me.

I be-lieve in mir - a-cles—I've seen a soul set free, Mi - rac - u-lous the

change in One Re-deemed thro' Cal-va - ry; I've seen the lil - y push its way Up

thro' the stub-born sod— I be-lieve in mir - a-cles, For I be-lieve in God!

FAITH AND HOPE

415

My Faith Has Found a Resting Place

" . . . In His great mercy he has given us new birth into a living hope through
the resurrection of Jesus Christ from the dead, and into an inheritance that can
never perish, spoil or fade . . . "—I Peter 1:3b, 4a

Lidie H. Edmunds

C.M.wR.
NO OTHER PLEA
Norwegian Melody

1. My faith has found a rest-ing place, Not in de-vice nor creed;
2. E - nough for me that Je - sus saves, This ends my fear and doubt;
3. My soul is rest - ing on the Word, The liv - ing Word of God:
4. The great Phy - si - cian heals the sick, The lost He came to save;

1. I trust the ev - er liv - ing One, That He for me will plead.
2. A sin - ful soul I come to Him, He will not cast me out.
3. Sal - va - tion in my Sav - ior's name, Sal - va - tion through His blood.
4. For me His pre - cious blood He shed, For me His life He gave.

I need no oth - er ar - gu - ment, I need no oth - er plea;

It is e - nough that Je - sus died And that He died for me.

FAITH AND HOPE

How Firm a Foundation

416

"Nevertheless, God's solid foundation stands firm . . . "—II Timothy 2:19a

Based on II Timothy 2:19; Hebrews 13:5;
Isaiah 43:1-2
Rippon's *Selection of Hymns*

11.11.11.11.
FOUNDATION
Early American Melody
Caldwell's *Union Harmony*

1 How firm a foun - da - tion, ye saints of the Lord,
2 "Fear not, I am with thee; O be not dis - mayed,
3 "When through fier - y tri - als thy path - way shall lie,
4 "The soul that on Je - sus hath leaned for re - pose

1 Is laid for your faith in His ex - cel - lent Word!
2 For I am thy God, and will still give thee aid;
3 My grace, all suf - fi - cient, shall be thy sup - ply:
4 I will not, I will not de - sert to its foes;

1 What more can He say than to you He hath said,
2 I'll strength-en thee, help thee, and cause thee to stand,
3 The flame shall not hurt thee; I on - ly de - sign
4 That soul, though all hell should en - deav - or to shake,

1 To you who for ref - uge to Je - sus have fled?
2 Up - held by My right - eous, om - nip - o - tent hand.
3 Thy dross to con - sume and thy gold to re - fine.
4 I'll nev - er, no nev - er, no nev - er for - sake!"

FAITH AND HOPE

417 I Know in My Heart What It Means

"The Spirit himself testifies with our spirit that we are God's children."
—Romans 8:16

12.9.12.9.wR.

D. Otis Teasley

I KNOW IN MY HEART
D. Otis Teasley

1 When I read how my Sav - ior was nailed to the cross For the
2 When the gos - pel is preached in the name of the Lord By the
3 When the sweet songs of Zi - on are float - ing a - bove, And the
4 And when oth - ers pro -claim that sal - va - tion is free, When they

1 sins of the world to a - tone, O I feel so un-wor - thy such
2 Spir - it sent down from a - bove, My soul thrills with joy at the
3 saints all re - joice in the Lord, I am hap - py in Je - sus and
4 tell of the soul-cleans-ing blood, I too can re-joice, for He

1 suf - f'ring and loss, For I know in my heart what it means.
2 sound of His word, For I know in my heart what it means.
3 lost in His love, For I know in my heart what it means.
4 sanc - ti -fied me, And I know in my heart what it means.

I know in my heart what it means, Sal - va - tion, that

FAITH AND HOPE

word so di-vine; His Spir - it has wit-nessed to
so di-vine; so

mine, And I know in my heart what it means.
clear - ly to mine,

Only Believe 418

" 'If you can?' said Jesus. 'Everything is possible for him who believes.' "
—Mark 9:23

Paul Rader

ONLY BELIEVE
Paul Rader

On - ly be - lieve, on - ly be - lieve; All things are

pos - si-ble, on - ly be - lieve; On - ly be - lieve,

on - ly be - lieve; All things are pos - si-ble, on - ly be - lieve.

FAITH AND HOPE

419 In the Name of the Lord

"And I will do whatever you ask in my name, so that the Son may bring glory to the Father."—John 14:13

Phill McHugh, Gloria Gaither
and Sandi Patti Helvering

NAME OF THE LORD
Phill McHugh, Gloria Gaither
and Sandi Patti Helvering

There is strength in the name of the Lord; There is pow'r in the
Hay po - der en el nom-bre del Se - ñor. Hay po - der en el

name of the Lord; There is hope in the name of the Lord!
nom-bre del Se - ñor. Y es per - an - za en el nom-bre del Se - ñor.

Bless - ed is He who comes in the name of the Lord.
Ben - di - to se a El que viene en el nom-bre del Señor.

Harmony

There is strength in the name of the Lord;
Hay po - der en el nom-bre del Se - ñor;

There is pow'r in the name of the Lord; There is hope in the
Hay po - der en el nom-bre del Se - ñor; Y es per - an - za en el

FAITH AND HOPE

2nd time
Fine

name of the Lord! Bless-ed is He who comes in the name of the Lord.
nom-bre del Se-ñor! Ben - di -to se a El que viene en el nom-bre del Señor.

The Solid Rock **420**

*"Therefore everyone who hears these words of mine and puts them into practice
is like a wise man who built his house on the rock."—Matthew 7:24*

Edward Mote

L.M.wR.
SOLID ROCK
William B. Bradbury

1 My hope is built on noth-ing less Than Je - sus' blood and
2 When dark-ness veils His love - ly face, I rest on His un-
3 His oath, His cov - e - nant, His blood, Sup - port me in the
4 When He shall come with trum-pet sound, O may I then in

1 right-eous-ness; I dare not trust the sweet-est frame, But whol-ly
2 chang-ing grace; In ev - ery high and storm - y gale, My an-chor
3 whelm-ing flood; When all a - round my soul gives way, He then is
4 Him be found; Dressed in His right-eous - ness a - lone, Fault - less to

1 lean on Je - sus' name.
2 holds with - in the veil.   On Christ, the sol - id Rock, I stand; All
3 all my hope and stay.
4 stand be - fore the throne.

oth - er ground is sink-ing sand, All oth - er ground is sink-ing sand.

FAITH AND HOPE

421 Take the Name of Jesus with You

"And whatever you do, whether in word or deed, do it all in the name of the Lord Jesus, giving thanks to God the Father through him."—Colossians 3:17

8.7.8.7.wR.
PRECIOUS NAME
William H. Doane

Lydia Baxter

1 Take the name of Je - sus with you, Child of sor-row and of woe.
2 Take the name of Je - sus ev - er As pro-tec-tion ev-ery - where;
3 At the name of Je - sus bow - ing, When in heav-en we shall meet,

1 It will joy and com-fort give you, Take it then wher-e'er you go.
2 If temp-ta-tions 'round you gath - er, Breathe that ho - ly name in prayer.
3 King of kings, we'll glad-ly crown Him When our jour-ney is com - plete.

Pre - cious name, O how sweet! Hope of earth and joy of heaven,

Pre - cious name, O how sweet— Hope of earth and joy of heaven.

Nothing But the Blood

422

" . . . and without the shedding of blood there is no forgiveness."
—Hebrews 9:22b

Robert Lowry

7.8.7.8.wR.
PLAINFIELD
Robert Lowry

1 What can wash a - way my sin? Noth-ing but the blood of Je - sus;
2 For my par - don this I see— Noth-ing but the blood of Je - sus;
3 Noth-ing can for sin a - tone— Noth-ing but the blood of Je - sus;
4 This is all my hope and peace— Noth-ing but the blood of Je - sus;

1 What can make me whole a - gain? Noth-ing but the blood of Je - sus.
2 For my cleans-ing this my plea— Noth-ing but the blood of Je - sus.
3 Naught of good that I have done— Noth-ing but the blood of Je - sus.
4 This is all my right - eous-ness— Noth-ing but the blood of Je - sus.

O! pre - cious is the flow That makes me white as snow;

No oth - er fount I know, Noth-ing but the blood of Je - sus.

FAITH AND HOPE

423 There's Power in the Blood

"They overcame him by the blood of the Lamb and by the word of their testimony; they did not love their lives so much as to shrink from death."
—Revelation 12:11

10.9.10.8.wR.
POWER
Lewis E. Jones

Lewis E. Jones

1 Would you be free from your bur - den of sin? There's pow'r in the blood,
2 Would you be free from your pas - sion and pride? There's pow'r in the blood,
3 Would you do serv - ice for Je - sus your King? There's pow'r in the blood,

1 pow'r in the blood; Would you o'er e - vil a vic - to - ry win? There's
2 pow'r in the blood; Come for a cleans-ing to Cal - va-ry's tide—There's
3 pow'r in the blood; Would you live dai - ly His prais - es to sing? There's

won - der - ful pow'r in the blood. There is pow'r, pow'r,
there is

won-der-work-ing pow'r In the blood of the Lamb; There is
In the blood of the Lamb;

pow'r,   pow'r, wonder-working pow'r In the pre-cious blood of the Lamb.
there is

Have Faith in God   424

" . . . According to your faith will it be done to you."—Matthew 9:29b

Daniel W. Whittle

HAVE FAITH
James McGranahan

1 Have faith in God; what can there be For Him too hard to do for thee?
2 Have faith thy par-don to be-lieve, Let God's own word thy fears re-lieve;
3 Have faith in God, and trust His might That He will con-quer as you fight,
4 Have faith in God, press near His side; Thy troub-led soul trust Him to guide;

1 He gave His Son, now all is free; Have faith, have faith in God.
2 Have faith the Spir-it to re-ceive; Have faith, have faith in God.
3 And give the tri-umph to the right; Have faith, have faith in God.
4 In life, in death, what-e'er be-tide, Have faith, have faith in God.

425 Power in the Blood of Jesus

"They overcame him by the blood of the Lamb and by the word of their testimony; they did not love their lives so much as to shrink from death."
—Revelation 12:11

Barney E. Warren

THE BLOOD OF JESUS
Barney E. Warren

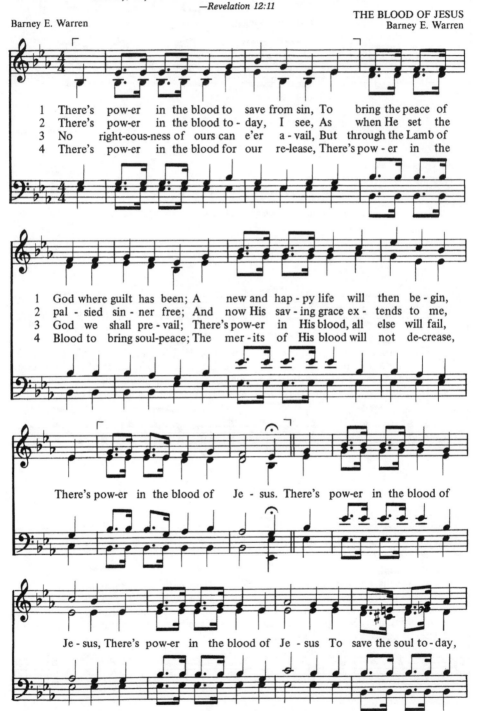

1 There's pow-er in the blood to save from sin, To bring the peace of God where guilt has been; A new and hap-py life will then be-gin,

2 There's pow-er in the blood to-day, I see, As when He set the pal-sied sin-ner free; And now His sav-ing grace ex-tends to me,

3 No right-eous-ness of ours can e'er a-vail, But through the Lamb of God we shall pre-vail; There's pow-er in His blood, all else will fail,

4 There's pow-er in the blood for our re-lease, There's pow-er in the Blood to bring soul-peace; The mer-its of His blood will not de-crease,

There's pow-er in the blood of Je - sus. There's pow-er in the blood of Je-sus, There's pow-er in the blood of Je - sus To save the soul to-day,

FAITH AND HOPE

Wash ev - 'ry sin a - way; There's pow - er in the blood of Je - sus.

Cleansing From Sin 426

This is the message we have heard from Him
and proclaim to you, that God is light and in
Him is no darkness at all.

**If we say we have fellowship with Him while
we walk in darkness, we lie and do not live
according to the truth;**

But if we walk in the light, as He is in the
light, we have fellowship with one another,
and the blood of Jesus His Son cleanses us
from all sin.

**If we say we have no sin, we deceive
ourselves, and the truth is not in us. If
we confess our sins, He is faithful and
just, and will forgive our sins and cleanse
us from all unrighteousness.**

—*I John 1:5-9 (RSV)*

FAITH AND HOPE

427 The Blood Will Never Lose Its Power

"But if we walk in the light, as he is in the light, we have fellowship with one another, and the blood of Jesus, his Son, purifies us from all sin."—I John 1:7

Andraé Crouch

THE BLOOD
Andraé Crouch

1 The blood that Je - sus shed for me, Way back on
2 It soothes my doubts and calms my fears, And it dries

1 Cal - va - ry, The blood that gives me strength from day to
2 all my tears; The blood that gives me strength from day to

1 day, It will nev - er lose its power.
2 day, It will nev - er lose its power.

It reach-es to the high - est moun - tain. It flows to the

low - est val - ley. The blood that gives me strength from

FAITH AND HOPE

day to day,   It will nev - er   lose   its   power.

Burdens Are Lifted at Calvary 428

"Take My yoke upon you and learn from me . . . and you will find rest for your souls."—Matthew 11:29

John M. Moore

BURDENS LIFTED
John M. Moore

1 Days are filled with sor-row and care, Hearts are lone - ly and drear;
2 Cast your care on Je - sus to - day, Leave your wor - ry and fear;
3 Trou-bled soul, the Sav-ior can see Ev - ery heart-ache and tear;

1 Bur-dens are lift - ed at Cal - va - ry, Je - sus is ver - y near.
2 Bur-dens are lift - ed at Cal - va - ry, Je - sus is ver - y near.
3 Bur-dens are lift - ed at Cal - va - ry, Je - sus is ver - y near.

Bur-dens are lift - ed at Cal - va - ry, Cal - va - ry, Cal - va - ry;

Bur-dens are lift - ed at Cal - va - ry, Je - sus is ver - y near.

FAITH AND HOPE

429 I Know

"Let us fix our eyes on Jesus, the author and perfecter of our faith . . . "
—Hebrews 12:2a

Charles W. Naylor

C.M.wR.
I KNOW
Andrew L. Byers

1 I know on Whom my faith is fixed, I know in Whom I trust;
2 They can-not quench the fire of love That burns with-in my breast,
3 They can-not bring a-gain the sins The blood has washed a-way,
4 I know God is, I know His word Un-fail-ing meets each test;

1 I know that Christ a-bides in me, And all His ways are just.
2 Nor break that ten-der fel-low-ship That makes my life so blest.
3 Nor make my heart like stone once more, Nor turn to night my day.
4 I calm-ly face a hos-tile world, With soul and mind at rest.

I know on Whom my faith is fixed, His mer-cy has set me free;
I know set me free;

I know that He will safe-ly keep, And His love is sweet to me.
yes, I know

FAITH AND HOPE

My Faith Still Holds

430

"You will keep in perfect peace him whose mind is steadfast, because he trusts in you."—Isaiah 26:3

Gloria Gaither
William J. Gaither

STRONG FAITH
William J. Gaither

My faith still holds on to the Christ of Cal - va - ry,

O bless - ed Rock of A - ges cleft for me.

I glad - ly place my trust in things I can - not see,

My faith still holds on to the Christ of Cal - va - ry.

FAITH AND HOPE

431 For All the Saints

"And into an inheritance that can never perish, spoil or fade—kept in heaven for you."—I Peter 1:4

William W. How

10.10.10. with Alleluias
SINE NOMINE
Ralph Vaughan Williams

Unison

1 For all the saints who from their la - bors rest, Who
2 Thou wast their Rock, their For - tress, and their Might:
3 O may Thy sol - diers, faith - ful, true, and bold,
4 And when the strife is fierce, the war - fare long,
5 From earth's wide bounds, from o - cean's far - thest coast, Thru

1 Thee by faith be - fore the world con - fessed, Thy
2 Thou, Lord, their Cap - tain in the well - fought fight;
3 Fight as the saints who no - bly fought of old, And
4 Steals on the ear the dis - tant tri - umph song, And
5 gates of pearl streams in the count - less host,

1 name, O Je - sus, be for - ev - er blest:
2 Thou, in the dark - ness drear, their one true Light:
3 win with them the vic - tor's crown of gold:
4 hearts are brave a - gain, and arms are strong:
5 Sing - ing to Fa - ther, Son, and Ho - ly Ghost:

Music from THE ENGLISH HYMNAL, by permission of Oxford University Press.
FAITH AND HOPE

Al - le - lu - ia! Al - le - lu - ia! A-men.

Hope and Comfort **432**

Do not be afraid, for I am with you;
stop being anxious and watchful, for
   I am your God.
I give you strength, I bring you help,
I uphold you with My victorious
   right hand.

The eye of Jehovah is on those
   who fear Him,
on those who rely on His love,
to rescue their souls from death
and keep them alive in famine.

It is by faith and through Jesus
that we have entered this state
   of grace
in which we can boast about looking
   forward to God's glory.

But that is not all we can
   boast about;
we can boast about our sufferings.
These sufferings bring patience, as
   we know,
and patience brings perseverance,
and perseverance brings hope,

and this hope is not deceptive,
because the love of God has been
   poured into our hearts by
   the Holy Spirit which has
   been given us.

May the God of hope
bring you such joy and peace in
   your faith
that the power of the Holy Spirit
will remove all bounds to hope.

—From Isaiah 41, Psalm 33, and
   Romans 5, 15 (TJB)

433 I Know Whom I Have Believed

" . . . I know whom I have believed . . . He is able to guard what I have entrusted to him for that day."—II Timothy 1:12

Based on II Timothy 1:12
Daniel W. Whittle

C.M.wR.
EL NATHAN
James McGranahan

1 I know not why God's won-drous grace To me He has made known,
2 I know not how this sav - ing faith To me He did im - part,
3 I know not how the Spir - it moves, Con - vinc - ing us of sin,
4 I know not when my Lord may come, At night or noon-day fair,

1 Nor why, un-wor - thy, Christ in love Re - deemed me for His own.
2 Nor how be -liev - ing in His word Wrought peace with-in my heart.
3 Re - veal - ing Je - sus through the word, Cre - at - ing faith in Him.
4 Nor if I'll walk the vale with Him, Or meet Him in the air.

But "I know whom I have be - liev - ed, and am per - suad - ed that He is

a - ble To keep that which I've com-mit-ted un-to Him a-gainst that day."

FAITH AND HOPE

My Hope Is in the Lord

434

"To them God has chosen to make known among the Gentiles the glorious riches of this mystery, which is Christ in you, the hope of glory."
—Colossians 1:27

6.6.12.wR.
WAKEFIELD
Norman J. Clayton

Norman J. Clayton

1 My hope is in the Lord Who gave Him-self for me,
2 No mer-it of my own His judge-ment to sup-press,
3 And now for me He stands Be-fore the Fa-ther's throne,
4 His grace has planned it all; 'Tis mine but to be-lieve,

1 And paid the price of all my sin at Cal-va-ry.
2 My on-ly hope is found in Je-sus' right-eous-ness.
3 And shows His wound-ed hands and names me as His own.
4 And rec-og-nize His work of love and Christ re-ceive.

For me He died, For me He lives,
For me He died, For me He lives,

And ev-er-last-ing life and light He free-ly gives.

FAITH AND HOPE

435 I Know My Name Is There

"However, do not rejoice that the spirits submit to you, but rejoice that your names are written in heaven."—Luke 10:20

Daniel S. Warner

MY NAME IS THERE
Barney E. Warren

1 My name is in the book of life, O bless the name of Je-sus!
2 With sin-ners lost my name once stood Up-on a pain-ful rec-ord;
3 Yet in-ward trou-ble of-ten cast A shad-ow o'er my ti-tle;
4 While oth-ers climb thru world-ly strife To carve a name of hon-or,

1 I rise a-bove all doubt and strife And read my ti-tle clear.
2 But now it's can-celed by the blood, And writ-ten on His roll.
3 But now with full sal-va-tion blest, Praise God, it's ev-er clear!
4 High up in heav-en's book of life, My name is writ-ten there.

I know, I know, my name is there;
I know, I tru-ly know, I know my name is there;

I know, I know my name is writ-ten there.
I know my name is there,

I'll Follow with Rejoicing

436

"Teach me your way O Lord; lead me in a straight path because of my oppressors."—Psalm 27:11

Charles W. Naylor

C.M.wR.
FOLLOW WITH REJOICING
Andrew L. Byers

1 The fu-ture lies un-seen a-head, It holds I know not what;
2 Does He not know what I shall meet Up-on life's rug-ged way?
3 No mat-ter how things look to me, Nor if they threat-en sore,
4 The glo-ry of e-ter-nal dawn Shines from His smil-ing face;

1 But still I know I need not dread, For Je-sus fails me not.
2 Will He not guide my halt-ing feet, Lest from the path I stray?
3 I know my way pre-pared shall be, For Christ leads on be-fore.
4 So trust-ing Him, I fol-low on, With heart made strong by grace.

I'll fol-low Him with re-joic-ing, With re-joic-ing, re-joic-ing;
I'll fol-low Him, I'll fol-low Him, With re-joic-ing I will fol-low Him;

I know He safe-ly will lead me To my e-ter-nal home.
I know He safe-ly will lead me on

FAITH AND HOPE

437 Surely Goodness and Mercy

"Surely goodness and love will follow me all the days of my life, and I will dwell in the house of the Lord forever."—Psalm 23:6

Based on Psalm 23
John W. Peterson
Alfred B. Smith

SURELY GOODNESS AND MERCY
John W. Peterson

1 A pil-grim was I and a wan-d'ring; In the cold night of
2 He re-stor-eth my soul when I'm wea-ry; He giv-eth me
3 When I walk through the dark, lone-some val-ley, My Sav-ior will

1 sin I did roam, When Je-sus, the kind Shep-herd found me, And
2 strength day by day. He leads me be-side the still wa-ters; He
3 walk with me there; And safe-ly His great hand will lead me To the

1 now I am on my way home.
2 guards me each step of the way. Sure-ly good-ness and mer-cy shall
3 man-sions He's gone to pre-pare.

fol-low me All the days, all the days of my life.

Sure-ly good-ness and mer-cy shall fol-low me All the days, all the

FAITH AND HOPE

days of my life. And I shall dwell in the house of the

Lord for - ev - er, And I shall feast at the ta - ble spread for me.

Yesterday, Today, and Tomorrow 438

There are three days—yesterday, today, and tomorrow, Each person in the world lives in one of these three days. Some are living in the present, some in the past, and some in the future. Where we are living with respect to time has a great influence upon our lives.

Those who live in yesterday are living on memories. Yesterday is gone forever. We can never recall it. Other people live in tomorrow. Their joys are the joys of anticipation, not of realization. True, anticipation has its real joys, but we should not picture a tomorrow so bright that it obscures today. We should not exalt tomorrow so much that today loses its meaning.

Our lives are wholly made of todays. Let us live in the time that is ours; make the best of it while we may. Let us enjoy its joys and do its work. Let us live to the full today, giving to the past and to the future only what is justly theirs and only what will profit us in the giving.

Yes, today will pass and tomorrow will come, and when tomorrow comes we shall have tomorrow's strength for its needs. Let us live today, in the strength that God gives, and not permit the shadows of yesterday or forebodings for tomorrow to hide the sunshine and beauty and gladness that come from trust and obedience today.

—Charles Wesley Naylor
from *The Secret of the Singing Heart*
© Copyright 1954 by Warner Press, Inc. Used With Permission.

FAITH AND HOPE

439 Lift Every Voice and Sing

"Come, let us sing for joy to the Lord; let us shout aloud to the Rock of our salvation."—Psalm 95:1

James Weldon Johnson

LIFT EVERY VOICE
J. Rosamond Johnson

1 Lift ev-'ry voice and sing, till earth and heav-en ring,
2 Ston-y the road we trod, bit-ter the chast-'ning rod,
3 God of our wea-ry years, God of our si-lent tears,

1 Ring with the har-mo-nies of lib-er-ty;
2 Felt in the days when hope un-born had died;
3 Thou who hast brought us thus far on the way,

1 Let our re-joic-ing rise, high as the lis-t'ning skies,
2 Yet with a stead-y beat, have not our wea-ry feet
3 Thou who hast by Thy might led us in-to the light,

1 Let it re-sound loud as the roll-ing sea.
2 Come to the place for which our fa-thers sighed?
3 Keep us for-ev-er in the path, we pray.

FAITH AND HOPE

1 Sing a song full of the faith that the dark past has taught us,
2 We have come o - ver a way that with tears has been wa - tered,
3 Lest our feet stray from the plac - es, our God, where we met Thee,

1 Sing a song full of the hope that the pres - ent has brought us;
2 We have come, tread -ing our path thru the blood of the slaugh - tered,
3 Lest our hearts, drunk with the wine of the world, we for - get Thee;

1 Fac - ing the ris - ing sun of our new day be - gun,
2 Out from the gloom - y past, till now we stand at last
3 Shad -owed be - neath Thy hand, May we for - ev - er stand,

1 Let us march on till vic - to - ry is won.
2 Where the white gleam of our bright star is cast.
3 True to our God, true to our na - tive land.

FAITH AND HOPE

440 By Faith and Not by Sight

"We live by faith, not by sight."—II Corinthians 5:7

Clara M. Brooks

NOT BY SIGHT
Andrew L. Byers

1 Fol - low - ing Je - sus from day to day, Gen - tly He leads me a-
2 Seek - ing to en - ter the ho - liest place, Bold - ly I came to the
3 When I was held in af - flic - tion's chain, Suf - fer-ing much from di-
4 Soon I shall has - ten my Lord to meet, And in His like - ness I'll

1 long the way. E'er will I trust Him, all foes de-spite, By
2 throne of grace, Sanc - ti - fied whol - ly, He's my de-light, By
3 sease and pain, Je - sus then touched me and healed me quite, By
4 stand com-plete, Where with the ran - somed in heav - en's light My

1 faith and not by sight.
2 faith and not by sight.
3 faith and not by sight. Walk-ing with Je - sus I'm in the light,
4 faith is lost in sight.

Walk-ing with Je - sus in robes of white, Walk-ing with Je - sus my

HEALING

way   is bright, By faith and not by sight.

Triumphant Living 441

The triumphant life results from courageous action, and courageous action is always based on faith. It has a hopeful outlook. It faces the future with confidence. This is the normal attitude of the Christian. But worry causes heaviness, discouragement, dissatisfaction, despondency, and perhaps despair.

We say God is our Father, that He is taking care of us. We say we have faith in Him. We say we believe God is faithful. Then we act in a way altogether contrary to this faith. If God is our God and if He is taking care of us, if we are safe in His care, if no evil can come to us without His permission, then what are we worrying about? If God really is what He says He is and what we believe He is, we have no reason to worry.

—Charles Wesley Naylor
from *The Secret of the Singing Heart*

442 He Is Just the Same Today

"Jesus Christ is the same yesterday and today and forever."—Hebrews 13:8

Based on Hebrews 13:8
Jacob W. Byers

THE SAME TODAY
Andrew L. Byers

1 Have you ev-er heard of Je-sus, How He came from heav'n to earth
2 Do you see the peo-ple gath-er 'Round that great and ho-ly Man,
3 Is it true that ev-'ry sick-ness May be laid at Je-sus' feet?
4 O that pre-cious, lov-ing Je-sus! His com-pas-sion still the same

1 With a name of might-y vir-tue, Tho' by ver-y hum-ble birth?
2 Bring-ing all the sick and suf-f'ring, Com-ing to Him all who can?
3 All my trou-ble, care, and sor-row, And I rest in joy com-plete?
4 For each sin-ful, suf-f'ring mor-tal Who seeks re-fuge in His name.

1 When the world was held in bond-age Un-der Sa-tan's dis-mal sway,
2 See Him look with great com-pas-sion As they faint-ed by the way!
3 Yes, my friend, in ev-'ry sad-ness, If by faith to Him you pray,
4 Heed the pre-sent in-vi-ta-tion, O you need not stay a-way!

1 Je-sus healed their dread dis-eas-es— He is just the same to-day.
2 How He called them gent-ly to Him! He is just the same to-day.
3 He'll re-move with ten-der mer-cy, For He's just the same to-day.
4 Come, re-ceive His heal-ing fa-vor, For He's just the same to-day.

HEALING

He is just the same to - day,
He is just the same to - day, just the same to - day,

He is just the same to - day (the same to - day);
He is just the same to - day, just the same to - day,

Yes, He healed in Gal - li - lee, Set the suf - f'ring cap - tives free,

And He's just the same to - day. (the same to - day).
And He's just the same, He is just the same to - day.

And He's just the same, the same to - day.

HEALING

443 The Healer

"For he had healed many, so that those with diseases were pushing forward to touch him."—Mark 3:10

Lois Irwin

HEALER
Lois Irwin

1 On the cross cru-ci-fied, in great sor-row He died— The giv-er of
2 Came the lep-er to Christ, say-ing, "Sure-ly I know That Thou, Lord, canst
3 He has healed my sick soul, made me ev-ery whit whole, And He'll do the

1 life was He; Yet my Lord was de-spised and re-ject-ed of
2 make me whole!" When his great faith was seen, Je-sus said, "Yes, I
3 same for you; He's the same yes-ter-day and to-day and for

1 men, This Je-sus of Cal-va-ry.
2 will," And touched him and made him clean. He was wound-ed for
3 aye, This heal-er of all to-day.

our trans-gres-sions, He was bruised for our in-iq-ui-ties;

Sure-ly He bore our sor-rows, And by His stripes we are healed.

HEALING

Rise and Be Healed

444

"Then Peter said, 'Silver or gold I do not have, but what I have I give you. In the name of Jesus Christ of Nazareth, walk.' "—Acts 3:6

RISE

Milton Bourgeois

Milton Bourgeois

Rise and be healed in the name of Je - sus,

Let faith a - rise in your soul;

Rise and be healed in the name of Je - sus,

He will make you ev - ery whit whole.

HEALING

445 He Is Just the Same Today

"Jesus Christ is the same yesterday and today and forever."—Hebrews 13:8

Based on Hebrews 13:8
Jacob W. Byers

8.7.8.7.D.
NETTLETON
John Wyeth

1 Have you ev-er heard of Je-sus, How He came from heav'n to earth
2 Do you see the peo-ple gath-er 'Round that great and ho-ly Man,
3 Is it true that ev-'ry sick-ness May be laid at Je-sus' feet?
4 O that pre-cious, lov-ing Je-sus! His com-pas-sion's still the same

1 With a name of might-y vir-tue, Tho' by ver-y hum-ble birth?
2 Bring-ing all the sick and suf-f'ring, Com-ing to Him all who can?
3 All my trou-ble, care, and sor-row, And I rest in joy com-plete?
4 For each sin-ful, suf-f'ring mor-tal Who seeks re-fuge in His name.

1 When the world was held in bond-age Un-der Sa-tan's dis-mal sway,
2 See Him look with great com-pas-sion As they faint-ed by the way!
3 Yes, my friend, in ev-'ry sad-ness, If by faith to Him you pray,
4 Heed the pre-sent in-vi-ta-tion, O you need not stay a-way!

1 Je-sus healed their dread dis-eas-es— He is just the same to-day.
2 How He called them gent-ly to Him! He is just the same to-day.
3 He'll re-move with ten-der mer-cy, For He's just the same to-day.
4 Come, re-ceive His heal-ing fa-vor, For He's just the same to-day.

HEALING

**Now we know that if the earthly tent we live
in is destroyed, we have a building from
God, an eternal house in heaven, not built by
human hands.**

Meanwhile we groan, longing to be
clothed with our heavenly dwelling,
because when we are clothed, we will
not be found naked.

**For while we are in this tent, we groan and
are burdened, because we do not wish to be
unclothed but to be clothed with our
heavenly dwelling, so that what is mortal
may be swallowed up by life.**

Now it is God who has made us for this
very purpose and has given us the Spirit
as a deposit, guaranteeing what is to
come.

**Therefore we are always confident and know
that as long as we are at home in the body we
are away from the Lord.**

We live by faith, not by sight.

—II Corinthians 5:1–7 (NIV)

447 Draw Me Close to Thee

"I have set the Lord always before me. Because he is at my right hand, I will not be shaken."—Psalm 16:8

Clara M. Brooks

C.M.wR.
DRAW ME CLOSE
W. H. Oldham

1 I would be near-er, my Sav-ior, Where I can hear Thy voice
2 I would be kept in Thy pres-ence, Free from the strife of tongues;
3 Keep me, O Lord, in Thy shad-ow, When the dark tem-pests low'r;
4 Swift-ly the shad-ows are deep-'ning, Light of my life, be near;

1 Fall - ing in ten-der-est whis - pers, Mak - ing my heart re - joice.
2 There shall the hum-ble a - dore Thee, Rais-ing their grate-ful songs.
3 Safe - ly to rest on Thy bos - om, Keep me for - ev - er - more.
4 Strength-en the trust I am keep - ing, Fill me with hope and cheer.

Draw me close to Thee, Draw me close to Thee;
Sav - ior, draw me close to Thee, Sav - ior, draw me close to Thee;

Keep me, dear Sav-ior, so near Thy side, Draw me close to Thee. A - men.

DEVOTION

Aspiration

448

LEADER: To Thee, O Lord, I lift up my soul,
ALL: *O, my God, in Thee I trust,*
LEADER: Let me not be put to shame;
ALL: *Let not my enemies exult over me.*
LEADER: Yea, let none that wait for Thee be put to shame:
ALL: *Let them be ashamed who are wantonly treacherous.*
LEADER: Make me to know Thy ways, O Lord;
ALL: *Teach me Thy paths.*
LEADER: Lead me in Thy truth and teach me,
ALL: *For Thou art the God of my salvation; for Thee I wait all the day long.*
LEADER: Be mindful of Thy mercy, O Lord, and of Thy steadfast love,
ALL: *For they have been from old.*

LEADER: Remember not the sins of my youth, or my transgressions;
ALL: *According to Thy steadfast love remember me for Thy goodness' sake, O Lord!*
LEADER: Good and upright is the Lord.
ALL: *Therefore He instructs sinners in the way.*
LEADER He leads the humble in what is right.
ALL: *And teaches the humble His way.*
LEADER: All the paths of the Lord are steadfast love and faithfulness.
ALL: *For those who keep His covenant and His testimonies.*

—Psalm 25:1–10

Nearer, My God, to Thee 449

"If we live, we live to the Lord; and if we die, we die to the Lord. So, whether we live or die, we belong to the Lord."—Romans 14:8

6.4.6.4.6.6.6.4.

Sarah F. Adams

BETHANY
Lowell Mason

1 Near-er, my God, to Thee, Near-er to Thee! E'en though it
2 Though like the wan-der-er, The sun gone down, Dark-ness be
3 There let the way ap-pear Steps un-to heav'n; All that Thou
4 Then, with my wak-ing thoughts Bright with Thy praise, Out of my
5 Or if on joy-ful wing, Cleav-ing the sky, Sun, moon, and

1 be a cross That rais-eth me; Still all my song shall be, Near-er, my
2 o-ver me, My rest a stone; Yet in my dreams I'd be Near-er, my
3 send-est me In mer-cy giv'n; An-gels to beck-on me Near-er, my
4 ston-y griefs, Beth-el I'll raise; So by my woes to be Near-er, my
5 stars for-got, Up-ward I fly, Still all my song shall be Near-er, my

God to Thee, Near-er, my God, to Thee, Near-er to Thee. A-men.

DEVOTION

450 Near the Cross

"May I never boast except in the cross of our Lord Jesus Christ, through which the world has been crucified to me, and I to the world."—Galatians 6:14

7.6.7.6.wR.

Fanny J. Crosby

NEAR THE CROSS
William H. Doane

1 Je - sus, keep me near the cross— There a pre - cious foun - tain,
2 At the cross I stood one day, Love and mer - cy found me;
3 Near the cross! O Lamb of God, Bring its scenes be - fore me;
4 Near the cross I'll watch and wait, Hop - ing, trust - ing ev - er,

1 Free to all, a heal - ing stream, Flows from Cal - vary's moun - tain.
2 There the Bright and Morn - ing Star Sheds its beams a - round me.
3 Help me walk from day to day With its shad - ow o'er me.
4 'Til I reach the gold - en strand Just be - yond the riv - er.

In the cross, in the cross, Be my glo - ry ev - er,

'Til my rap - tured soul shall find Rest be - yond the riv - er.

DEVOTION

Let Me See Jesus Only

"When they looked up, they saw no one except Jesus."—Matthew 17:8

W. Dale Oldham

JESUS ONLY
W. Dale Oldham

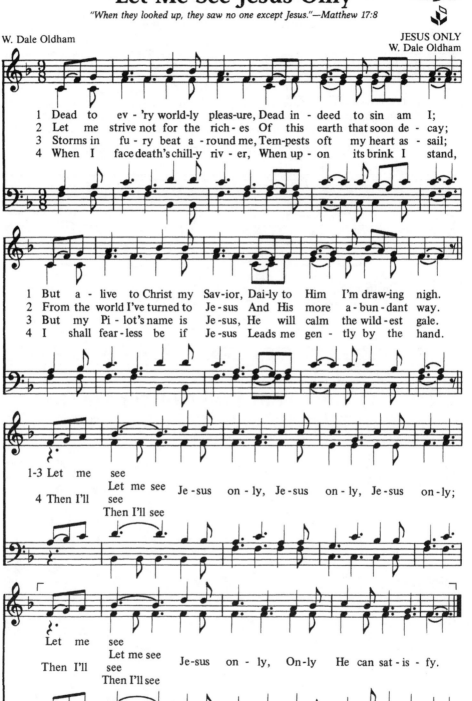

1 Dead to ev - 'ry world-ly pleas-ure, Dead in - deed to sin am I;
2 Let me strive not for the rich - es Of this earth that soon de - cay;
3 Storms in fu - ry beat a - round me, Tem-pests oft my heart as - sail;
4 When I face death's chill-y riv - er, When up - on its brink I stand,

1 But a - live to Christ my Sav-ior, Dai-ly to Him I'm draw-ing nigh.
2 From the world I've turned to Je - sus And His more a - bun - dant way.
3 But my Pi - lot's name is Je - sus, He will calm the wild-est gale.
4 I shall fear-less be if Je - sus Leads me gen - tly by the hand.

1-3 Let me see
Let me see Je - sus on - ly, Je - sus on - ly, Je - sus on - ly;
4 Then I'll see
Then I'll see

Let me see
Let me see
Then I'll see Je - sus on - ly, On - ly He can sat - is - fy.
Then I'll see

DEVOTION

452 Just a Closer Walk with Thee

"But he said to me, 'My grace is sufficient for you, for my power is made perfect in weakness.' "—II Corinthians 12:9

Traditional

CLOSER WALK
Traditional Folk Song

1 I am weak but Thou art strong; Je - sus, keep me from all wrong;
2 Through this world of toil and snares, If I fal - ter, Lord, who cares?
3 When my fee - ble life is o'er, Time for me will be no more;

Refrain: Just a clos - er walk with Thee, Grant, Grant it, Je - sus, is my plea,

D.C. for Refrain

1 I'll be sat - is - fied as long As I walk, let me walk close to Thee.
2 Who with me my bur - den shares? None but Thee, dear Lord, none but Thee.
3 Guide me gen - tly, safe - ly o'er To Thy king-dom shore, to Thy shore.

Ref.: Dai - ly walk-ing close to Thee, Let it be, dear Lord, let it be.

453 O Love That Will Not Let Me Go

"Neither height nor depth, nor anything else in all creation, will be able to separate us from the love of God that is in Christ Jesus our Lord."
—Romans 8:39

George Matheson

8.8.8.8.6.

ST. MARGARET
Albert L. Peace

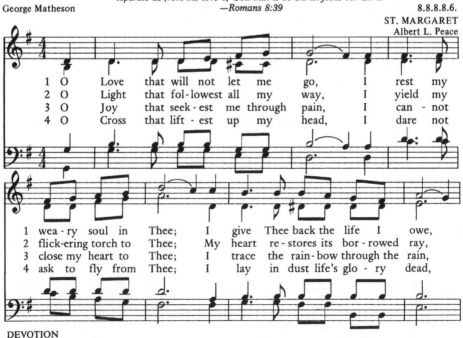

1 O Love that will not let me go, I rest my
2 O Light that fol-lowest all my way, I yield my
3 O Joy that seek - est me through pain, I can - not
4 O Cross that lift - est up my head, I dare not

1 wea - ry soul in Thee; I give Thee back the life I owe,
2 flick-ering torch to Thee; My heart re - stores its bor - rowed ray,
3 close my heart to Thee; I trace the rain-bow through the rain,
4 ask to fly from Thee; I lay in dust life's glo - ry dead,

DEVOTION

1 That in Thine o - cean depths its flow May rich - er, full - er be.
2 That in Thy sun-shine's blaze its day May bright-er, fair - er be.
3 And feel the prom-ise is not vain That morn shall tear - less be.
4 And from the ground there blos-soms red, Life that shall end - less be. A-men.

O for a Closer Walk with God 454

"Rather, clothe yourselves with the Lord Jesus Christ, and do not think about
how to gratify the desires of the sinful nature."—Romans 13:14

C.M.
ST. AGNES
John B. Dykes

William Cowper

1 O for a clos - er walk with God, A calm and heav'n - ly frame,
2 Where is the bless - ed - ness I knew, When first I saw the Lord?
3 The dear-est i - dol I have known, What-e'er that i - dol be,
4 So shall my walk be close with God, Calm and se - rene my frame;

1 A light to shine up - on the road That leads me to the Lamb.
2 Where is the soul - re - fresh-ing view Of Je - sus and His Word?
3 Help me to tear it from Thy throne, And wor-ship on - ly Thee.
4 So pur - er light shall mark the road That leads me to the Lamb.

455   Close to Thee

*"Come near to God and he will come near to you. Wash your hands, you
sinners, and purify your hearts, you double-minded."—James 4:8*

8.7.8.7.6.6.8.7.
CLOSE TO THEE

Fanny J. Crosby

Silas J. Vail

1 Thou, my ev-er-last-ing por-tion, More than friend or life to me,
2 Not for ease or world-ly pleas-ure Nor for fame my prayer shall be;
3 Lead me through the vale of shad-ows, Bear me o'er life's fit-ful sea;

1 All a-long my pil-grim jour-ney, Sav-ior, let me walk with Thee.
2 Glad-ly will I toil and suf-fer, On-ly let me walk with Thee.
3 Then the gate of life e-ter-nal May I en-ter, Lord, with Thee.

1 Close to Thee, close to Thee, Close to Thee, close to Thee; All a-
2 Close to Thee, close to Thee, Close to Thee, close to Thee; Glad-ly
3 Close to Thee, close to Thee, Close to Thee, close to Thee; Then the

1 long my pil-grim jour-ney, Sav-ior, let me walk with Thee.
2 will I toil and suf-fer, On-ly let me walk with Thee.
3 gate of life e-ter-nal May I en-ter, Lord, with Thee.

DEVOTION

I Am Thine, O Lord — 456

*" . . . let us draw near to God with a sincere heart in full assurance of faith,
having our hearts sprinkled to cleanse us from a guilty conscience and having
our bodies washed with pure water."—Hebrews 10:22*

Fanny J. Crosby

10.7.10.7.wR.
I AM THINE
William H. Doane

1. I am Thine, O Lord— I have heard Thy voice, And it
2. Con-se-crate me now to Thy ser-vice, Lord, By the
3. O the pure de-light of a sin-gle hour That be-
4. There are depths of love that I can-not know 'Til I

1. told Thy love to me; But I long to rise in the
2. power of grace di-vine; Let my soul look up with a
3. fore Thy throne I spend, When I kneel in prayer and with
4. cross the nar-row sea; There are heights of joy that I

1. arms of faith And be clos-er drawn to Thee.
2. stead-fast hope, And my will be lost in Thine.
3. Thee, my God, I com-mune as friend with friend.
4. may not reach 'Til I rest in peace with Thee.

Draw me near-er, near-er, bless-ed Lord, To the cross where Thou hast died; Draw me near-er, near-er, near-er, bless-ed Lord, To Thy pre-cious, bleed-ing side.

DEVOTION

457 O, How I Love Jesus

"We love because he first loved us."—I John 4:19

Frederick Whitfield

O HOW I LOVE JESUS
American Melody
Descant by Ralph H. Good Pasteur

1 There is a name I love to hear, I love to sing its worth;
2 It tells me of a Sav-ior's love, Who died to set me free;
3 It tells of One whose lov-ing heart Can feel my deep-est woe,

Descant: To

1 It sounds like mu - sic in my ear, The sweet-est name on earth.
2 It tells me of His pre-cious blood, The sin-ner's per-fect plea.
3 Who in each sor - row bears a part That none can bear be - low.

me, it's won-der-ful, To me, it's won-der-ful! To

O, how I love Je - sus, O, how I love Je - sus,

me, it's won-der-ful To know that Je-sus is mine!

O, how I love Je - sus— Be-cause He first loved me!

DEVOTION

In the Garden

458

" . . . And surely I will be with you always, to the very end of the age."
—Matthew 28:20b

C. Austin Miles

GARDEN
C. Austin Miles

1 I come to the gar-den a-lone, While the dew is still on the
2 He speaks, and the sound of His voice Is so sweet the birds hush their
3 I'd stay in the gar-den with Him Though the night a-round me be

1 ros - es; And the voice I hear, fall-ing on my ear, The
2 sing - ing, And the mel - o-dy that He gave to me With-
3 fall - ing, But He bids me go; through the voice of woe, His

1 Son of God dis - clos - es.
2 in my heart is ring - ing. And He walks with me, and He
3 voice to me is call - ing.

talks with me, And He tells me I am His own; And the

joy we share as we tar - ry there, None oth-er has ev - er known.

DEVOTION

459 I'd Rather Have Jesus

"What is more, I consider everything a loss compared to the surpassing greatness of knowing Christ Jesus my Lord . . . "—Philippians 3:8a

Rhea F. Miller

I'D RATHER HAVE JESUS
George Beverly Shea

1 I'd rath-er have Je-sus than sil-ver or gold, I'd rath-er be
2 I'd rath-er have Je-sus than vain ap - plause, I'd rath-er be
3 He's fair - er than lil-ies of rar-est bloom, He's sweet-er than

1 His than have rich-es un - told; I'd rath-er have Je-sus than
2 faith-ful to His dear cause; I'd rath-er have Je-sus than
3 hon - ey from out the comb; He's all that my hun-ger - ing

1 hous-es or lands, I'd rath-er be led by His nail-pierced hand.
2 world-wide fame, I'd rath-er be true to His ho - ly name.
3 spir - it needs, I'd rath-er have Je-sus and let Him lead.

Than to be the king of a vast do-main Or be held in sin's dread sway;

I'd rath-er have Je-sus than an - y - thing This world af-fords to-day.

DEVOTION

Nearer, Still Nearer

460

*"(For the law made nothing perfect), and a better hope is introduced, by which
we draw near to God."—Hebrews 7:19*

9.10.9.10.
MORRIS
Lelia N. Morris

Lelia N. Morris

1 Near-er, still near-er, close to Thy heart, Draw me, my
2 Near-er, still near-er, noth-ing I bring, Naught as an
3 Near-er, still near-er, while life shall last, 'Til safe in

1 Sav-ior, so pre-cious Thou art; Fold me, O fold me
2 of-fering to Je-sus my King; On-ly my sin-ful,
3 glo-ry my an-chor is cast; Through end-less a-ges,

1 close to Thy breast, Shel-ter me safe in that "Ha-ven of
2 now con-trite heart, Grant me the cleans-ing Thy blood doth im-
3 ev-er to be, Near-er, my Sav-ior, still near-er to

1 Rest," Shel-ter me safe in that "Ha-ven of Rest."
2 part, Grant me the cleans-ing Thy blood doth im-part.
3 Thee, Near-er, my Sav-ior, still near-er to Thee.

DEVOTION

461   I Ought to Love My Savior

"But God demonstrates his own love for us in this: While we were still sinners,
Christ died for us."—Romans 5:8

Daniel S. Warner

7.6.7.6.D.
FISHER
Joseph C. Fisher

1. I ought to love my Savior; He loved me long a-go,
   Looked on my soul with favor, When deep in guilt and woe:
   And though my sin had grieved Him, His Father's law had crossed,
   Love drew Him down from heaven To seek and save the lost,

2. I ought to love my Savior; He bore my sin and shame;
   From glory to the manger On wings of love He came:
   He trod this earth in sorrow, Endured the pains of hell,
   That I should not be banished, But in His glory dwell,

3. I ought to love my Savior; He pardoned all my sin,
   Then sanctified my nature, And keeps me pure within:
   He fills me with His glory, And bears my soul above;
   This world, O wondrous story! 'Tis love, redeeming love,

4. O Christ, I can but love Thee: What heart could e'er withhold
   A love that cost so dearly The off'ring of Thy soul?
   O King of love immortal, Reign in my heart alone,
   And flood this earthen temple With glory from Thy throne,

DEVOTION

1 Love drew him down from heav - en   To   seek and save the lost.
2 That I should not be ban -ished, But   in His glo - ry dwell.
3 This world, O   won-drous sto - ry! 'Tis love, re - deem-ing love!
4 And flood this earth - en tem - ple With   glo - ry from Thy throne. A-men.

Open Our Eyes, Lord

462

"Blessed are the pure in heart, for they will see God."—Matthew 5:8

Robert Cull

OPEN OUR EYES
Robert Cull

1 O - pen our   eyes,   Lord,   we want to see Je - sus,
2 O - pen our   ears,   Lord,   and help us to lis - ten.

1.

1   to   reach out and   touch   Him,   and say that we love
2   O - pen our   eyes,

2.

Him.   Lord,   we want to see Je - sus.

DEVOTION

463 The Greatest Thing

" . . . 'Love the Lord your God with all your heart, and with all your soul, and with all your mind.' "—Matthew 22:37b

Mark Pendergrass

THE GREATEST THING
Mark Pendergrass

1 The great-est thing in all my life is know-ing You;
2 The great-est thing in all my life is lov-ing You;
3 The great-est thing in all my life is serv-ing You;

1 The great-est thing in all my life is know-ing You;
2 The great-est thing in all my life is lov-ing You;
3 The great-est thing in all my life is serv-ing You;

1 I want to know You more, I want to know You more;
2 I want to love You more, I want to love You more;
3 I want to serve You more, I want to serve You more;

1 The great-est thing in all my life is know-ing You.
2 The great-est thing in all my life is lov-ing You.
3 The great-est thing in all my life is serv-ing You.

DEVOTION

My Jesus, I Love Thee

464

"I love the Lord, for he heard my voice; he heard my cry for mercy."
—Psalm 116:1

11.11.11.11.
GORDON
Adoniram J. Gordon

William R. Featherstone

1 My Je - sus, I love Thee, I know Thou art mine; For Thee all the
2 I love Thee be - cause Thou hast first lov - ed me, And pur-chased my
3 I'll love Thee in life, I will love Thee in death, And praise Thee as
4 In man-sions of glo - ry and end - less de - light, I'll ev - er a-

1 fol - lies of sin I re - sign; My gra - cious Re - deem - er, my
2 par - don on Cal - va - ry's tree; I love Thee for wear - ing the
3 long as Thou lend - est me breath; And say when the death - dew lies
4 dore Thee in heav - en so bright; I'll sing with the glit - ter - ing

1 Sav - ior art Thou: If ev - er I loved Thee, my Je - sus, 'tis now.
2 thorns on Thy brow: If ev - er I loved Thee, my Je - sus, 'tis now.
3 cold on my brow: If ev - er I loved Thee, my Je - sus, 'tis now.
4 crown on my brow: If ev - er I loved Thee, my Je - sus, 'tis now.

DEVOTION

465 Jesus, Thou Joy of Loving Hearts

"I have told you this so that my joy may be in you and that your joy may be complete."—John 15:11

Attr. to Bernard of Clairvaux
Tr. by Ray Palmer

L.M.
QUEBEC
Henry Baker

1 Je - sus, Thou joy of lov - ing hearts, Thou fount of life, light all can see, From the best bliss that earth im-parts We turn un - filled a - gain to Thee.

2 Thy truth un - changed hath ev - er stood, Thou sav - est those that on Thee call; To them that seek Thee, Thou art good, To them that find Thee, all in all.

3 We taste Thee, O Thou liv - ing Bread, And long to feast up - on Thee still; We drink of Thee, the Foun - tain-head, And thirst our souls from Thee to fill.

4 Our rest - less spir - its yearn for Thee, Wher - e'er our change - ful lot is cast, Glad when Thy gra - cious smile we see, Blest when our faith can hold Thee fast.

5 O Je - sus, ev - er with us stay, Make all our mo - ments calm and bright; Chase the dark night of sin a - way, Shed o'er the world Thy ho - ly light. A - men.

466 Jesus, the Very Thought of Thee

"Consider him who endured such opposition from sinful men, so that you will not grow weary and lose heart."—Hebrews 12:3

Latin: 12th Century
Tr. by Edward Caswall

C.M.
ST. AGNES
John B. Dykes

1 Je - sus, the ver - y thought of Thee With sweet-ness fills my breast;

2 No voice can sing, no heart can frame, Nor can the mem-ory find

3 O hope of ev - ery con - trite heart, O joy of all the meek,

4 But what to those who find? Ah, this No tongue or pen can show;

5 Je - sus, our on - ly joy be Thou, As Thou our prize will be;

DEVOTION

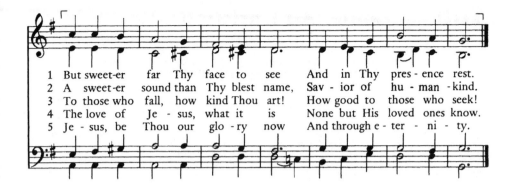

1 But sweet-er far Thy face to see And in Thy pres - ence rest.
2 A sweet-er sound than Thy blest name, Sav - ior of hu - man - kind.
3 To those who fall, how kind Thou art! How good to those who seek!
4 The love of Je - sus, what it is None but His loved ones know.
5 Je - sus, be Thou our glo - ry now And through e - ter - ni - ty.

More Love to Thee, O Christ 467

*"And this is my prayer: that your love may abound more and more in
knowledge and depth of insight."—Philippians 1:9*

6.4.6.4.6.6.4.4.

Elizabeth P. Prentiss

MORE LOVE TO THEE
William H. Doane

1 More love to Thee, O Christ, More love to Thee! Hear Thou the
2 Once earth-ly joy I craved, Sought peace and rest; Now Thee a-
3 Then shall my ev - ery breath Sing out Your praise; This be the

1 prayer I make On bend - ed knee; This is my ear - nest plea:
2 lone I seek, Give what is best; This all my prayer shall be:
3 on - ly song My heart shall raise; This still my prayer shall be:

More love, O Christ, to Thee, More love to Thee, More love to Thee!

DEVOTION

468 Come, All Christians, Be Committed

"Therefore, I urge you, brothers, in view of God's mercy, to offer your bodies as living sacrifices, holy and pleasing to God—which is your spiritual worship."
—Romans 12:1

Eva B. Lloyd

8.7.8.7.D.
BEACH SPRING
"The Sacred Harp"
Arr. by James H. Wood

Unison

1. Come, all Chris-tians, be com-mit-ted To the ser-vice of the Lord.
2. Of your time and tal-ents give ye, They are gifts from God a-bove,
3. God's com-mand to love each oth-er Is re-quired of ev-'ry one.
4. Come in praise and ad-o-ra-tion, All who on Christ's name be-lieve.

1. Make your lives for Him more fit-ted, Tune your hearts with one ac-cord.
2. To be used by Chris-tians free-ly To pro-claim His won-drous love.
3. Show-ing mer-cy to an-oth-er Mir-rors His re-demp-tive plan.
4. Wor-ship Him with con-se-cra-tion, Grace and love will you re-ceive.

1. Come in-to His courts with glad-ness, Each his sa-cred vows re-new.
2. Come a-gain to serve the Sav-ior, Tithes and of-f'rings with you bring.
3. In com-pas-sion He has giv-en Of His love that is di-vine;
4. For His grace give Him the glo-ry, For the Spir-it and the Word,

1. Turn a-way from sin and sad-ness, Be trans-formed with life a-new.
2. In your work, with Him find fa-vor, And with joy His prais-es sing.
3. On the cross sins were for-giv-en; Joy and peace are ful-ly thine.
4. And re-peat the gos-pel sto-ry Un-til all His name have heard.

DEDICATION AND COMMITMENT

Have Thine Own Way, Lord 469

"Yet, O Lord, you are our Father. We are the clay, you are the potter; we are all the work of your hand."—Isaiah 64:8

Adelaide A. Pollard

5.4.5.4.D.
ADELAIDE
George C. Stebbins

1 Have Thine own way, Lord! Have Thine own way!
2 Have Thine own way, Lord! Have Thine own way!
3 Have Thine own way, Lord! Have Thine own way!
4 Have Thine own way, Lord! Have Thine own way!

1 Thou art the pot - ter, I am the clay!
2 Search me and try me, Mas - ter, to - day!
3 Wound - ed and wea - ry, Help me, I pray!
4 Hold o'er my be - ing Ab - so - lute sway!

1 Mold me and make me Aft - er Thy will,
2 Cleanse me from sin, Lord, Wash me just now,
3 Pow - er— all pow - er— Sure - ly is Thine!
4 Fill with Thy Spir - it 'Til all shall see

1 While I am wait - ing, Yield - ed and still.
2 As in Thy pres - ence Hum - bly I bow.
3 Touch me and heal me, Sav - ior di - vine!
4 Christ on - ly, al - ways, Liv - ing in me! A - men.

470

Take My Life
and Let It Be Consecrated

"Now, who is willing to consecrate himself today to the Lord?"
—I Chronicles 29:5b

7.7.7.7.wRPT.

Frances R. Havergal

HENDON
Henri A. César Malan

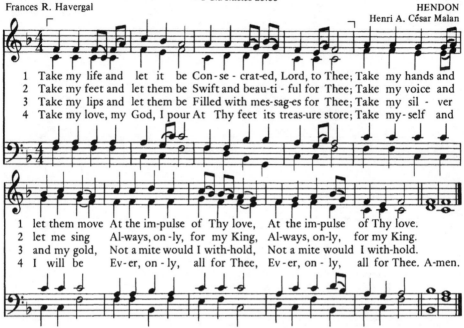

1 Take my life and let it be Con-se-crat-ed, Lord, to Thee; Take my hands and
2 Take my feet and let them be Swift and beau-ti-ful for Thee; Take my voice and
3 Take my lips and let them be Filled with mes-sag-es for Thee; Take my sil - ver
4 Take my love, my God, I pour At Thy feet its treas-ure store; Take my-self and

1 let them move At the im-pulse of Thy love, At the im-pulse of Thy love.
2 let me sing Al-ways, on-ly, for my King, Al-ways, on-ly, for my King.
3 and my gold, Not a mite would I with-hold, Not a mite would I with-hold.
4 I will be Ev-er, on-ly, all for Thee, Ev-er, on-ly, all for Thee. A-men.

471

Is Your All on the Altar?

"You see that a person is justified by what he does and not by faith alone."
—James 2:24

Elisha A. Hoffman

ALL ON THE ALTAR
Elisha A. Hoffman

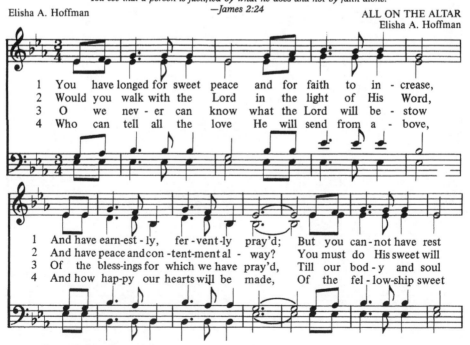

1 You have longed for sweet peace and for faith to in - crease,
2 Would you walk with the Lord in the light of His Word,
3 O we nev - er can know what the Lord will be - stow
4 Who can tell all the love He will send from a - bove,

1 And have earn-est-ly, fer-vent-ly pray'd; But you can-not have rest
2 And have peace and con-tent-ment al - way? You must do His sweet will
3 Of the bless-ings for which we have pray'd, Till our bod-y and soul
4 And how hap-py our hearts will be made, Of the fel-low-ship sweet

DEDICATION AND COMMITMENT

1 or be per-fect-ly blest Un-til all on the al-tar is laid.
2 to be free from all ill, On the al-tar your all you must lay.
3 He doth ful-ly con-trol, And our all on the al-tar is laid.
4 we shall share at His feet, When our all on the al-tar is laid?

Is your all on the al-tar of sac-ri-fice laid?

Your heart does the Spir-it con-trol? You will sure-ly be blest

and have peace and sweet rest, As you yield Him your bod-y and soul.

DEDICATION AND COMMITMENT

472 His Way with Thee

"For God did not call us to be impure, but to live a holy life."
—I Thessalonians 4:7

Cyrus S. Nusbaum

HIS WAY
Cyrus S. Nusbaum

1 Would you live for Je - sus and be al - ways pure and good?
2 Would you have Him make you free, and fol - low at His call?
3 Would you in His king - dom find a place of con - stant rest?

1 Would you walk with Him with - in the nar - row road? Would you have Him
2 Would you know the peace that comes by giv - ing all? Would you have Him
3 Would you prove Him true in prov - i - den - tial test? Would you in His

1 bear your bur - den, car - ry all your load? Let Him have His way with thee.
2 save you, so that you need nev - er fall? Let Him have His way with thee.
3 serv - ice la - bor al - ways at your best? Let Him have His way with thee.

His pow'r can make you what you ought to be; His

blood can cleanse your heart and make you free; His love can fill your soul, and

you will see 'Twas best for Him to have His way with thee.

Where He Leads Me 473

"My sheep listen to my voice; I know them, and they follow me."—John 10:27

E. W. Blandy

8.8.8.9.wR.
NORRIS
John S. Norris

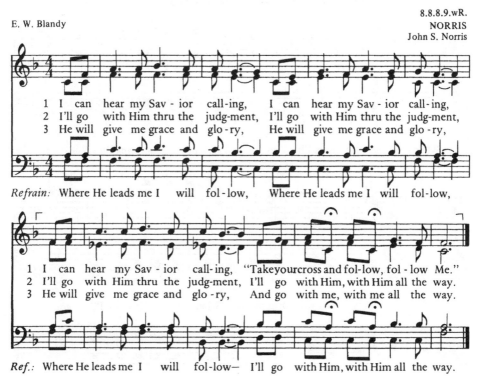

1 I can hear my Sav - ior call - ing, I can hear my Sav - ior call - ing,
2 I'll go with Him thru the judg-ment, I'll go with Him thru the judg-ment,
3 He will give me grace and glo - ry, He will give me grace and glo - ry,

Refrain: Where He leads me I will fol-low, Where He leads me I will fol-low,

1 I can hear my Sav - ior call - ing, "Take your cross and fol-low, fol - low Me."
2 I'll go with Him thru the judg-ment, I'll go with Him, with Him all the way.
3 He will give me grace and glo - ry, And go with me, with me all the way.

Ref.: Where He leads me I will fol-low— I'll go with Him, with Him all the way.

DEDICATION AND COMMITMENT

474 Wherever He Leads I'll Go

"If anyone would come after me, he must deny himself and take up his cross daily and follow me."—Luke 9:23b

B. B. McKinney

8.6.8.7.wR.
FALLS CREEK
B. B. McKinney

1 "Take up thy cross and fol-low me," I heard my Mas-ter say;
2 He drew me clos-er to His side, I sought His will to know,
3 It may be through the shad-ows dim, Or o'er the storm-y sea,
4 My heart, my life, my all I bring To Christ who loves me so;

1 "I gave My life to ran-som thee, Sur-ren-der your all to-day."
2 And in that will I now a-bide, Wher-ev-er He leads I'll go.
3 I take my cross and fol-low Him, Wher-ev-er He lead-eth me.
4 He is my Mas-ter, Lord, and King, Wher-ev-er He leads I'll go.

Wher-ev-er He leads I'll go, Wher-ev-er He leads I'll go,

I'll fol-low my Christ who loves me so, Wher-ev-er He leads I'll go.

DEDICATION AND COMMITMENT

Consecration

" . . . Now, who is willing to consecrate himself today to the Lord?"
—I Chronicles 29:5b

475

Mildred E. Howard

C.M.wR.
CONSECRATION
Andrew L. Byers

1 Since Je-sus gave His life for me Should I not give Him mine?
2 I care not where my Lord di-rects, His pur-pose I'll ful-fill;
3 My home and friends are dear to me, Yet He is dear-er still;
4 My all, O Lord, to Thee I give, Ac-cept it as Thine own;

1 I'm con-se-crat-ed, Lord, to Thee, I shall be whol-ly Thine.
2 I know He ev-'ry one pro-tects Who does His ho-ly will.
3 In my af-fec-tion first He'll be, And first His right-eous will.
4 For Thee a-lone I'll ev-er live, My heart shall be Thy throne.

My life, O Lord, I give to Thee, My tal-ents, time and all; I'll

serve Thee, Lord, and faith-ful be, I'll hear Thy faint-est call. A-men.

DEDICATION AND COMMITMENT

476

My Heart Says Amen

"Yet, not as I will, but as you will."—Matthew 26:39c

Charles W. Naylor

MY HEART SAYS AMEN
Clarence E. Hunter

1 I have yield-ed my-self to Thy serv-ice, And Thy pres-ence my
2 All the heart-ties of earth may be sun-dered, So that I may Thy
3 Tho my plans and my hopes may seem blight-ed, I will love Thee and
4 When I pass to that heav-en-ly coun-try, And my soul with its

1 soul Thou doth fill; O my Sav-ior, I haste to o-bey Thee, And my
2 pur-pose ful-fill; Help me glad-ly sub-mit and not mur-mur, Ev-er
3 trust in Thee still, For I know all is well that Thou do-est, And my
4 glo-ry doth thrill, This for-ev-er shall be my re-joic-ing, That my

1 heart says a-men to Thy will.
2 say-ing a-men to Thy will.
3 heart says a-men to Thy will.
4 heart said a-men to Thy will.

Yes, my heart says a-men to Thy

will, Lord, And I know that Thou lov-est me still, While I bow low in

478 Holiness unto the Lord

" . . . and put on the new self, which in the likeness of god has been created in righteousness and holiness of the truth."—Ephesians 4:24

Lelia N. Morris

HOLINESS UNTO THE LORD
Lelia N. Morris

1 "Called un-to ho-li-ness," church of our God, Pur-chase of
2 "Called un-to ho-li-ness," chil-dren of light, Walk-ing with
3 "Called un-to ho-li-ness," praise His dear name! This bless-ed
4 "Called un-to ho-li-ness," Bride of the Lamb, Wait-ing the

1 Je - sus, re-deemed by His blood; Called from the world and its
2 Je - sus in gar-ments of white; Rai-ment un-sul-lied, nor
3 se - cret to faith now made plain: Not our own right-eous-ness,
4 Bride-groom's re-turn-ing a-gain! Lift up your heads, for the

1 i - dols to flee, Called from the bond-age of sin to be free.
2 tar - nished with sin; God's Ho-ly Spir-it a-bid-ing with-in.
3 but Christ with-in, Liv-ing, and reign-ing, and sav-ing from sin.
4 day draw-eth near When in His beau-ty the King shall ap-pear.

SANCTIFICATION AND HOLINESS

hum - ble sub - mis - sion, And my heart says a-men to Thy will.

Dear Lord and Father of Mankind 477

"After the earthquake came a fire, but the Lord was not in the fire. And after the fire came a gentle whisper."—I Kings 19:12

John Greenleaf Whittier

8.6.8.8.6.
REST
Frederick C. Maker

1 Dear Lord and Fa - ther of man - kind, For - give our fool - ish ways!
2 In sim - ple trust like theirs who heard, Be - side the Syr - ian sea,
3 O sab - bath rest by Gal - i - lee! O calm of hills a - bove!
4 Drop Thy still dews of qui - et - ness 'Til all our striv - ings cease;
5 Breathe through the heat of our de - sire Thy cool - ness and Thy balm;

1 Re - clothe us in our right - ful mind; In pur - er lives Thy
2 The gra - cious call - ing of the Lord, Let us, like them, with-
3 Where Je - sus knelt to share with Thee The si - lence of e -
4 Take from our souls the strain and stress, And let our or - dered
5 Let sense be dumb, let flesh re - tire; Speak through the earth-quake,

1 serv - ice find, In deep - er rev - erence, praise.
2 out a word, Rise up and fol - low Thee.
3 ter - ni - ty, In - ter - pret - ed by love.
4 lives con - fess The beau - ty of Thy peace.
5 wind, and fire, O still, small voice of calm. A - men.

"Ho - li - ness un-to the Lord" is our watch - word and song,

"Ho - li - ness un - to the Lord" as we're march - ing a - long.

Sing it, shout it, loud and long.
"Ho - li - ness un - to the Lord," Sing, "Ho - li - ness un - to the Lord,"

"Ho - li - ness un - to the Lord" now and for - ev - er!

479 Higher Ground

"I press on toward the goal to win the prize for which God has called me heavenward in Christ Jesus."—Philippians 3:14

Johnson Oatman, Jr.

L.M.wR.
HIGHER GROUND
Charles H. Gabriel

1 I'm press-ing on the up-ward way, New heights I'm gain - ing ev - ery
2 My heart has no de-sire to stay Where doubts a - rise and fears dis-
3 I want to live a-bove the world, Though Sa - tan's darts at me are
4 I want to scale the ut-most height And catch a gleam of glo - ry

1 day; Still pray - ing as I'm on - ward bound, "Lord, plant my
2 may; Though some may dwell where these a - bound, My prayer, my
3 hurled; For faith has caught the joy - ful sound, The song of
4 bright; But still I'll pray, 'til heaven I've found, "Lord, lead me

1 feet on high - er ground."
2 aim is high - er ground.
3 saints on high - er ground.
4 on to high - er ground."

Lord, lift me up and let me

stand By faith on heav - en's ta - ble - land, A high - er

plane than I have found: Lord, plant my feet on high - er ground.

SANCTIFICATION AND HOLINESS

Are You Adorning the Doctrine?

480

" 'Sir,' they said, 'we would like to see Jesus.' "—John 12:21b

Charles W. Naylor

ADORNING THE DOCTRINE
Andrew L. Byers

1 Are you a-dorn-ing the doc-trine, The glo-ri-ous doc-trine of God,
2 Are you a-dorn-ing the doc-trine, And mak-ing at-trac-tive the way,
3 Are you a-dorn-ing the doc-trine, By meek-ness and love and good-will,
4 If you're a-dorn-ing the doc-trine, Its beau-ties your soul will ar-ray;

1 Walk-ing so ho-ly be-fore Him, Fol-low-ing where He has trod,
2 Hon-or-ing Christ by your ac-tions And by the words that you say?
3 Gen-tle-ness, pa-tience and true-ness, Lib-er-ty's law to ful-fill?
4 Show-ers of grace will be giv-en— Strength from the Lord as your day:

1 So when the world looks up-on you Noth-ing but Christ is in view?
2 Are you, my broth-er and sis-ter, Prov-ing the Bi-ble is true?
3 Je-sus will shine if with-in you, Show-ing these grac-es di-vine.
4 Light from on high will be stream-ing O-ver the path-way you tread,

1 So when the world looks up-on you Noth-ing but Christ is in view?
2 Are you, my broth-er and sis-ter, Prov-ing the Bi-ble is true?
3 Je-sus will shine if with-in you, Show-ing these grac-es di-vine.
4 Light from on high will be stream-ing O-ver the path-way you tread.

SANCTIFICATION AND HOLINESS

481 The Kingdom of Peace

"For the kingdom of God is not a matter of eating and drinking, but of righteousness, peace and joy in the Holy Spirit."—Romans 14:17

Barney E. Warren

KINGDOM OF PEACE
Barney E. Warren

1 There's a theme that is sweet to my mem'ry, There's a joy that I
2 There's a scene of its grand-ness be - fore me, Of its great-ness there
3 I am lost in its splen-dor and beau-ty, To its ne'er- fad - ing
4 What a pleas-ure in life it is bring-ing! What as-sur-ance and

1 can - not ex - press, There's a treas-ure that glad-dens my be-ing, 'Tis the
2 can be no end; It is joy, it is peace, it is glo-ry, In my
3 heights I would rise, Till I see the King come to re - ceive me, And ex -
4 hope ev - er bright! O what rap-ture and bliss are a - wait-ing, When our

1 king - dom of God's right-eous - ness.
2 heart, how these rich - es do blend!
3 plore it with Him in the skies.
4 faith shall be lost in the sight!

'Tis a king-dom of peace, it is

reign-ing with-in, It shall ev-er in-crease in my soul; We pos-sess it right

here when He saves from all sin, And 'twill last while the a-ges shall roll.

Take Time to Be Holy 482

"But solid food is for the mature, who by constant use have trained themselves
to distinguish good from evil."—Hebrews 5:14

William D. Longstaff

6.5.6.5.D.
LONGSTAFF
George C. Stebbins

1 Take time to be ho-ly, Speak of-ten with God; Find rest in Him
2 Take time to be ho-ly, The world rush-es on; Spend much time in
3 Take time to be ho-ly, Let Him be your guide, And run not be-

1 al-ways, And feed on His Word. Make friends of God's chil-dren, Help
2 se-cret With Je-sus a-lone. By look-ing to Je-sus, Like
3 fore Him, What-ev-er be-tide. In joy or in sor-row, Still

1 those who are weak, For-get-ting in noth-ing His bless-ing to seek.
2 Him you shall be; Your friends in your con-duct His like-ness shall see.
3 fol-low your Lord, And, look-ing to Je-sus, Still trust in His word.

483 Let the Fire Fall on Me

" . . . but if by the Spirit you put to death the misdeeds of the body, you will live . . . "—Romans 8:13b

William J. Henry

LET THE FIRE FALL
William J. Henry

1 Lord, I would be whol-ly Thine, I would do Thy will di-vine, From the
2 I would have suf-fi-cient grace Ev-'ry foe to brave-ly face, And an
3 Ho-ly Spir-it from a-bove, Fill my long-ing soul with love, Till the
4 In the king-dom I would stay, There to la-bor night and day, An-y

1 world and sin and self I would be free; On the al-tar now I lie, And with
2 o-ver-com-er ev-er-more to be; That I well may fill my place, And that
3 Mas-ter's im-age all in me may see; Make me gen-tle, true and kind, Meek of
4 way and an-y-where Thy will may be; But that I may do my best, And that

1 all my heart I cry, Let the ho-ly fire from heav-en fall on me.
2 I may win the race, Let the ho-ly fire from heav-en fall on me.
3 heart and hum-ble mind, Let the ho-ly fire from heav-en fall on me.
4 oth-ers may be blest, Let the ho-ly fire from heav-en fall on me.

D.S. ho-ly fire from heav-en fall on me.

Fine

Let the fire fall on me, Let the fire fall on me;
Let the fire fall on me, Let the fire fall on me;

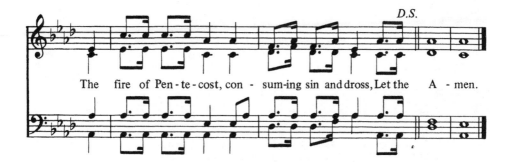

The fire of Pen-te-cost, con-sum-ing sin and dross, Let the   A-men.

Sanctification   484

Count yourselves dead to sin but alive to
God in Christ Jesus.

**Therefore do not let sin reign in your
mortal body so that you obey its evil
desires.**

Do not offer the parts of your body to sin,
as instruments of wickedness, but rather
offer yourselves to God, as those who
have been brought from death to life; and
offer the parts of your body to Him as
instruments of righteousness.

**For sin shall not be your master,
because you are not under law, but
under grace.**

Just as you used to offer the parts of your
body to slavery to impurity and to ever-
increasing wickedness, so now offer them
in slavery to righteousness leading to
holiness.

**When you were slaves to sin, you
were free from the control of
righteousness.**

What benefit did you reap at that time
from the things you are now ashamed of?
Those things result in death!

**But now that you have been set free
from sin and have become slaves to
God, the benefit you reap leads to
holiness, and the result is eternal life.**

So I say, live by the Spirit, and you will
not gratify the desires of the sinful nature.

**For the sinful nature desires what is
contrary to the Spirit, and the Spirit
what is contrary to the sinful nature.
They are in conflict with each other,
so that you do not do what you want.**

But if you are led by the Spirit, you are
not under law.

**The acts of the sinful nature are
obvious: sexual immorality, impurity
and debauchery;**

Idolatry and witchcraft; hatred, discord,
jealousy, fits of rage, selfish ambition,
dissensions, factions and envy;
drunkenness, orgies, and the like.

**I warn you, as I did before, that those
who live like this will not inherit the
kingdom of God.**

But the fruit of the Spirit is love, joy,
peace, patience, kindness, goodness,
faithfulness,

**Gentleness and self-control. Against
such things there is no law.**

Those who belong to Christ Jesus have
crucified the sinful nature with its passions
and desires.

**Since we live by the Spirit, let us keep
in step with the Spirit.**

*—Rom. 6:11-14, 19-22;
Gal. 5:16-25 (NIV)*

485 River of Peace

"There is a river whose streams make glad the city of God . . . "—Psalm 46:4a

Daniel S. Warner

L.M.wR.
RIVER OF PEACE
Barney E. Warren

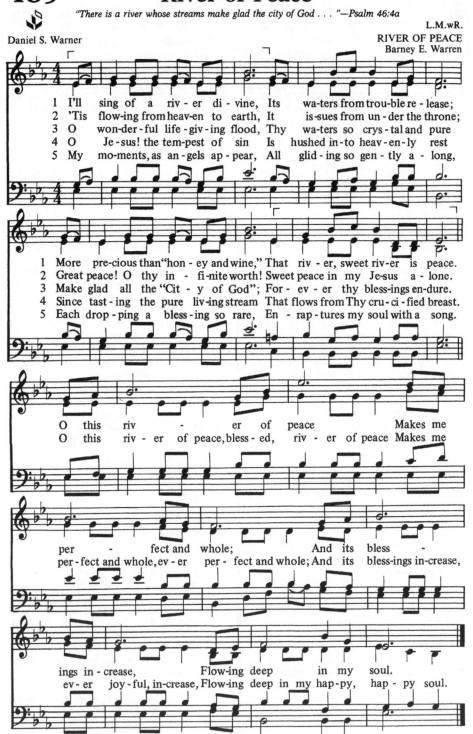

1 I'll sing of a riv-er di-vine, Its wa-ters from trou-ble re-lease;
2 'Tis flow-ing from heav-en to earth, It is-sues from un-der the throne;
3 O won-der-ful life-giv-ing flood, Thy wa-ters so crys-tal and pure
4 O Je-sus! the tem-pest of sin Is hushed in-to heav-en-ly rest
5 My mo-ments, as an-gels ap-pear, All glid-ing so gen-tly a-long,

1 More pre-cious than "hon-ey and wine," That riv-er, sweet riv-er is peace.
2 Great peace! O thy in-fi-nite worth! Sweet peace in my Je-sus a-lone.
3 Make glad all the "Cit-y of God"; For-ev-er thy bless-ings en-dure.
4 Since tast-ing the pure liv-ing stream That flows from Thy cru-ci-fied breast.
5 Each drop-ping a bless-ing so rare, En-rap-tures my soul with a song.

O this riv - er of peace Makes me
O this riv-er of peace, bless-ed, riv-er of peace Makes me

per - fect and whole; And its bless -
per-fect and whole, ev-er per-fect and whole; And its bless-ings in-crease,

ings in-crease, Flow-ing deep in my soul.
ev-er joy-ful, in-crease, Flow-ing deep in my hap-py, hap-py soul.

SANCTIFICATION AND HOLINESS

He gave some as apostles, and some as prophets, and some as evangelists, and some as pastors and teachers, for the equipping of the saints, for the work of service, to the building up of the body of Christ;

> **Until we all attain to the unity of the faith, and of the knowledge of the Son of God, to a mature man, to the measure of the stature which belongs to the fulness of Christ.**

As a result, we are no longer to be children, tossed here and there by waves, and carried about by every wind of doctrine, by the trickery of men, by craftiness in deceitful scheming;

> **But speaking the truth in love, we are to grow up in all aspects into Him, who is the head, even Christ, from whom the whole body, being fitted and held together by that which every joint supplies, according to the proper working of each individual part, causes the growth of the body for the building up of itself in love.**

Though by this time you ought to be teachers, you have need again for someone to teach you the elementary principles of the oracles of God, and you have come to need milk and not solid food.

> **For everyone who partakes only of milk is not accustomed to the word of righteousness, for he is a babe.**

But solid food is for the mature, who because of practice have their senses trained to discern good and evil.

> **Therefore leaving the elementary teaching about the Christ, let us press on to maturity.**

—*Eph. 4:11–16; Heb. 5:12–6:1 (NASB)*

487 "Are Ye Able," Said the Master

"Are you able to drink the cup that I am to drink?"—Matthew 20:22c

Based on Mark 10:35-40
Earl B. Marlatt

8.7.8.7.wR.
BEACON HILL
Harry S. Mason

1 "Are ye a-ble," said the Mas-ter, "To be cru-ci-fied with Me?"
2 "Are ye a-ble" to re-mem-ber, When a thief lifts up his eyes,
3 "Are ye a-ble?" still the Mas-ter Whis-pers down e-ter-ni-ty,

1 "Yea," the stur-dy dream-ers an-swered, "To the death we fol-low Thee:"
2 That his par-doned soul is wor-thy Of a place in par-a-dise?
3 And he-ro-ic spir-its an-swer, Now, as then in Gal-i-lee:

"Lord, we are a-ble"—our spir-its are Thine; Re-mold them—

make us like Thee, di-vine. Thy guid-ing ra-diance a-

bove us shall be A bea-con to God, to love and loy-al-ty.

DISCIPLESHIP: GROWING IN THE LIKENESS OF CHRIST

Abiding in Christ

I am the true vine and my Father is the gardener.

He cuts off every branch in me that bears no
fruit, while every branch that does bear fruit he
trims clean so that it will be even more fruitful.

**You are already clean because of the word I have
spoken to you.**

Remain in me and I will remain in you. No
branch can bear fruit by itself; it must remain in
the vine. Neither can you bear fruit unless you
remain in me.

**I am the vine; you are the branches. If a man
remains in me and I in him, he will bear much fruit;
apart from me you can do nothing.**

If anyone does not remain in me, he is like a
branch that is thrown away and withers; such
branches are picked up, thrown into the fire
and burned.

**If you remain in me and my words remain in you,
ask whatever you wish, and it will be given you.**

This is to my Father's glory, that you bear
much fruit, showing yourselves to be my
disciples.

**As the Father has loved me, so have I loved you.
Now remain in my love.**

If you obey my commands, you will remain in
my love, just as I have obeyed my Father's
commands and remain in his love.

**I have told you this so that my joy may be in you
and that your joy may be complete. My command is
this: Love each other as I have loved you.**

Greater love has no one than this, that one lay
down his life for his friends.

You are my friends if you do what I command.

I no longer call you servants, because a servant
does not know his master's business. Instead I
have called you friends, for everything that I
learned from my Father I have made known
to you.

**You did not choose me, but I chose you to go and
bear fruit—fruit that will last. Then the Father will
give you whatever you ask in my name.**

This is my command: Love each other.

—John 15:1–17

489 O to Be Like Thee!

"My dear children, for whom I am again in the pains of childbirth until Christ is formed in you."—Galatians 4:19

10.9.10.9. wR.

Thomas O. Chisholm

RONDINELLA
William J. Kirkpatrick

1 O to be like Thee! Bless-ed Re - deem - er, This is my con - stant
2 O to be like Thee! Full of com - pas - sion, Lov-ing, for - giv - ing,
3 O to be like Thee! Low - ly in spir - it, Ho - ly and harm - less,
4 O to be like Thee! Lord, I am com - ing, Now to re - ceive th'a-
5 O to be like Thee! While I am plead-ing, Pour out Thy Spir - it,

1 long-ing and prayer; Glad-ly I'll for - feit all of earth's treas - ures,
2 ten - der and kind, Help-ing the help - less, cheer-ing the faint - ing,
3 pa - tient and brave; Meek-ly en - dur - ing cru - el re - proach - es,
4 noint-ing di - vine; All that I am and have I am bring - ing.
5 fill with Thy love; Make me a tem - ple deemed to re - ceive You:

1 Je - sus, Thy per - fect like-ness to wear.
2 Seek-ing the wan-dering sin - ner to find!
3 Will - ing to suf - fer oth-ers to save. O to be like Thee!
4 Lord, from this mo - ment all shall be Thine.
5 Fit me for life and heav-en a - bove.

O to be like Thee, Bless-ed Re - deem - er, pure as Thou art! Come in Thy

DISCIPLESHIP: GROWING IN THE LIKENESS OF CHRIST

sweet - ness, come in Thy full - ness; Stamp Thine own im - age deep on my heart.

Imitating Christ 490

If you have any encouragement from being united with Christ, if any comfort from his love, if any fellowship with the Spirit, if any tenderness and compassion, then make my joy complete by being like-minded, having the same love, being one in spirit and purpose. Do nothing out of selfish ambition or vain conceit, but in humility consider others better than your-selves. Each of you should look not only to your own interests, but also to the interests of others.

Your attitude should be the same as that of Christ Jesus:

Who, being in very nature God,
    did not consider equality with God something to be grasped,
but made himself nothing,
    taking the very nature of a servant,
    being made in human likeness.
And being found in appearance as a man,
    he humbled himself
    and became obedient to death—
        even death on a cross!
Therefore God exalted him to the highest place
    and gave him the name that is above every name,
that at the name of Jesus every knee should bow,
    in heaven and on earth and under the earth,
and every tongue confess that Jesus Christ is Lord
    to the glory of God the Father.

—Philippians 2:1–11 (NIV)

491 More About Jesus Would I Know

"But grow in the grace and knowledge of our Lord and Savior Jesus Christ. To him be glory both now and forever! Amen."—II Peter 3:18

Eliza E. Hewitt

L.M.wR.
SWENEY
John R. Sweney

1. More a-bout Je-sus would I know, More of His grace to oth-ers show;
2. More a-bout Je-sus let me learn, More of His ho-ly will dis-cern;
3. More a-bout Je-sus, in His Word, Hold-ing com-mun-ion with my Lord;
4. More a-bout Je-sus on His throne, Rich-es in glo-ry all His own;

1. More of His sav-ing full-ness see, More of His love who died for me.
2. Spir-it of God, my teach-er be, Show-ing the things of Christ to me.
3. Hear-ing His voice in ev-'ry line, Mak-ing each faith-ful say-ing mine.
4. More of His king-dom's sure in-crease, More of His com-ing, Prince of Peace.

More, more a-bout Je-sus, More, more a-bout Je-sus;

More of His sav-ing full-ness see, More of His love who died for me.

DISCIPLESHIP: GROWING IN THE LIKENESS OF CHRIST

The More I Learn About Jesus 492

"We ought always to thank God for you, brothers, and rightly so, because your faith is growing more and more, and the love every one of you has for each other is increasing."—II Thessalonians 1:3

Barney E. Warren

LEARN ABOUT JESUS
Barney E. Warren

1 The more I learn a-bout Je-sus, The more I know He loves me;
2 I long for great-er com-pas-sion, I would more sym-pa-thy show,
3 The more with Him in com-mun-ion, The near-er heav-en I rise;

1 His love is great-er and strong-er Than hu-man love can be.
2 And be more ten-der and ho-ly, More of His full-ness know.
3 And sweet-er far is our un-ion Than an-y hu-man ties.

1 The more I live in His pres-ence, The more His true-ness ap-pears,
2 I would be gen-tle and low-ly, Dis-play His love so di-vine,
3 I thirst for more of His Spir-it, His will to work in my soul:

1 The more I'm learn-ing to trust Him, Thru all the chang-ing years.
2 And have sub-mis-sion and meekness, And more of His life in mine.
3 I want to be in His im-age, While cease-less a-ges roll. A-men.

DISCIPLESHIP: GROWING IN THE LIKENESS OF CHRIST

493

May the Mind of Christ, My Savior

"Your attitude should be the same as that of Christ Jesus."—Philippians 2:5

Kate B. Wilkinson

8.7.8.5.
ST. LEONARDS
Cyril Barham-Gould

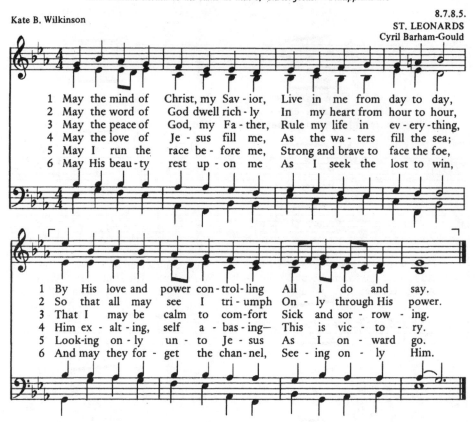

1 May the mind of Christ, my Sav-ior, Live in me from day to day,
2 May the word of God dwell rich-ly In my heart from hour to hour,
3 May the peace of God, my Fa-ther, Rule my life in ev-ery-thing,
4 May the love of Je-sus fill me, As the wa-ters fill the sea;
5 May I run the race be-fore me, Strong and brave to face the foe,
6 May His beau-ty rest up-on me As I seek the lost to win,

1 By His love and power con-trol-ling All I do and say.
2 So that all may see I tri-umph On-ly through His power.
3 That I may be calm to com-fort Sick and sor-row-ing.
4 Him ex-alt-ing, self a-bas-ing— This is vic-to-ry.
5 Look-ing on-ly un-to Je-sus As I on-ward go.
6 And may they for-get the chan-nel, See-ing on-ly Him.

494

Prayer of My Heart

"But grow in the grace and knowledge of our Lord and Savior Jesus Christ. To him be glory both now and forever! Amen."—II Peter 3:18

K. Y. Plank

C.M.
PRAYER OF MY HEART
K. Y. Plank

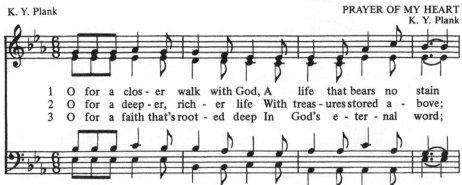

1 O for a clos-er walk with God, A life that bears no stain
2 O for a deep-er, rich-er life With treas-ures stored a-bove;
3 O for a faith that's root-ed deep In God's e-ter-nal word;

DISCIPLESHIP: GROWING IN THE LIKENESS OF CHRIST

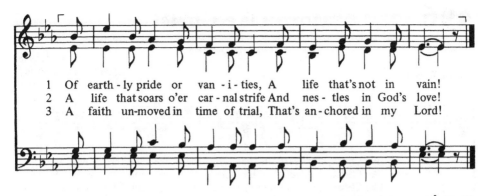

1 Of earth-ly pride or van-i-ties, A life that's not in vain!
2 A life that soars o'er car-nal strife And nes-tles in God's love!
3 A faith un-moved in time of trial, That's an-chored in my Lord!

Teach Me Thy Way, O Lord 495

"Teach me your way, O Lord; lead me in a straight path because of my oppressors."—Psalm 27:11

6.4.6.4.6.6.6.4.
CAMACHA

B. Mansell Ramsey

B. Mansell Ramsey

1 Teach me Thy way, O Lord, Teach me Thy way! Thy guid-ing grace af-ford—
2 When I am sad at heart, Teach me Thy way! When earth-ly joys de-part,
3 When doubts and fears a-rise, Teach me Thy way! When storms o'erspread the skies,
4 Long as my life shall last, Teach me Thy way! Wher-e'er my lot be cast,

1 Teach me Thy way! Help me to walk a-right, More by faith,
2 Teach me Thy way! In hours of lone-li-ness, In times of
3 Teach me Thy way! Shine thro' the cloud and rain, Thro' sor-row,
4 Teach me Thy way! Un-til the race is run, Un-til the

1 less by sight; Lead me with heav'n-ly light, Teach me Thy way!
2 dire dis-tress, In fail-ure or suc-cess, Teach me Thy way!
3 toil and pain; Make Thou my path-way plain, Teach me Thy way!
4 jour-ney's done, Un-til the crown is won, Teach me Thy way! A-men.

DISCIPLESHIP: GROWING IN THE LIKENESS OF CHRIST

496 More Like Christ

"For this very reason, make every effort to add to your faith goodness; and to goodness, knowledge."—II Peter 1:5

Charles W. Naylor

8.7.8.7.wR.
MORE LIKE CHRIST
Barney E. Warren

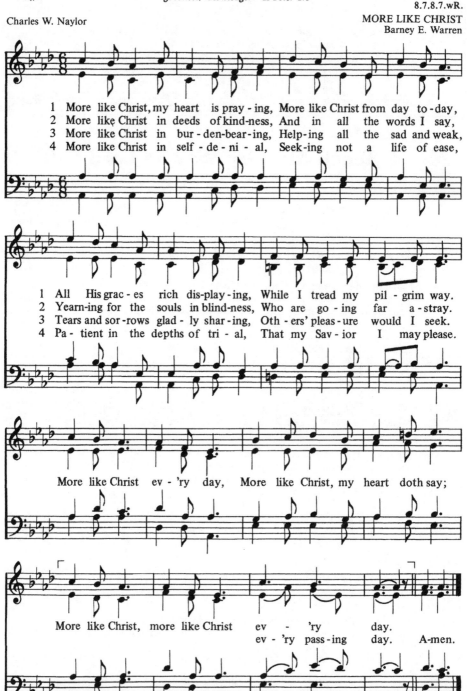

1 More like Christ, my heart is pray - ing, More like Christ from day to - day,
2 More like Christ in deeds of kind-ness, And in all the words I say,
3 More like Christ in bur - den-bear-ing, Help-ing all the sad and weak,
4 More like Christ in self - de - ni - al, Seek-ing not a life of ease,

1 All His grac - es rich dis-play - ing, While I tread my pil - grim way.
2 Yearn-ing for the souls in blind-ness, Who are go - ing far a - stray.
3 Tears and sor -rows glad - ly shar - ing, Oth - ers' pleas - ure would I seek.
4 Pa - tient in the depths of tri - al, That my Sav - ior I may please.

More like Christ ev - 'ry day, More like Christ, my heart doth say;

More like Christ, more like Christ ev - 'ry day.
ev - 'ry pass-ing day. A-men.

DISCIPLESHIP: GROWING IN THE LIKENESS OF CHRIST

Take Thou Our Minds, Dear Lord

497

"Jesus replied: 'Love the Lord your God with all your heart and with all your soul and with all your mind.' "—Matthew 22:37

William H. Foulkes

10.10.10.10.
HALL
Calvin W. Laufer

1 Take Thou our minds, dear Lord, we hum-bly pray;
2 Take Thou our hearts, O Christ— they are Thine own;
3 Take Thou our wills, Most High! Hold Thou full sway;
4 Take Thou our-selves, O Lord— heart, mind, and will;

1 Give us the mind of Christ each pass-ing day.
2 Come Thou with-in our souls and claim Thy throne.
3 Have in our in-most souls Thy per-fect way.
4 Through our sur-ren-dered souls Thy plans ful-fill.

1 Teach us to know the truth that sets us free;
2 Help us to shed a-broad Thy death-less love;
3 Guard Thou each sa-cred hour from self-ish ease;
4 We yield our-selves to Thee— time, tal-ents, all;

1 Grant us in all our thoughts to hon-or Thee.
2 Use us to make the earth like heaven a-bove.
3 Guide Thou our or-dered lives as Thou dost please.
4 We hear, and hence-forth heed Thy sov-ereign call. A-men.

DISCIPLESHIP: GROWING IN THE LIKENESS OF CHRIST

498

O Master Teacher, Teach Us Now

"Each one should use whatever gift he has received to serve others, faithfully administering God's grace in its various forms."—I Peter 4:10

Carlton C. Buck

C.M.
DUNDEE
Scottish Psalter, 1615

1 O Mas-ter Teach-er, teach us now, That we in turn may teach;
2 En-light-en now each seek-ing mind With Thy great mind of love,
3 In-struct our souls that we may learn The les-sons of the heart,
4 Give us a grasp up-on Thy Word, The truth that comes from Thee;

1 Re-veal Thy truth and teach us how The hearts of all to reach.
2 That in our seek-ing we may find The wis-dom from a bove.
3 That taught by Thee, we may in turn Thy sav-ing truth im-part.
4 Help us to teach till all have heard And ev-'ry mind is free. A-men.

499 Savior, Teach Me, Day by Day

"And to put on the new self, created to be like God in true righteousness and holiness."—Ephesians 4:24

Based on I John 4:19
Jane E. Leeson

7.7.7.7.
SEYMOUR
Carl M. von Weber

1 Sav-ior, teach me, day by day, Love's sweet les-son to o-bey:
2 With a child-like heart of love, At Thy bid-ding may I move,
3 Teach me all Thy steps to trace, Strong to fol-low in Thy grace,
4 Love in lov-ing finds em-ploy, In o-be-dience all her joy;

1 Sweet-er les-son can-not be— Lov-ing Him who first loved me.
2 Prompt to serve and fol-low Thee— Lov-ing Him who first loved me.
3 Learn-ing how to love from Thee— Lov-ing Him who first loved me.
4 Ev-er new that joy will be— Lov-ing Him who first loved me. A-men.

DISCIPLESHIP: GROWING IN THE LIKENESS OF CHRIST

Help Us, O Lord, to Learn　500

" . . . that whenever I open my mouth, words may be given me so that I will
fearlessly make known the mystery of the gospel . . . "—Ephesians 6:19b,c,d

S.M.
William W. Reid, Jr.

TRENTHAM
Robert Jackson

1 Help us, O Lord, to learn The truths Thy word im - parts;
2 Help us, O Lord, to live The faith which we pro - claim,
3 Help us, O Lord, to teach The beau - ty of Thy ways,

1 To stud - y that Thy laws may be In-scribed up - on our hearts.
2 That all our thoughts and words and deeds May glo - ri - fy Thy name.
3 That yearn-ing souls may find the Christ And sing a - loud His praise. A - men.

The Beatitudes　501

Happy are those who know they are spiritually poor;
　　the Kingdom of Heaven belongs to them!
　　Happy are those who mourn:
　　　God will comfort them!
Happy are the meek:
　　They will receive what God has promised.
　　Happy are those whose greatest desire is to do what God requires:
　　　God will satisfy them fully!
Happy are those who show mercy to others:
　　God will show mercy to them.
　　Happy are the pure in heart:
　　　they will see God.
Happy are those who work for peace among men;
　　God will call them His sons!
　　Happy are those who suffer persecution because
　　they do what God requires:
　　　The Kingdom of Heaven belongs to them!
Happy are you when men insult and mistreat you
and tell all kinds of evil lies against you
　　because you are My followers.
　　Rejoice and be glad, because a great reward is kept for you in heaven.
　　This is how men mistreated the prophets who lived before you.

—*Matthew 5:3–11 (GNB)*

DISCIPLESHIP: GROWING IN THE LIKENESS OF CHRIST

502 Sitting at the Feet of Jesus

*"Now when he saw the crowds, he went up on a mountainside and sat down.
His disciples came to him, and he began to teach them, saying: ... "*
—Matthew 5:1-2

Author Unknown

8.7.8.7.D.
AT THE FEET OF JESUS
Asa Hull

1 Sit - ting at the feet of Je - sus, O what words I hear Him say!
2 Sit - ting at the feet of Je - sus, Where can mor - tal be more blest?
3 Bless me, O my Sav-ior, bless me, As I sit low at Your feet;

1 Hap - py place! so near, so pre-cious! May it find me there each day;
2 There I lay my sins and sor - rows, And when wea-ry, find sweet rest;
3 O look down in love up - on me, Let me see Your face so sweet.

1 Sit - ing at the feet of Je - sus, I would look up - on the past;
2 Sit - ing at the feet of Je - sus, There I love to weep and pray,
3 Give me, Lord, the mind of Je - sus, Make me ho - ly as He is.

1 For His love has been so gra - cious, It has won my heart at last.
2 While I from His full-ness gath - er Grace and com-fort ev - 'ry day.
3 May I prove I've been with Je - sus, Who is all my right-eous-ness.

Lord, Be Glorified

503

"I eagerly expect and hope that I will in no way be ashamed, but will have sufficient courage so that now as always Christ will be exalted in my body, whether by life or by death."—Philippians 1:20

Bob Kilpatrick

GLORIFIED
Bob Kilpatrick

1 In my life, Lord, Be glo-ri-fied, be glo-ri-fied.
2 In my song, Lord, Be glo-ri-fied, be glo-ri-fied.
3 In my home, Lord, Be glo-ri-fied, be glo-ri-fied.
4 In Your church, Lord, Be glo-ri-fied, be glo-ri-fied.
En mi vi - da glo-ria te doy, glo-ria te doy.

1 In my life, Lord, Be glo-ri-fied to - day.
2 In my song, Lord, Be glo-ri-fied to - day.
3 In my home, Lord, Be glo-ri-fied to - day.
4 In Your church, Lord, Be glo-ri-fied to - day.
En mi vi - da, glo-ria te doy, Se - ñor.

Risen with Christ

504

LEADER: You have been raised to life with Christ. Set your hearts, then, on the things that are in heaven, where Christ sits on His throne at the right side of God. Keep your minds fixed on things there, not on things here on earth.

PEOPLE: *For you have died, and your life is hidden with Christ in God. Your real life is Christ, and when He appears, then you too will appear with Him and share His glory!*

LEADER: You are the people of God; He loved you and chose you for His own. So then, you must put on compassion, kindness, humility, gentleness, and patience. Be helpful to one another, and forgive one another, whenever any of you has a complaint against someone else.

PEOPLE: *You must forgive each other in the same way that the Lord has forgiven you. And to all these add love, which binds all things together in perfect unity. The peace that Christ gives is to be the judge in your hearts; for to this peace God has called you together in the one body.*

LEADER: And be thankful. Christ's message, in all its richness, must live in your hearts. Teach and instruct each other with all wisdom. Sing psalms, hymns, and sacred songs; sing to God, with thanksgiving in your hearts.

PEOPLE: *Everything you do or say, then, should be done in the name of the Lord Jesus, as you give thanks through Him to God the Father.*

—Colossians 3:1–4, 12–17 (GNB)

DISCIPLESHIP: GROWING IN THE LIKENESS OF CHRIST

505 Humble Yourself to Walk with God

"And being found in appearance as a man, he humbled himself and became obedient to death—even death on a cross!"—Philippians 2:8

Johnson Oatman, Jr.

HUMBLE YOURSELF
W. J. Rogers

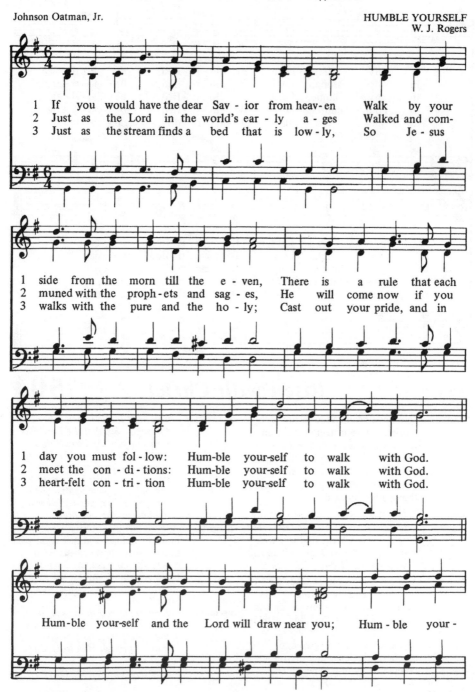

1 If you would have the dear Sav - ior from heav - en Walk by your
2 Just as the Lord in the world's ear - ly a - ges Walked and com-
3 Just as the stream finds a bed that is low - ly, So Je - sus

1 side from the morn till the e - ven, There is a rule that each
2 muned with the proph - ets and sag - es, He will come now if you
3 walks with the pure and the ho - ly; Cast out your pride, and in

1 day you must fol - low: Hum-ble your-self to walk with God.
2 meet the con - di - tions: Hum-ble your-self to walk with God.
3 heart-felt con - tri - tion Hum-ble your-self to walk with God.

Hum-ble your-self and the Lord will draw near you; Hum - ble your -

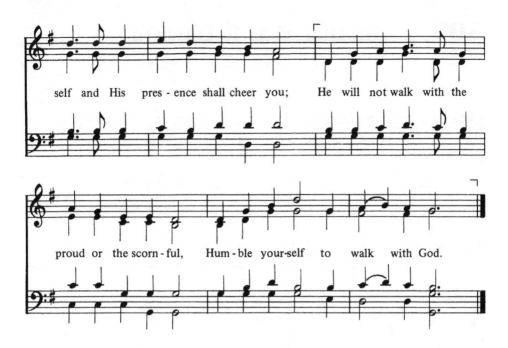

self and His pres-ence shall cheer you; He will not walk with the

proud or the scorn-ful, Hum-ble your-self to walk with God.

New Year

506

Our heavenly Father, as the old year ends and a new year begins, forgive us for the failures of the vanished days. Keep us from vain regrets, and let us face forward in the light of the best that we have learned from the past.

The Lord's mercies are new every morning.
Great is Thy faithfulness!

O God, who art from everlasting to everlasting, and hast granted to us a new beginning of days; grant us, throughout this coming year, such prosperity as Thou seest to be good for us.

The Lord's mercies are new every morning.
Great is Thy faithfulness!

O Lord, make us to abound in such works as are pleasing unto Thee; purge our hearts both of shallow self-confidence and of cowardly fear, so that we may know that without Thee we can do nothing, but that in Thee all things are possible.

The Lord's mercies are new every morning.
Great is Thy faithfulness!

O Lord, as days and years pass over us, teach us to be more thankful for past mercies, more penitent for past faults, and more earnest to serve Thee in the years ahead.

The Lord's mercies are new every morning.
Great is Thy faithfulness!

—James Earl Massey

507 Another Year Is Dawning

"Teach us to number our days aright, that we may gain a heart of wisdom."
—Psalm 90:12

7.6.7.6.D.

Frances R. Havergal

AURELIA
Samuel S. Wesley

1 An - oth - er year is dawn - ing: Dear Fa - ther, let it be,
2 An - oth - er year of mer - cies, Of faith - ful - ness and grace;
3 An - oth - er year of serv - ice, Of wit - ness for Thy love;

1 In work-ing or in wait - ing, An - oth - er year with Thee;
2 An - oth - er year of glad - ness In the shin - ing of Thy face;
3 An - oth - er year of train - ing For ho - lier work a - bove.

1 An - oth - er year of prog - ress, An - oth - er year of praise,
2 An - oth - er year of lean - ing Up - on Thy lov - ing breast;
3 An - oth - er year is dawn - ing: Dear Fa - ther, let it be,

1 An - oth - er year of prov - ing Thy pres - ence all the days.
2 An - oth - er year of trust - ing, Of qui - et, hap - py rest.
3 On earth or else in heav - en, An - oth - er year for Thee.

DISCIPLESHIP: GROWING IN THE LIKENESS OF CHRIST

Hark, the Voice of Jesus Calling

508

"Do you not say, 'Four months more and then the harvest'? I tell you, open your eyes and look at the fields! They are ripe for harvest."—John 4:35

Daniel March

8.7.8.7.D.
HYMN TO JOY
Ludwig van Beethoven
Adapted by Edward Hodges

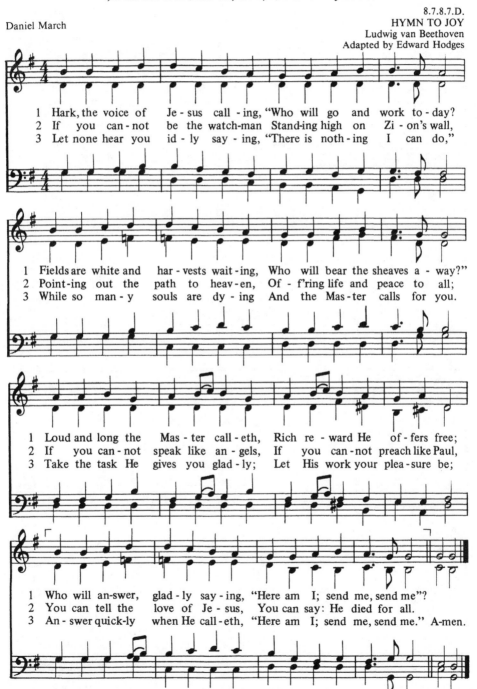

1 Hark, the voice of Jesus call-ing, "Who will go and work to-day?
2 If you can-not be the watch-man Stand-ing high on Zi-on's wall,
3 Let none hear you id-ly say-ing, "There is noth-ing I can do,"

1 Fields are white and har-vests wait-ing, Who will bear the sheaves a-way?"
2 Point-ing out the path to heav-en, Of-f'ring life and peace to all;
3 While so man-y souls are dy-ing And the Mas-ter calls for you.

1 Loud and long the Mas-ter call-eth, Rich re-ward He of-fers free;
2 If you can-not speak like an-gels, If you can-not preach like Paul,
3 Take the task He gives you glad-ly; Let His work your plea-sure be;

1 Who will an-swer, glad-ly say-ing, "Here am I; send me, send me"?
2 You can tell the love of Je-sus, You can say: He died for all.
3 An-swer quick-ly when He call-eth, "Here am I; send me, send me." A-men.

DISCIPLESHIP: OBEDIENCE TO CHRIST

509

I Then Shall Live

"Whoever tries to keep his life will lose it, and whoever loses his life will preserve it."—Luke 17:33

Gloria Gaither

11.10.11.10.11.10.
FINLANDIA
Jean Sibelius

1. I then shall live as one who's been for-giv-en; I'll walk with
2. I then shall live as one who's learned com-pas-sion; I've been so
3. Your king-dom come a-round and through and in me, Your pow'r and

1. joy to know my debts are paid. I know my name is
2. loved that I'll risk lov-ing, too. I know how fear builds
3. glo-ry, let them shine through me; Your Hal-lowed Name, O

1. clear be-fore my Fa-ther; I am His child, and I am not a-
2. walls in-stead of bridg-es; I dare to see an-oth-er's point of
3. may I bear with hon-or, And may Your liv-ing King-dom come in

1. fraid. So great-ly par-doned, I'll for-give my broth-er;
2. view. And when re-la-tion-ships de-mand com-mit-ment,
3. me. The Bread of Life, O may I share with hon-or,

DISCIPLESHIP: OBEDIENCE TO CHRIST

1 The law of love I glad-ly will o - bey.
2 Then I'll be there to care and fol - low through.
3 And may You feed a hun-gry world through me.

A - men.

A Charge to Keep I Have 510

"In the presence of God and of Christ Jesus, who will judge the living and the dead, and in view of his appearing and his kingdom, I give you this charge."
—II Timothy 4:1

S.M.
BOYLSTON
Lowell Mason

Charles Wesley

1 A charge to keep I have, A God to glo - ri - fy,
2 To serve the pres - ent age, My call - ing to ful - fill,
3 Arm me with jeal - ous care, As in Thy sight to live;
4 Help me to watch and pray, And on Thy-self re - ly,

1 A nev - er - dy - ing soul to save, And fit it for the sky.
2 O may it all my pow'rs en - gage To do my Mas - ter's will!
3 And O thy serv - ant, Lord, pre-pare, A strict ac - count to give!
4 As - sured if I my trust be - tray I shall for - ev - er die.

DISCIPLESHIP: OBEDIENCE TO CHRIST

511

I Would Be True

" . . . Be faithful, even to the point of death, and I will give you the crown of life."—Revelation 2:10b

Howard A. Walter

11.10.11.10.10.
PEEK
Joseph Y. Peek

1 I would be true, for there are those who trust me;
2 I would be friend of all, the foe, the friend - less;

1 I would be pure, for there are those who care;
2 I would be giv - ing, and for - get the gift;

1 I would be strong, for there is much to suf - fer;
2 I would be hum - ble, for I know my weak - ness;

1 I would be brave, for there is much to dare,
2 I would look up, and laugh, and love, and lift,

1 I would be brave, for there is much to dare.
2 I would look up, and laugh, and love, and lift.

DISCIPLESHIP: OBEDIENCE TO CHRIST

Come Forth, O Christian Youth

512

"This is to my Father's glory, that you bear much fruit, showing yourselves to be my disciples."—John 15:8

Mary Ellen Jackson

S.M.D.
DIADEMATA
George J. Elvey

1 Come forth, O Chris-tian youth, A task be - fore us lies;
2 Stand firm, O Chris-tian youth, With trust in God a - lone,
3 Grow strong, O Chris-tian youth, Be loy - al, brave and true,
4 Give all, O Chris-tian youth, And naught from Christ with - hold;

1 The world a - waits the strength and zeal Which youth-ful heart sup - plies.
2 That we may live our Chris - tian faith And make Christ tru - ly known.
3 And strive with cour - age for the right In what we say and do.
4 His king - dom claims us for its own; His Spir - it keep us bold!

1 We seek to win the lost To choose Christ's no - bler way,
2 Be ours to show the earth The path His feet have trod,
3 Thus may our words and deeds Be wor - thy in God's sight,
4 As pil - grims in the world Yet fol - lowers of the Way,

1 And ush - er in true u - ni - ty For ev - 'ry - one to - day.
2 To make all life a sa - cra - ment And ho - ly un - to God.
3 And man - i - fest to all the world His way of truth and light.
4 God make us faith - ful cit - i - zens Till His e - ter - nal day.

DISCIPLESHIP: OBEDIENCE TO CHRIST

513 Faith for Thy Service

"And now these three remain: faith, hope and love. But the greatest of these is love."—I Corinthians 13:13

Mrs. L. H. Figh, Jr.

10.10.10.10.
SLANE
Traditional Irish Melody
Arranged by Norman Johnson

1 Faith for Thy ser-vice, my Fa-ther, I ask—
2 Hope for new cour-age and hope for new sight,
3 Love for my neigh-bor and love for my God,

1 Faith for the fac-ing and faith for the task,
2 Hope in my heav-en-ly Fa-ther's great might,
3 Love that will cause me to car-ry His Word—

1 Faith for the mo-ment and faith for the day,
2 Hope that He'll help me His mes-sage to bear,
3 Car-ry it on-ward and out-ward to win

1 Faith that my God will throw o-pen the way.
2 Hope that His truth with the lost I may share.
3 All who should know of sal-va-tion from sin.

DISCIPLESHIP: OBEDIENCE TO CHRIST

I Will Serve Thee

514

"It is the Lord Christ you are serving."—Colossians 3:24b

Gloria Gaither
William J. Gaither

SERVING
William J. Gaither

I will serve Thee be-cause I love Thee, You have giv-en life to me; I was noth-ing be-fore You found me, You have giv-en life to me. Heart-aches, bro-ken piec-es, Ru-ined lives are why You died on Cal-vary; Your touch was what I longed for, You have giv-en life to me.

DISCIPLESHIP: OBEDIENCE TO CHRIST

515 Wholehearted Service

"Then Jesus said to his disciples, 'If anyone would come after me, he must deny himself and take up his cross and follow me.' "—Matthew 16:24

Charles W. Naylor

9.8.9.8.wR.
WHOLEHEARTED SERVICE
Andrew L. Byers

1 I've turned from the world and its fol - lies, For - ev - er for -
2 I will not be lan - guid or care - less, Or for - mal, or
3 Since Je - sus gave all to re - deem me, Since on - ly through
4 O help me, dear Lord, to be read - y The task that Thou

1 sak - en all sin; I've giv - en my-self un - to Je - sus
2 cold, or un - true; But, striv - ing with ear - nest en - deav - or,
3 mer - cy I live, It now is my joy and my pur - pose
4 giv - est to do, Not shrink - ing from la - bor or du - ty,

1 To ev - er and on - ly serve Him.
2 The will of my Lord I will do. I'll put my whole heart in His
3 A whole-heart-ed serv-ice to give.
4 De - vot-ed and faith-ful and true.

serv - ice, And do all He ask-eth of me; I mean to live

DISCIPLESHIP: OBEDIENCE TO CHRIST

ho - ly and blame - less— A Chris-tian in - deed will I be.

I Have Decided to Follow Jesus   516

"Then Jesus said to his disciples, 'If anyone would come after me, he must deny himself and take up his cross and follow me.' " —Matthew 16:24

Unknown

ASSAM
Folk Melody From India

1 I have de - cid - ed to fol - low Je - sus; I have de -
2 The world be - hind me, the cross be - fore me; The world be -
3 Tho none go with me, I still will fol - low; Tho none go
4 Will you de - cide now to fol - low Je - sus? Will you de -
5 He de - ci - di - do se - guir á Cri - sto; He di - ci -

1 cid - ed to fol - low Je - sus; I have de - cid - ed to fol - low
2 hind me, the cross be - fore me; The world be - hind me, the cross be -
3 with me, I still will fol - low; Tho none go with me, I still will
4 cide now to fol - low Je - sus? Will you de - cide now to fol - low
5 di - do se - guir á Cri - sto; He de - ci - di - do se - guir á

1 Je - sus; No turn - ing back, no turn - ing back.
2 fore me; No turn - ing back, no turn - ing back.
3 fol - low; No turn - ing back, no turn - ing back.
4 Je - sus? No turn - ing back, no turn - ing back.
5 Cri - sto; No vuel - vo a - trás, No vuel - vo a - trás.

DISCIPLESHIP: OBEDIENCE TO CHRIST

517 The Longer I Serve Him

"Not that I have already obtained all this, or have already been made perfect, but I press on to take hold of that for which Christ Jesus took hold of me."
—Philippians 3:12

William J. Gaither

8.6.8.11.wR.

THE SWEETER HE GROWS
William J. Gaither

1 Since I start-ed for the King-dom, Since my life He con-
2 Ev-ery need He is sup-ply-ing, Plen-teous grace He be-

1 trols, Since I gave my heart to Je-sus, The long-er I
2 stows; Ev-ery day my way gets bright-er, The long-er I

1 serve Him, the sweet-er He grows. The long-er I serve Him the sweet-er
2 serve Him, the sweet-er He grows.

He grows, The more that I love Him, more love He be-stows; Each day is like

heav-en, my heart o-ver-flows, The long-er I serve Him the sweet-er He grows.

DISCIPLESHIP: OBEDIENCE TO CHRIST

Must Jesus Bear the Cross Alone 518

"Then he called the crowd to him along with his disciples and said: 'If anyone would come after me, he must deny himself and take up his cross and follow me.' "—Mark 8:34

Thomas Shepherd

C.M.
MAITLAND
George N. Allen

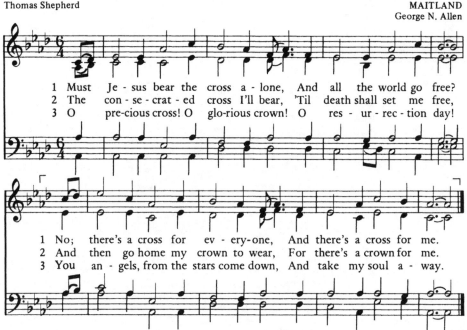

1 Must Je - sus bear the cross a - lone, And all the world go free?
2 The con - se - crat - ed cross I'll bear, 'Til death shall set me free,
3 O pre-cious cross! O glo-rious crown! O res - ur - rec - tion day!

1 No; there's a cross for ev - ery-one, And there's a cross for me.
2 And then go home my crown to wear, For there's a crown for me.
3 You an - gels, from the stars come down, And take my soul a - way.

Adoration Unto the Lord 519

LEADER: What the Lord gives us is the wisdom to conceive and the courage to believe. He will give us the power to achieve.

PEOPLE: *An exhilarating life of daring discipleship begins with an unreserved commitment of our lives to the Lord.*

LEADER: We say with Paul, "For I know whom I have believed and am persuaded that He is able to keep what I have committed to Him." *(II Timothy 1:12)*

MEN: *All that we have and are is a gift from the Lord. Let us adore Him!*

WOMEN: *He is Lord of the future. Let us trust Him!*

LEADER: There is no limit to what the Lord is able to do when we leave the results to Him. We adore Him when we lay our lives before Him in complete surrender.

ALL: *Lord, we adore You. Here are our minds, think through them; here are our emotions, love through them; here are our bodies, fill us with Your healing and shine through them. This is our prayer as we sing together:*

—Lloyd John Ogilvie

DISCIPLESHIP: OBEDIENCE TO CHRIST

520 We Will Work for Jesus

"He told them, 'The harvest is plentiful, but the workers are few. Ask the Lord of the harvest, therefore, to send out workers into his harvest field.' "
—Luke 10:2

Daniel S. Warner

WORK FOR JESUS
Andrew L. Byers

1 We will work for Je-sus and a-dore the plan That ex-alt-eth so a
2 We will work for Je-sus, all to Him we owe; On-ly for His mer-cy
3 We will work for Je-sus, we are not our own; Je-sus, we can nev-er
4 We will work for Je-sus, bless His ho-ly name! Ev-'ry-where the rip-ened

1 fall-en race, Join-ing with the Sav-ior, do-ing what we can To ex-
2 we would be Lost in sin for-ev-er; but we tru-ly know That His
3 i-dle be; Souls a-round us dy-ing, pur-chased for Thy throne; We will
4 grain we see; From the ear-ly morn-ing till the day is gone, Je-sus,

1 tend the won-ders of His grace.
2 might-y love has set us free.
3 gath-er all we can for Thee.
4 we will la-bor on for Thee.

We will work for Je-sus, We will

We will work for Je-sus,

1. work for Je-sus, We will live for Him who died for all;

We will work for Je-sus,

work   for Je - sus, Till we hear the fi - nal trum-pet call.
We will work for   Je - sus,

Jesus Calls Us O'er the Tumult **521**

" 'Come, follow me,' Jesus said, 'and I will make you fishers of men.' "
—Matthew 4:19

8.7.8.7.
GALILEE
William H. Jude

Cecil Frances Alexander
Jeff Redd, alt.

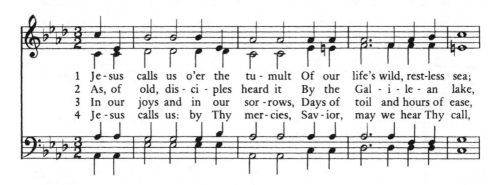

1 Je - sus calls us o'er the tu - mult Of our life's wild, rest-less sea;
2 As, of old, dis - ci - ples heard it By the Gal - i - le - an lake,
3 In our joys and in our sor - rows, Days of toil and hours of ease,
4 Je - sus calls us: by Thy mer - cies, Sav - ior, may we hear Thy call,

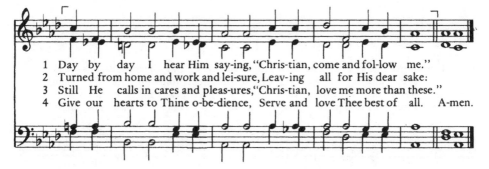

1 Day by day I hear Him say-ing, "Chris-tian, come and fol-low me."
2 Turned from home and work and lei-sure, Leav-ing all for His dear sake:
3 Still He calls in cares and pleas-ures, "Chris-tian, love me more than these."
4 Give our hearts to Thine o-be-dience, Serve and love Thee best of all. A-men.

DISCIPLESHIP: OBEDIENCE TO CHRIST

522 I Love to Serve My Jesus

"But you are a chosen people, a royal priesthood . . . that you may declare the praise of him . . . "—I Peter 2:9a,c

Barney E. Warren

SERVE MY JESUS
Elisha A. Hoffman

1. I love to serve my Je - sus, a priv - i - lege sub - lime,
2. I love to serve my Je - sus, the world I do give up,
3. I love to serve my Je - sus and lean up - on His arm
4. I love to serve my Je - sus for all His ten - der care,

1. My life a - fresh with beau - ty bright is spar - kling all the time;
2. I'll drink with my dear Sav - ior from that bit - ter, bit - ter cup;
3. In health or in af - flic - tion, in the calm or in the storm;
4. O joy, and what a pleas - ure in this life we all may share!

1. 'Mid scenes that are un - fad - ing of rap - ture and of bliss,
2. I know that if I suf - fer, with Him I too shall reign
3. In dark - ness, clouds, or sun - shine, in heat or in the cold,
4. O depth of great com - pas - sion! 'tis like a might - y flood;

1. Trans-port - ed I am soar - ing in my Sav - ior's right-eous - ness.
2. In life, and up in glo - ry bright sweet prom - ise sure I claim.
3. In pov - er - ty or rich - es, I have peace and joy un - told.
4. He gave His pledge of love to us and sealed it with His blood.

DISCIPLESHIP: OBEDIENCE TO CHRIST

I love to serve my Je - sus, He's all in all to me;

He helps me bear each bur - den, He is my vic - to - ry.

Use Me, Lord 523

Make me a channel, a riverbed, of Your love
to others. Help me act on the inspiration You
give me rather than stifling Your guidance.
Take charge of my tongue so that it becomes
an instrument of healing. Make me a commu-
nicator of love and forgiveness as I cheer oth-
ers on to their best. I commit my schedule to
You, Lord; help me to know and do Your will.
I long to be the person You created me to be
and not anyone else. Forgive me when I take
my signals of success from others and not You.
Most of all, Lord, help me to catch the drum-
beat of Your guidance and live by Your timing.
Here is my life—invade it, fill it, transform it.
And I thank You in advance for the healing of
my life. Amen.

—Unknown

524
The Way of the Cross
Leads Home

"Salvation is found in no one else, for there is no other name under heaven given to me by which we must be saved."—Acts 4:12

Jessie B. Pounds

WAY OF THE CROSS
Charles H. Gabriel

1 I must go home by the way of the cross, There's
2 I must go on in the blood-sprin-kled way, The
3 Then I bid fare-well to the way of the world, To

1 no oth-er way but this; I shall ne'er get sight of the
2 path that the Sav-ior trod, If I ev-er climb to the
3 walk in it nev-er-more; For my Lord says, "Come," and I

1 gates of light, If the way of the cross I miss.
2 heights sub-lime, Where the soul is at home with God.
3 seek my home, Where He waits at the o-pen door.

The way of the cross leads home, The way of the cross leads home;
leads home, leads home;

It is sweet to know as I on-ward go, The way of the cross leads home.

DISCIPLESHIP: OBEDIENCE TO CHRIST

Trust and Obey

"But the man who looks intently into the perfect law that gives freedom, and continues to do this, not forgetting what he has heard, but doing it—he will be blessed in what he does."—James 1:25

6.6.9.D.wR.

James H. Sammis

TRUST AND OBEY
Daniel B. Towner

1 When we walk with the Lord In the light of His Word, What a glo-ry He
2 Not a shad-ow can rise, Not a cloud in the skies, But His smile quick-ly
3 Not a bur-den we bear, Not a sor-row we share, But our toil He does
4 Then in fel-low-ship sweet We will sit at His feet, Or we'll walk by His

1 sheds on our way! While we do His good will, He a-bides with us still,
2 drives it a-way; Not a doubt or a fear, Not a sigh or a tear
3 rich-ly re-pay; Not a grief or a loss, Not a frown or a cross,
4 side in the way; What He says we will do, Where He sends we will go,

1 And with all who will trust and o-bey.
2 Can re-main when we trust and o-bey.
3 But is blest if we trust and o-bey.
4 Nev-er fear, on-ly trust and o-bey.

Trust and o-bey, for there's

no oth-er way To be hap-py in Je-sus, but to trust and o-bey.

DISCIPLESHIP: OBEDIENCE TO CHRIST

526

Our Best

"For everyone who has will be given more, and he will have an abundance.
Whoever does not have, even what he has will be taken from him."
—Matthew 25:29

S.C. Kirk

OUR BEST
Grant C. Tullar

1 Hear ye the Mas-ter's call, "Give me thy best!" For, be it
2 Wait not for those who laud, Heed not their slight; Win-ning the
3 Night soon comes on a-pace, Day has-tens by; Work-ers and

1 great or small, That is His test. Do then the best you can,
2 smile of God Brings its de-light! Aid-ing the good and true
3 work must face Test-ing on high. Oh, may we in that day

1 Not for re-ward, Not seek-ing hu-man praise, But for the Lord.
2 Ne'er goes un-blest, All that we think or do, Be it the best.
3 Find rest, sweet rest, Which God has prom-ised those Who do their best.

Ev-'ry work for Je-sus will be blest, But He

DISCIPLESHIP: OBEDIENCE TO CHRIST

asks from ev - 'ry - one his best. Our tal - ents may be few,

These may be small, But un - to Him is due Our best, our all.

Seek Ye First 527

"But seek first his kingdom and his righteousness, and all these things will be given to you as well."—Matthew 6:33

Matthew 6:33

LAFFERTY
Karen Lafferty

1 Seek ye first the king - dom of God And His
2 Ask and it shall be giv -en un - to you; Seek and
Bus - ca pri - mer - o el rei - no de Dios Y su ju -

1 right - eous - ness, And all these things shall be
2 ye shall find. Knock and the door shall be
sti - cia, To - das las co - sas se

1 add - ed un - to you. Al - le - lu, al - le - lu - ia.
2 o-pened un - to you. Al - le - lu, al - le - lu - ia.
te añ - a - di - rán. A - le - lu, A - le - lu - ya.

DISCIPLESHIP: OBEDIENCE TO CHRIST

528 Every Hour for Jesus

"Be very careful, then, how you live—not as unwise but as wise, making the most of every opportunity, because the days are evil."—Ephesians 5:15-16

Based on Ephesians 5:15-16
Barney E. Warren

EVERY HOUR
Barney E. Warren

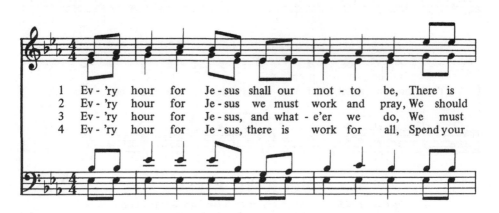

1 Ev - 'ry hour for Je - sus shall our mot - to be, There is
2 Ev - 'ry hour for Je - sus we must work and pray, We should
3 Ev - 'ry hour for Je - sus, and what - e'er we do, We must
4 Ev - 'ry hour for Je - sus, there is work for all, Spend your

1 plen - ty of work we may do; We may all keep bus - y till the
2 nev - er be sloth - ful, or tire; For the time is com - ing, so His
3 have His ap-prov - al to - day; If we do heart serv - ice with the
4 time in His serv - ice a - lone; Be ye read - y, wait - ing for His

1 Lord we see, Till He comes for His faith - ful few.
2 Word does say, When our work shall be tried by fire.
3 Lord in view, He will bless us a - long life's way.
4 ev - 'ry call, Soon He'll say, "'Tis e - nough, come home."

DISCIPLESHIP: OBEDIENCE TO CHRIST

Ev - 'ry hour for the Lord, Ev - 'ry
Ev - 'ry hour for the Lord,

hour for the Lord let us spend; Ev - 'ry hour for Je - sus till He

comes a - gain, When the la - bor of life shall end.

529

I'll Go Where You Want Me to Go

"Speak, for your servant is listening."—I Samuel 3:10b

Mary Brown, stanza 1
Charles E. Prior, stanzas 2, 3

9.7.9.7.9.8.wR.
I'LL GO
Carrie E. Rounsefell

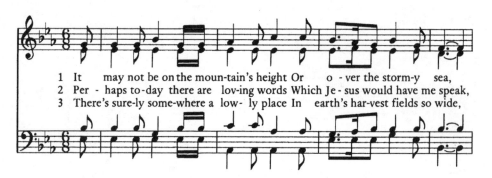

1 It   may not be on the moun-tain's height Or   o - ver the storm-y   sea,
2 Per - haps to-day there are lov-ing words Which Je - sus would have me speak,
3 There's sure-ly some-where a low- ly place In   earth's har-vest fields so wide,

1 It   may not be at the   bat - tle-front My   Lord will have need of   me;
2 There may be now, in the   paths of sin, Some wan-derer whom I should seek;
3 Where I   may la - bor thru life's short day For   Je - sus the Cru - ci - fied;

1 But   if   by a still, small voice He calls To   paths I   do   not know,
2 O   Sav - ior, if Thou wilt   be my Guide, Tho' dark and rug-ged the way,
3 So, trust-ing my all   un - to Thy care—I   know Thou lov - est   me—

DISCIPLESHIP: OBEDIENCE TO CHRIST

1 I'll an-swer, dear Lord, with my hand in Thine, I'll go where You want me to go.
2 My voice shall ech-o the mes-sage sweet, I'll say what You want me to say.
3 I'll do Thy will with a heart sin-cere, I'll be what You want me to be.

I'll go where You want me to go, dear Lord, O'er moun-tain or plain or sea;

I'll say what You want me to say, dear Lord, I'll be what You want me to be.

530 Follow On!

"My sheep listen to my voice; I know them, and they follow me."—John 10:27

William O. Cushing

FOLLOW ON
Robert Lowry

1 Down in the val - ley with my Sav - ior I would go,
2 Down in the val - ley with my Sav - ior I would go,
3 Down in the val - ley or up - on the moun - tain steep,

1 Where the flow'rs are bloom-ing and the sweet wa - ters flow;
2 Where the storms are sweep-ing and the dark wa - ters flow;
3 Close be - side my Sav - ior would my soul ev - er keep;

1 Ev - 'ry - where He leads me I would fol - low, fol - low on,
2 With His hand to lead me I will nev - er, nev - er fear,
3 He will lead me safe - ly in the path that He has trod,

1 Walk - ing in His foot - steps till the crown be won.
2 Dan - ger can - not fright me if my Lord is near.
3 Up to where they gath - er on the hills of God.

DISCIPLESHIP: OBEDIENCE TO CHRIST

Fol - low! fol - low! I would fol-low Je - sus! An - y-where, ev-'ry-where,

I would fol-low on! Fol-low! fol - low! I would fol - low Je - sus!

Ev - 'ry - where He leads me I would fol - low on!

531

I Will Follow Thee

"Peter replied, 'Even if all fall away on account of you, I never will.'"
—Matthew 26:33

James Lawson

8.7.8.7.D.

I WILL FOLLOW THEE
James Lawson

1 I will fol-low Thee my Sav-ior, Where-so - e'er my lot may be;
2 Tho the road be rough and thorn-y, Track-less as the foam-ing sea,
3 Tho 'tis lone, and dark, and drear-y, Cheer-less tho my path may be,
4 Tho I meet with trib - u - la-tion, Sore-ly tempt-ed tho I be,
5 Tho Thou lead-est thru af -flic-tions, Poor, for -sak - en tho I be,

1 Where Thou go - est I will fol-low, Yes, my Lord, I'll fol-low Thee.
2 Thou hast trod this way be - fore me, And I glad-ly fol-low Thee.
3 If Thy voice I hear be - fore me, Fear-less-ly I'll fol-low Thee.
4 I re-mem-ber Thou wast tempt-ed, And re-joice to fol-low Thee.
5 Thou wast des-ti-tute, af - flict-ed, And I on-ly fol-low Thee.

I will fol-low Thee, my Sav-ior, Thou didst shed Thy blood for me;

And tho oth - ers should for-sake Thee, By Thy grace I'll fol-low Thee. A-men.

DISCIPLESHIP: OBEDIENCE TO CHRIST

Let Your Heart Be Broken 532

"When he saw the crowds, he had compassion on them, because they were harassed and helpless, like sheep without a shepherd."—Matthew 9:36

Bryan Jeffery Leech

6.5.6.5.D.
WYE VALLEY (Abridged)
James Mountain

1 Let your heart be bro - ken For a world in need— Feed the mouths that
2 Here on earth ap - ply - ing Prin - ci - ples of love— Vis - i - ble ex -
3 Blest to be a bless - ing, Priv - i - leged to care, Chal-lenged by the
4 Add to your be - liev - ing Deeds that prove it true— Know-ing Christ as
5 Let your heart be ten - der And your vi - sion clear— See man-kind as

1 hun - ger, Soothe the wounds that bleed, Give the cup of wa - ter And the
2 pres-sion God still rules a - bove, Liv - ing il - lus - tra - tion Of the
3 need Ap - par - ent ev - 'ry - where, Where the world is want-ing Fill the
4 Sav - ior, Make Him Mas - ter too: Fol - low in His foot-steps, Go where
5 God sees, Serve Him far and near; Let your heart be bro - ken By an -

1 loaf of bread— Be the hands of Je - sus, Serv - ing in His stead.
2 Liv-ing Word To the minds of all who've Nev - er seen and heard.
3 va - cant place, Be the means thru which the Lord re - veals His grace.
4 He has trod, In the world's great trou - ble Risk your-self for God.
5 oth-er's pain, Share your rich re - sourc - es— Give and give a - gain.

DISCIPLESHIP: SERVANTHOOD

533 Reach Out and Touch

"He said, . . . 'Do you love Me? . . . feed My sheep.' "—John 21:17

Charles F. Brown

REACH OUT
Charles F. Brown

Unison

1 Reach out and touch a soul that is hun-gry, Reach out and touch a
2 Reach out and touch a friend who is wea-ry, Reach out and touch a

1 spir-it in de-spair, Reach out and touch a life torn and
2 seek-er un-a-ware, Reach out and touch, though touch-ing means

1 dirt-y, The one who is lone-ly— If you care! Reach out and
2 los-ing A part of your own self— If you dare! Reach out and

1 touch that neigh-bor who hates you, Reach out and touch that stran-ger who
2 give your love to the love-less, Reach out and make a home for the

1 meets you, Reach out and touch the per-son who needs you, Reach out
2 home-less, Reach out and shed God's light in the dark-ness, Reach out

DISCIPLESHIP: SERVANTHOOD

1 and let the smile of God touch thru you.
2 and let the smile of God touch thru you.

The Character of a Christian 534

LEADER: If I speak in the tongues of men and of angels, but have not love, I am only a resounding gong or a clanging cymbal.

PEOPLE: *If I have the gift of prophecy and can fathom all mysteries and all knowledge, and if I have a faith that can move mountains, but have not love, I am nothing.*

LEADER: If I give all I possess to the poor and surrender my body to the flames, but have not love, I gain nothing.

PEOPLE: *Love is patient, love is kind.*

LEADER: It does not envy, it does not boast, it is not proud.

PEOPLE: *It is not rude, it is not self-seeking, it is not easily angered, it keeps no record of wrongs.*

LEADER: Love does not delight in evil but rejoices with the truth.

PEOPLE: *It always protects, always trusts, always hopes, always perseveres.*

LEADER: Love never fails. But where there are prophecies, they will cease; where there are tongues, they will be stilled; where there is knowledge, it will pass away. For we know in part and we prophesy in part.

PEOPLE: *And now these three remain: faith, hope and love. But the greatest of these is love.*
          —from I Corinthians 13 (NIV)

535

All for Jesus

"I have been crucified with Christ and I no longer live, but Christ lives in me. The life I live in the body, I live by faith in the Son of God, who loved me and gave himself for me."—Galatians 2:20

Mary D. James

8.7.8.7.D.
CONSTANCY
Unknown

1 All for Je - sus, all for Je - sus! All my be - ing's ran-somed powers:
2 Let my hands per-form His bid - ding, Let my feet run in His ways;
3 Since my eyes were fixed on Je - sus, I've lost sight of all be - side,
4 O what won-der! how a - maz - ing! Je - sus, glo-rious King of kings,

1 All my thoughts and words and do - ings, All my days and all my hours:
2 Let my eyes see Je - sus on - ly, Let my lips speak forth His praise:
3 So en-thralled my spir - it's vi - sion, Look-ing at the Cru - ci - fied:
4 Deigns to call me His be - lov - ed, Lets me rest be - neath His wings:

1 All for Je - sus! all for Je - sus! All my days and all my hours;
2 All for Je - sus! all for Je - sus! Let my lips speak forth His praise;
3 All for Je - sus! all for Je - sus! Look-ing at the Cru - ci - fied;
4 All for Je - sus! all for Je - sus! Rest - ing now be - neath His wings;

1 All for Je - sus! all for Je - sus! All my days and all my hours.
2 All for Je - sus! all for Je - sus! Let my lips speak forth His praise.
3 All for Je - sus! all for Je - sus! Look-ing at the Cru - ci - fied.
4 All for Je - sus! all for Je - sus! Rest - ing now be - neath His wings.

DISCIPLESHIP: SERVANTHOOD

O Master, Let Me Walk with Thee

536

"And see if there is any wicked way in me, and lead me in the way everlasting."—Psalm 139:24

Washington Gladden

L.M.
MARYTON
H. Percy Smith

1 O Mas-ter, let me walk with Thee In low-ly
2 Help me the slow of heart to move By some clear,
3 Teach me Thy pa-tience: still with Thee In clos-er,
4 In hope that sends a shin-ing ray Far down the

1 paths of serv-ice free; Tell me Thy se-cret— help me
2 win-ning word of love; Teach me the way-ward feet to
3 dear-er com-pa-ny, In work that keeps faith sweet and
4 fu-ture's broad-ening way, In peace that on-ly Thou canst

1 bear The strain of toil, the fret of care.
2 stay, And guide them in the home-ward way.
3 strong, In trust that tri-umphs o-ver wrong.
4 give, With Thee, O Mas-ter, let me live. A-men.

DISCIPLESHIP: SERVANTHOOD

537 Lord, Light My Soul with Holy Flame

"For this reason I remind you to fan into flame the gift of God, which is in you through the laying on of my hands."—II Timothy 1:6

Robert E. Brickhouse

L.M.
CANONBURY
Robert Schumann

1 Lord, light my soul with ho - ly flame, That I may glo - ri - fy Thy name,
2 Dear Sav-ior, guide my feet to - day, For I would walk in Thy good way,
3 Show me the path to ser-vice true And give me faith Thy work to do,
4 Up - on Thine al - tar now I lay My-self, my all, this ho - ly day,

1 In all I say and do and give, While by Thy grace I dai - ly live.
2 O use me, Lord, to do Thy will And Thy great pur-pose to ful - fill!
3 With mind and heart on hu-man needs And us - ing life for no - ble deeds.
4 That all my strength may tru - ly be In faith-ful ser-vice, Lord, to Thee.

538 *Micah 6:8*

"He has showed you, O man, what is good;
and what does the Lord require of you
but to do justice,
and to love kindness,
and to walk humbly with your God?"

This is often called the greatest single verse in the Old Testament. With remarkable insight, the author has focused our attention on three broad avenues of Christian concern. As you meditate upon these words, relate them to your own life.

Have I done justly?
with those whose lives touch mine?
with those who can do me no harm?
with those who are weak?
with those who would not know justice is being done?

Have I loved kindness?
In kindness there is power.
The kind thing is always the right thing to do;
the unkind thing is always the wrong thing.
If I am not kind, all else I am or do will be as a clanging cymbal.

Have I walked humbly with God?
If I really walk with God,
I shall learn the meaning of humility.

—Marvin J. Hartman

DISCIPLESHIP: SERVANTHOOD

In Joyous Celebration

539

"Therefore, I urge you, brothers, in view of God's mercy, to offer your bodies as living sacrifices, holy and pleasing to God—which is your spiritual worship."
—Romans 12:1

Lloyd Larson

C.M.D.
ELLACOMBE
"Gesängbuch der Herzogl," Württemburg

1 In joy - ous cel - e - bra - tion, Lord, We join to bring our praise.
2 We yearn to know Your per - fect plan Of love be - yond com - pare.
3 The fel - low-ship of Chris-tian love Re - news our soul in - deed.
4 In Je - sus Christ, the ser - vant life, Is seen as Your de - cree.

1 With hearts in full - est grat - i - tude, Our voic - es now we raise.
2 And as we seek e - ter - nal truth; Lord, keep us in Your care.
3 And hands ex - tend - ed in Your name Bring strength to those in need.
4 That call a - waits our firm re - ply; In an - swer: "Here are we."

1 Ac - cept our gifts of wor - ship now, And songs of love this day.
2 To grow each day in faith and hope; Lord, nur - ture us, we pray.
3 May we re - flect the one - ness, Lord, De - signed in heav'n a - bove.
4 De - mand the ver - y best of us. We'll share Your love, O Lord.

1 We seek to know Your will and way; O teach us, Lord, we pray.
2 Then we shall lend the help - ing hand That guides some-one to - day.
3 Then help us to be used by You As chan-nels of Your love.
4 In faith-ful ser - vice we will be, Your church to all the world. A-men.

DISCIPLESHIP: SERVANTHOOD

540 Lord, Whose Love Through Humble Service

*"I urge you to offer your bodies as living sacrifices, holy and pleasing to God
—this is your spiritual act of worship." —Romans 12:1*

Albert F. Bayly

8.7.8.7.D.
BEECHER
John Zundel

1 Lord, whose love through hum-ble ser-vice Bore the weight of hu-man need,
2 Still the chil-dren wan-der home-less; Still the hun-gry cry for bread;
3 As we wor-ship, grant us vi-sion Till Your love's re-veal-ing light
4 Called from wor-ship un-to ser-vice, Forth in Your dear name we go

1 Who did on the cross, for-sak en, Work Your mer-cy's per-fect deed:
2 Still the cap-tives long for free-dom; Still in grief we mourn our dead.
3 In its height and depth and great-ness Dawns up-on our quick-ened sight,
4 To the child, the youth, the a-ged, Love in liv-ing deeds to show.

1 We, Your ser-vants, bring the wor-ship Not of voice a-lone, but heart,
2 As, O Lord, Your deep com-pas-sion Healed the sick and freed the soul,
3 Mak-ing known the needs and bur-dens Your com-pas-sion bids us bear,
4 Hope and health, good will and com-fort, Coun-sel, aid, and peace we give,

1 Con-se-crat-ing to Your pur-pose Ev-'ry gift which You im-part.
2 Use the love Your spir-it kin-dles Still to save and make us whole.
3 Stir-ring us to tire-less striv-ing Your a-bun-dant life to share.
4 That Your chil-dren, Lord, in free-dom May Your mer-cy know, and live. A-men.

DISCIPLESHIP: SERVANTHOOD

As Channels of Thy Healing Grace 541

"Heal the sick, raise the dead, cleanse those who have leprosy, drive out demons. Freely you have received, freely give."—Matthew 10:8

Donald R. Frederick

C.M.D.
ALL SAINTS NEW
Henry S. Cutler

1 As chan-nels of Thy heal-ing grace, We would be used, O God,
2 Where bro-ken health and wan-ing strength Are caused by want of food,
3 When bro-ken spir-its reach for light, And grope for vi-sion clear,
4 When neigh-bor-hoods are bro-ken wide With ha-treds seeth-ing deep,

1 To heal the bro-ken, guide the halt On paths the Mas-ter trod.
2 Give us the heart to share our store That health may be re-newed.
3 Re-veal Thy truth and wis-dom, Lord; Re-move the stunt-ing fear.
4 Make real through us true u-ni-ty: Our Fa-ther's will to keep.

1 May we be chan-nels of Thy love Where strife and hate a-bound;
2 Where bro-ken bod-ies writhe in pain, And cry for heal-ing balm,
3 Where bro-ken homes need heal-ing love: Where self-ish pride holds sway,
4 Where bro-ken na-tions strain for power, And vie the stars to gain,

1 We would pro-claim the Mas-ter's way, Where peace and love are found.
2 May we be in-stru-ments of Thine To bring Thy sooth-ing calm.
3 May we be used to rec-on-cile And show the Christ-like way.
4 Use us: our hearts, our minds, our hands To bring Thy peace a-gain. A-men.

DISCIPLESHIP: SERVANTHOOD

542   **Eternal Life**

"Therefore, as we have opportunity, let us do good to all people . . . "
—Galatians 6:10a

St. Francis of Assisi

ETERNAL LIFE
Olive Dungan

Lord, make me an in-stru-ment of Thy peace;

Where there is ha-tred, let me sow love; Where there is in-ju-ry,

par-don; Where there is doubt, faith; Where there is de-spair, hope;

Where there is dark-ness, light; Where there is sad-ness, joy.

DISCIPLESHIP: SERVANTHOOD

O Di-vine Mas-ter, grant that I may not so much seek To be con-soled as to con-sole, To be un-der-stood as to un-der-stand, To be loved as to love; For it is in giv-ing that we re-ceive; It is in par-don-ing that we are par-doned; It is in dy-ing that we are born to e-ter-nal life!

DISCIPLESHIP: SERVANTHOOD

543 Lord, Speak to Me

"Therefore I have reason to glory in Christ Jesus in the things which pertain to God."—Romans 15:17

Frances R. Havergal

L.M.
CANONBURY
Robert Schumann

1 Lord, speak to me, that I may speak In
2 O lead me, Lord, that I may lead The
3 O teach me, Lord, that I may teach The
4 O fill me with Thy full-ness, Lord, Un-
5 O use me, Lord, use e-ven me, Just

1 liv-ing ech-oes of Thy tone; As Thou hast sought, so
2 wan-dering and the wa-vering feet; O feed me, Lord, that
3 pre-cious things Thou dost im-part; And wing my words, that
4 til my ver-y heart o'er-flow In kin-dling thought and
5 as Thou wilt, and when, and where, Un-til Thy bless-ed

1 let me seek Thy err-ing chil-dren lost and lone.
2 I may feed Thy hun-gering ones with man-na sweet.
3 they may reach The hid-den depths of man-y a heart.
4 glow-ing word, Thy love to tell, Thy praise to show.
5 face I see— Thy rest, Thy joy, Thy glo-ry share. A-men.

544 I Cannot Be Idle

"Ask the Lork of the harvest, therefore, to send out workers into His harvest field."—Matthew 9:38

William J. Henry

I CANNOT BE IDLE
William J. Henry

1 I can-not be i-dle, for Je-sus says, "Go And
2 I can-not be i-dle, the fields are so white. And
3 I can-not be i-dle, soon time will be o'er, And
4 I can-not be i-dle, no time for re-pose, My

DISCIPLESHIP: EVANGELISM

1 work in my har-vest to - day; And then at the eve-ning when
2 num-ber-less sheaves will be lost; They per-ish for want of more
3 reap-ing be end-ed for aye; I'll gath-er the lost from the
4 rest-ing shall be o - ver there, Where all of the faith-ful in

1 la - bor is done, What - ev - er is right I will pay."
2 reap-ers to save— How aw - ful to think of the cost!
3 by - ways of sin To walk in the beau - ti - ful way.
4 heav - en a - bove A crown of bright glo - ry shall wear.

Then a - way to the work I will go And
(I'll go)

join in the reap-ing of grain, And back from the har-vest with
(I'll go,)

beau - ti - ful sheaves I'll come with re - joic-ing a - gain.

DISCIPLESHIP: EVANGELISM

545

Pass It On

" . . . as I have loved you, that you also should love one another."
—John 13:34

Kurt Kaiser

PASS IT ON
Kurt Kaiser

1 It on-ly takes a spark to get a fire go-ing,
2 What a won-drous time is spring—when all the trees are bud-ding,
3 I wish for you, my friend, this hap-pi-ness that I've found—

1 And soon all those a-round can warm up in its glow-ing;
2 The birds be-gin to sing, the flow-ers start their bloom-ing;
3 You can de-pend on Him, it mat-ters not where you're bound;

1 That's how it is with God's love, once you've ex-per-i-enced it:
2 That's how it is with God's love, once you've ex-per-i-enced it:
3 I'll shout it from the moun-tain top, I want my world to know:

1 You spread His love to ev-ery-one, you want to pass it on.
2 You want to sing, it's fresh like spring, you want to pass it on.
3 The Lord of love has come to me, I want to pass it on.

DISCIPLESHIP: EVANGELISM

Lord, Lay Some Soul Upon My Heart

546

" . . . I have become all things to all men, that I might by all means save some."—I Corinthians 9:22

Leon Tucker

UPON MY HEART
Ira D. Sankey

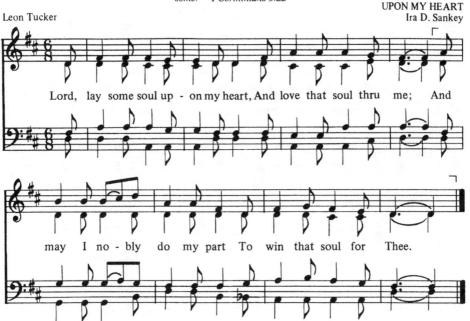

Lord, lay some soul up - on my heart, And love that soul thru me; And may I no - bly do my part To win that soul for Thee.

Help Us to Witness, Lord **547**

LEADER: Listen to Jesus' Commission for our ministry as individuals and a church. "You did not choose Me, but I chose you and appointed you that you should go and bear fruit..." (*John 15:16a*)

PEOPLE: *We accept our calling!*

LEADER: Jesus said, "All authority has been given to Me in heaven and on earth. Go therefore and make disciples of all nations, baptizing them in the name of the Father and of the Son and of the Holy Spirit, teaching them to observe all things that I have commanded you; and lo, I am with you always, even to the end of the age." (*Matthew 28:18-20*)

ALL: *Lord, we hear Your call. Fill us anew with Your Spirit and empower us to share Your love as individuals and as a church with a mission. In Your powerful name. Amen.*

—Lloyd John Ogilvie

DISCIPLESHIP: EVANGELISM

548 Get All Excited

"... the King of kings, and Lord of lords."—I Timothy 6:15

William J. Gaither

GET ALL EXCITED
William J. Gaither

Get all ex-cit-ed, go tell ev-ery-bod-y that Je-sus Christ is King! Get all ex-cit-ed, go tell ev-ery-bod-y that Je-sus Christ is King! Get all ex-cit-ed, go tell ev-ery-bod-y that Je-sus Christ is King, Je-sus Christ is still the King of kings, King of kings!

DISCIPLESHIP: EVANGELISM

The Wise May Bring Their Learning 549

" . . . Silver or gold I do not have, but what I have I give you."—Acts 3:6a 7.6.7.6.D.

Anonymous
From The Book of Praise for Children

FOREST GREEN
Traditional English Melody
Arr. by Ralph Vaughan Williams

1 The wise may bring their learn - ing, The rich may bring their wealth,
2 We'll bring Him hearts that love Him, We'll bring Him thank-ful praise,
3 We'll come and show the Sav - ior The things we do each day;

1 And some may bring their bril - liance, And some bring strength and health;
2 And young souls hum-bly striv - ing To walk in ho - ly ways;
3 We'll try our best to please Him At home, at school or play;

1 We, too, would bring our trea - sures To of - fer to the King;
2 And these shall be our trea - sures We of - fer to the King.
3 And bet - ter are these trea - sures To of - fer to our King.

1 We have no gifts de - serv - ing: What shall we chil - dren bring?
2 And these are gifts that ev - en The young-est child may bring.
3 Than rich-est gifts with - out them; Yet these a child may bring. A-men.

550 God, Whose Giving Knows No Ending

"Now it is required that those who have been given a trust must prove faithful."
—I Corinthians 4:2

8.7.8.7.D.

Robert L. Edwards

HYFRYDOL
Rowland H. Prichard

1 God, whose giv-ing knows no end-ing, All our life is
2 Skills and time are ours for press-ing Toward the goals of
3 Trea-sure, too, Thou hast en-trust-ed, Gain thru powers Thy
4 Lend Thy joy to all our giv-ing, Let it light our

1 from Thy store: Na-ture's won-der, Je-sus' wis-dom, Cost-ly
2 Christ, Thy Son: We at peace in health and free-dom, Rac-es
3 grace con-ferred; Ours to use for home and kin-dred And to
4 pil-grim way; From the dark of anx-ious keep-ing, Loose us

1 cross, grave's shat-tered door. Gift-ed by Thee, turn we to Thee,
2 joined, the church made one. Now di-rect our dai-ly la-bor,
3 spread the Gos-pel Word. O-pen wide our hands in shar-ing,
4 in-to gen-er-ous day. Then when years on earth are o-ver,

1 Of-fering up our-selves in praise; Thank-ful song shall rise for-
2 Lest we strive for self a-lone; Born with ta-lents, make us
3 As we heed Christ's age-less call, Heal-ing, teach-ing and re-
4 Hav-ing sought to fol-low Thy plan, Lord, ful-fill be-yond our

DISCIPLESHIP: STEWARDSHIP OF LIFE

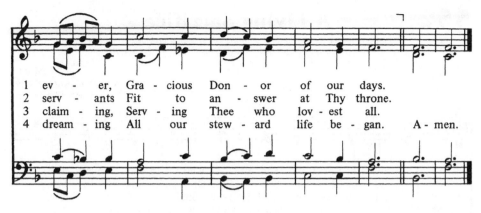

1	ev - er,	Gra - cious	Don - or	of our	days.		
2	serv - ants	Fit to	an - swer	at Thy	throne.		
3	claim - ing,	Serv - ing	Thee who	lov - est	all.		
4	dream - ing	All our	stew - ard	life be - gan.		A - men.	

Giving 551

Give, and it will be given to you. A good measure,
pressed down, shaken together and running over,
will be poured into your lap. For with the measure
you use, it will be measured to you.

> **In everything I did, I showed you that by this
> kind of hard work we must help the weak,
> remembering the words the Lord Jesus Himself
> said: It is more blessed to give than to receive.**

On the first day of every week, each one of you
should set aside a sum of money in keeping with his
income, saving it up, so that when I come no
collections will have to be made.

> **Just as you excel in everything—in faith, in
> speech, in knowledge, in complete earnestness
> and in your love for us—see that you also excel
> in this grace of giving.**

For you know the grace of our Lord Jesus Christ,
that though He was rich, yet for your sakes He
became poor, so that you through His poverty might
become rich.

> **If the willingness is there, the gift is acceptable
> according to what one has, not according to
> what he does not have.**

Remember this: Whoever sows sparingly will also
reap sparingly, and whoever sows generously will
also reap generously. Each man should give what he
has decided in his heart to give, not reluctantly or
under compulsion, for God loves a cheerful giver.

> **Thanks be to God for His indescribable Gift!**

*—Luke 6:38; Acts 20:35; 1 Cor. 16:2;
2 Cor. 8:7,9,12; 9:6–7,15*

552

A Living Sacrifice

*"If anyone serves, he should do it with the strength God provides, so that in all
things God may be praised through Jesus Christ."—I Peter 4:11b*

Lucena Byrum

C.M.wR.
A LIVING SACRIFICE
Henry C. Clausen

1 I love the Christ, the Son of God, Who died that I might live;
2 I fail to find a sac - ri -fice, Or fit -ting gift to bring;
3 No gift, how - ev - er grand or great, Could pay the debt I owe;
4 My tal - ents all I glad - ly yield For serv - ice, Lord, to Thee;

1 I would my grat - i - tude ex - press, A gift un - to Him give.
2 Earth's trea-sures have too lit - tle worth To of - fer to my King.
3 I bring my-self, my life, my all, A liv - ing gift be - stow.
4 To bear the bless - ed gos - pel light, That oth - ers Christ may see.

My gift is small, it is my all; Ac - cept it, Lord, I pray:

Let self be slain, let Je - sus reign With - in my heart al - way.

DISCIPLESHIP: STEWARDSHIP OF LIFE

Give of Your Best to the Master

553

"Never be lacking in zeal, but keep your spiritual fervor, serving the Lord."
—Romans 12:11

Howard B. Grose

8.7.8.7.D.wR.
BARNARD
Charlotte A. Barnard

1 Give of your best to the Mas - ter, Give of the strength of your youth;
2 Give of your best to the Mas - ter, Give Him first place in your heart;
3 Give of your best to the Mas - ter, Naught else is wor - thy His love;
Refrain – Give of your best to the Mas - ter, Give of the strength of your youth;

Fine

1 Throw your soul's fresh, glow-ing ar - dor, In - to the bat - tle for truth.
2 Give Him first place in your serv - ice, Con - se - crate ev - 'ry part.
3 He gave Him-self for your ran - som, Gave up His glo - ry a - bove:
Ref– Clad in sal - va-tion's full ar - mor, Join in the bat - tle for truth.

1 Je - sus has set the ex - am - ple— Daunt-less was He, young and brave;
2 Give and to you shall be giv - en— God His be - lov - ed Son gave;
3 Laid down His life with - out mur - mur, You from sin's ru - in to save;

D.C.

1 Give Him your loy - al de - vo - tion, Give Him the best that you have.
2 Grate-ful - ly seek - ing to serve Him, Give Him the best that you have.
3 Give Him your heart's ad - o - ra - tion, Give Him the best that you have.

DISCIPLESHIP: STEWARDSHIP OF LIFE

554 *Do Not Be Anxious*

"Therefore I tell you, do not worry about your life, what you will eat or drink; or about your body, what you will wear. Is not life more important than food, and the body more important than clothes?

Look at the birds of the air; they do not sow or reap or store away in barns, yet your heavenly Father feeds them. Are you not much more valuable than they?

Who of you by worrying can add a single hour to his life?

And why do you worry about clothes? See how the lilies of the field grow. They do not labor or spin.

Yet I tell you that not even Solomon in all his splendor was dressed like one of these.

If that is how God clothes the grass of the field, which is here today and tomorrow is thrown into the fire, will he not much more clothe you, O you of little faith?

So do not worry, saying, 'What shall we eat?' or 'What shall we drink?' or 'What shall we wear?'

For the pagans run after all these things, and your heavenly Father knows that you need them.

But seek first his kingdom and his righteousness, and all these things will be given to you as well.

Therefore do not worry about tomorrow, for tomorrow will worry about itself. Each day has enough trouble of its own."

—Matthew 6:25-34 (NIV)

555 We Give Thee But Thine Own

"But who am I, and who are my people, that we should be able to give as generously as this? Everything comes from you, and we have given you only what comes from your hand."—I Chronicles 29:14

S.M.
William W. How

SCHUMANN
Mason and Webb's *Cantica Laudis*

1 We give Thee but Thine own, What-e'er the gift may be:
2 May we Thy boun-ties thus As stew-ards true re-ceive,
3 To com-fort and to bless, To find a balm for woe,
4 And we be-lieve Thy word, Though dim our faith may be:

1 All that we have is Thine a-lone, A trust, O Lord, from Thee.
2 And glad-ly, as Thou bless-est us, To Thee our first-fruits give.
3 To tend the lone and par-ent-less Is our great task be-low.
4 What-ev-er task we do, O Lord, We do it un-to Thee. A-men.

DISCIPLESHIP: STEWARDSHIP OF LIFE

As Those of Old Their Firstfruits Brought

556

"Honor the Lord with your wealth, with the firstfruits of all your crops."
—Proverbs 3:9

C.M.
ELLACOMBE
Gesangbuch, Wirtemberg

Frank von Christierson

1 As those of old their first-fruits brought Of or-chard, flock, and field
2 A world in need now sum-mons us To la-bor, love and give,
3 In gra-ti-tude and hum-ble trust We bring our best to Thee

1 To God the Giv-er of all good, The Source of boun-teous yield;
2 To make our life an of-fer-ing To God, that all may live;
3 To serve Thy cause and share Thy love With all hu-man-i-ty.

1 So we to-day first fruits would bring, The wealth of this good land,
2 The church of Christ is call-ing us To make the dream come true
3 O God who gav-est us Thy-self In Je-sus Christ Thy Son,

1 Of farm and mar-ket, shop and home, Of mind and heart and hand.
2 A world re-deemed by Christ-like love, All life in Christ made new.
3 Teach us to give our-selves each day Un-til life's work is done. A-men.

Words Copyright © 1961. Renewal 1989 by The Hymn Society of America. All Rights Reserved. Used By Permission.

DISCIPLESHIP: STEWARDSHIP OF LIFE

557   What Gift Can We Bring?

"We give thanks to you, O God, we give thanks, for your Name is near; men
tell of your wonderful deeds."—Psalm 75:1

11.11.11.11.

ANNIVERSARY SONG
Jane Marshall

Jane Marshall

Unison

1 What gift can we bring, what pres - ent, what to - ken?
2 Give thanks for the Past, for those who had vi - sion,
3 Give thanks for To - mor - row, full of sur - pris - es,
4 This gift we now bring, this pres - ent, this to - ken,

1 What words can con - vey it— the joy of this day?
2 Who plant - ed and wa - tered so dreams could come true.
3 For know - ing what - ev - er To - mor - row may bring,
4 These words can con - vey it— the joy of this day!

1 When grate - ful we come, re - mem - bering, re - joic - ing,
2 Give thanks for the Now, for stud - y, for wor - ship,
3 God gives us His Word that al - ways, for - ev - er,
4 When grate - ful we come, re - mem - bering, re - joic - ing,

1 What song can we of - fer in hon - or and praise?
2 For mis - sion that bids us turn prayer in - to deed.
3 We rest in His keep - ing and live in His love.
4 This song we now of - er in hon - or and praise!

DISCIPLESHIP: STEWARDSHIP OF LIFE

Because I Have Been Given Much

558

"Therefore, as we have opportunity, let us do good to all people, especially to those who belong to the family of believers."—Galatians 6:10

8.4.8.4.8.8.8.8.

Grace Noll Crowell

THY GREAT BOUNTY
Blanche Douglas Byles

1 Be - cause I have been giv - en much, I too must give:
2 Be - cause I have been shel - tered, fed, By Thy good care,
3 Be - cause love has been lav - ished so Up - on me, Lord,

1 Be - cause of Thy great boun - ty, Lord, Each day I live,
2 I can - not see an - oth - er's lack And I not share
3 A wealth I know that was not meant For me to hoard,

1 I shall di - vide my gifts from Thee With all the peo - ple
2 My glow - ing fire, my loaf of bread, My roof's safe shel - ter
3 I shall give love to those in need, Shall show that love by

1 that I see Who have the need of help from me.
2 o - ver-head,That each, too, may be com - fort - ed.
3 word and deed;Thus shall my thanks be thanks in - deed. A-men.

DISCIPLESHIP: STEWARDSHIP OF LIFE

559 Glorious Is Thy Name, Most Holy

"Now, who is willing to consecrate himself to the Lord?"—I Chronicles 29:5b

Ruth Elliott

8.7.8.7.D.

HOLY MANNA
William Moore

1 Glo - rious is Thy name, Most Ho - ly, God and Fa - ther of us all;
2 For our world of need and an - guish We would lift to Thee our prayer.
3 In the midst of time we jour - ney, From Thy hand comes each new day;

1 We Thy ser - vants bow be - fore Thee, Strive to an - swer ev - 'ry call.
2 Faith - ful stew - ards of Thy boun - ty, May we with all peo - ple share.
3 We would use it in Thy ser - vice, Hum - bly, wise - ly, while we may.

1 Thou with life's great good hast blest us, Cared for us from ear - liest years;
2 In the name of Christ our Sav - ior, Who re - deems and sets us free,
3 So to Thee, Lord and Cre - a - tor, Praise and hon - or we ac - cord;

1 Un - to Thee our thanks we ren - der; Thy deep love o'er - comes all fears.
2 Gifts we bring of heart and trea - sure, That our lives may wor - thier be.
3 Thine the earth and Thine the heav - ens, Through all the E - ter - nal Word.

DISCIPLESHIP: STEWARDSHIP OF LIFE

I Gave My Life for Thee

560

"Greater love has no one than this, that one lay down his life for his friends."
—John 15:13

Frances R. Havergal

6.6.6.6.8.6.
KENOSIS
Philip P. Bliss

1. I gave My life for thee, My pre-cious blood I shed,
   That thou might'st ran-somed be, And quick-ened from the dead,
   I gave, I gave My life for thee, What hast thou giv'n for Me?

2. My Fa-ther's house of light, My glo-ry-cir-cled throne,
   I left for earth-ly night For wan-d'rings sad and lone;
   I left, I left it all for thee, Hast thou left aught for Me?

3. I suf-fered much for thee, More than thy tongue can tell
   Of bit-t'rest ag-o-ny, To res-cue thee from hell;
   I've borne, I've borne it all for thee, What hast thou borne for Me?

4. And I have brought to thee, Down from My home a-bove,
   Sal-va-tion full and free, My par-don and My love;
   I bring, I bring rich gifts to thee, What hast thou brought to Me?

A Living Sacrifice

561

Therefore, I urge you, brothers, in view of God's mercy to offer your bodies as living sacrifices. holy and pleasing to God—this is your spiritual act of worship. Do not conform any longer to the pattern of this world, but be transformed by the renewing of your mind. Then you will be able to test and approve what God's will is—his good, pleasing and perfect will.

For by the grace given me I say to every one of you: Do not think of yourself more highly than you ought, but rather think of yourself with sober judgment, in accordance with the measure of faith God has given you. Just as each of us has one body with many members, and these members do not all have the same function, so in Christ we who are many form one body, and each member belongs to all the others. We have different gifts, according to the grace given us. If a man's gift is prophesying, let him use it in proportion to his faith. If it is serving, let him serve; if it is teaching, let him teach; if it is encouraging, let him encourage; if it is contributing to the needs of others, let him give generously; if it is leadership, let him govern diligently; if it is showing mercy, let him do it cheerfully.

—Romans 12:1–8 (NIV)

DISCIPLESHIP: STEWARDSHIP OF LIFE

562 Bless Thou the Gifts

"Then the disciples went out and preached everywhere, and the Lord worked with them and confirmed his word by the signs that accompanied it."
—Mark 16:20

Samuel Longfellow

L.M.
CANONBURY
Robert Schumann

Bless thou the gifts our hands have bro't; Bless Thou the work our hearts have planned; Ours is the faith, the will, the thought; The rest, O God, is in Thy hand. A-men.

563 O God of Love, Who Gave Us Life

"Serve wholeheartedly, as if you were serving the Lord, not men."
—Ephesians 6:7

E. Urner Goodman

C.M.
ST. ANNE
William Croft

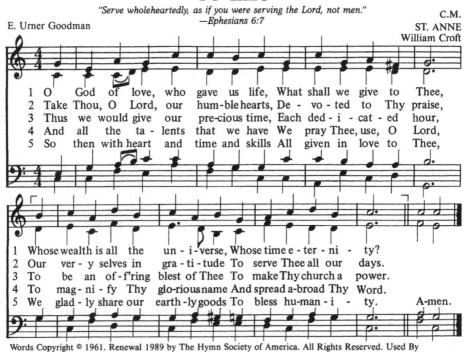

1 O God of love, who gave us life, What shall we give to Thee,
2 Take Thou, O Lord, our hum-ble hearts, De-vo-ted to Thy praise,
3 Thus we would give our pre-cious time, Each ded-i-cat-ed hour,
4 And all the ta-lents that we have We pray Thee, use, O Lord,
5 So then with heart and time and skills All given in love to Thee,

1 Whose wealth is all the un-i-verse, Whose time e-ter-ni-ty?
2 Our ver-y selves in gra-ti-tude To serve Thee all our days.
3 To be an of-f'ring blest of Thee To make Thy church a power.
4 To mag-ni-fy Thy glo-rious name And spread a-broad Thy Word.
5 We glad-ly share our earth-ly goods To bless hu-man-i-ty. A-men.

DISCIPLESHIP: STEWARDSHIP OF LIFE

Something for Thee

"Do your best to present yourself as one approved . . . " —II Timothy 2:15a

6.4.6.4.6.6.6.4.
SOMETHING FOR THEE

Sylvanus D. Phelps

Robert Lowry

1 Sav - ior, Thy dy - ing love Thou gav - est me,
2 At the blest mer - cy seat, Plead - ing for me,
3 Give me a faith - ful heart, Like - ness to Thee,
4 All that I am and have, Thy gifts so free,

1 Nor should I e'er with - hold, Dear Lord, from Thee:
2 My fee - ble faith looks up, Je - sus, to Thee:
3 That each de - part - ing day Hence - forth may see
4 In joy, in grief, thro' life, Dear Lord, for Thee!

1 In love my soul would bow, My heart ful - fill its vow,
2 Help me the cross to bear, Thy won - drous love de - clare,
3 Some work of love be - gun, Some deed of kind-ness done,
4 And when Thy face I see, My ran - som'd soul shall be,

1 Some of - f'ring bring Thee now, Some - thing for Thee.
2 Some song to raise, or pray'r, Some - thing for Thee.
3 Some wan - d'rer sought and won, Some - thing for Thee.
4 Thro' all e - ter - ni - ty, Some - thing for Thee.

DISCIPLESHIP: STEWARDSHIP OF LIFE

565 Little Is Much, When God Is in It

"Here is a boy with five small barley loaves and two small fish, but how far will they go among so many?"—John 6:9

Kittie Louise Suffield

STEWARDSHIP
Kittie Louise Suffield

1 In the har-vest field now rip-ened, There's a work for all to do;
2 Does the place you're called to la-bor Seem so small and lit-tle known?
3 When the con-flict here is end-ed And our race on earth is run;

1 Hark, the voice of God is call-ing, To the har-vest call-ing you.
2 It is great if God is in it, And He'll not for-get His own.
3 He will say, if we are faith-ful, "Wel-come home, my child, well done."

Lit-tle is much when God is in it, La-bor not for wealth or fame;

There's a crown and you can win it, If you go in Je-sus' name.

DISCIPLESHIP: STEWARDSHIP OF LIFE

I Will Sing the Wondrous Story 566

"And he showed me a pure river . . . of life, clear as crystal, proceeding from the throne of God and of the Lamb."—Revelation 22:1

8.7.8.7.wR.
WONDROUS STORY
Peter P. Bilhorn

Francis H. Rowley

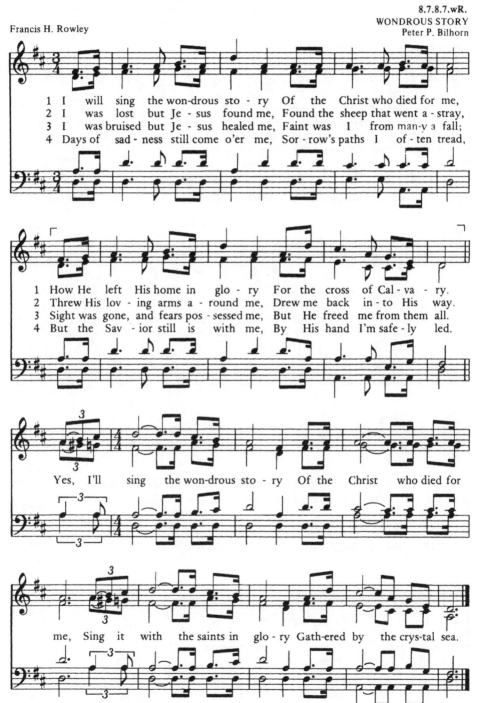

1 I will sing the won-drous sto - ry Of the Christ who died for me,
2 I was lost but Je - sus found me, Found the sheep that went a - stray,
3 I was bruised but Je - sus healed me, Faint was I from man-y a fall;
4 Days of sad - ness still come o'er me, Sor - row's paths I of - ten tread,

1 How He left His home in glo - ry For the cross of Cal - va - ry.
2 Threw His lov - ing arms a - round me, Drew me back in - to His way.
3 Sight was gone, and fears pos - sessed me, But He freed me from them all.
4 But the Sav - ior still is with me, By His hand I'm safe - ly led.

Yes, I'll sing the won-drous sto - ry Of the Christ who died for me, Sing it with the saints in glo - ry Gath-ered by the crys-tal sea.

WITNESS AND TESTIMONY

567 A Child of God

"The Spirit himself testifies with our spirit that we are God's children."
—Romans 8:16

Barney E. Warren

11.6.11.6.wR.
CHILD OF GOD
Barney E. Warren

1 Praise the Lord! my heart with His love is beam-ing, I am a child of
2 Let the saints re-joice with my rap-tured spir-it, I am a child of
3 Let a ho-ly life tell the gos-pel sto-ry, I am a child of
4 Saved from sin to-day, ev-ery band is riv-en, I am a child of

1 God; Heav-en's gold-en light o-ver me is stream-ing, I am a child of God.
2 God; I will tes-ti-fy that the world may hear it, I am a child of God.
3 God; How He fills the soul with His grace and glo-ry, I am a child of God.
4 God; Thro' the tests of life I have peace from heav-en, I am a child of God.

I am a child of God, I am a child of God; I have
I am a child, a child of God, I am a child, a child of God;

washed my robes in the cleans-ing foun-tain, I am a child of God.

WITNESS AND TESTIMONY

It Is Truly Wonderful

*"If we confess our sins, he is faithful and just and will forgive us our sins and
purify us from all unrighteousness."—I John 1:9*

7.6.7.6.wR.

Barney E. Warren

TRULY WONDERFUL
Barney E. Warren

1 He par-doned my trans-gres-sions, He sanc-ti-fied my soul;
2 He brings me thro' af-flic-tion, He leaves me not a-lone;
3 He keeps me firm and faith-ful, His love I do en-joy;

1 He hon-ors my con-fes-sions, Since by His blood I'm whole.
2 He's with me in temp-ta-tion, He keeps me for His own.
3 For this I shall be grate-ful And live in His em-ploy.

It is tru-ly won-der-ful what the Lord has done, It is
tru-ly won-der-ful, It is tru-ly won-der-ful; It is
tru-ly won-der-ful what the Lord has done. Glo-ry to His name!

WITNESS AND TESTIMONY

569 I'm Redeemed

"Who gave himself for us to redeem us . . . "—Titus 2:14a

Joseph C. Fisher

I'M REDEEMED
Joseph C. Fisher

1 I'm re-deemed, I'm re-deemed, From the dark-ness of the night That so
2 I'm re-deemed by Thy blood, From the pow-er of the grave, And the
3 I'm re-deemed from all sin, And I'm walk-ing in the light, And Thy
4 The re-deemed ones shall walk In The path-way of the just, Which shines

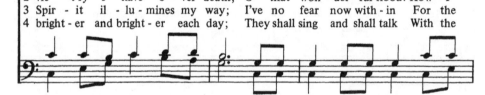

1 thick-ly en-vel-oped my soul; In my heart there have gleamed Rays of
2 vic-t'ry I have o-ver death; O that won-der-ful flood! How I
3 Spir-it il-lu-mines my way; I've no fear now with-in For the
4 bright-er and bright-er each day; They shall sing and shall talk With the

1 won-der-ful light, Where the waves of Thy glo-ry now roll.
2 felt its pow'r to save, When I plunged in its fath-om-less depth!
3 ter-ror of the night, Nor the ar-row that fli-eth by day.
4 bright an-gel-ic host, Where all sor-row and sighs flee a-way.

I'm re-deemed, praise the Lord! I'm re-
I'm re-deemed, praise the Lord!

deemed by the blood of the Lamb; I am saved from all sin, and I'm

walk-ing in the light, I'm re-deemed by the blood of the Lamb.

WITNESS AND TESTIMONY

570 Tell What He's Done for You

"Return home and tell how much God has done for you."—Luke 8:39a

Lizzie DeArmond

TELL WHAT HE'S DONE
Andrew L. Byers

1 Have you found rest and peace with - in, Rolled
2 Have you a Friend whose won - drous grace Lights
3 Have you been saved His love to show, Who
4 Have you a joy that ne'er shall fail E'en

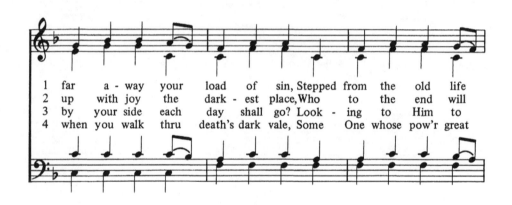

1 far a - way your load of sin, Stepped from the old life
2 up with joy the dark - est place, Who to the end will
3 by your side each day shall go? Look - ing to Him to
4 when you walk thru death's dark vale, Some One whose pow'r great

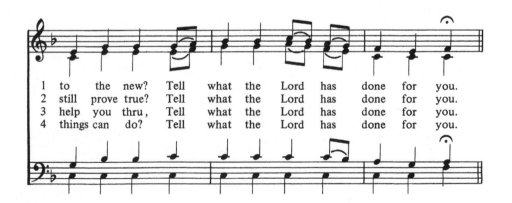

1 to the new? Tell what the Lord has done for you.
2 still prove true? Tell what the Lord has done for you.
3 help you thru, Tell what the Lord has done for you.
4 things can do? Tell what the Lord has done for you.

O   tell   what He's   done   for   you,   Of His
Tell   what He's done,   what He's   done   for   you;

love   so   strong and   true;   O   tell   what He's done,
Tell   of His love   so   strong and   true;

what He's   done   for   you;   Oth - ers   may   need   Him,   too.

WITNESS AND TESTIMONY

571   A New Name in Glory

"However, do not rejoice that the spirits submit to you, but rejoice that your names are written in Heaven."—Luke 10:20

C. Austin Miles

NEW NAME
C. Austin Miles

1. I was once a sin-ner, but I came Par-don to re-ceive from my
2. I was hum-bly kneel-ing at the cross, Fear-ing naught but God's an-gry
3. In the Book 'tis writ-ten, "Saved by Grace," O the joy that came to my

1. Lord: This was free-ly giv-en and I found That He al-ways kept His
2. frown; When the heav-ens o-pened and I saw That my name was writ-ten
3. soul! Now I am for-giv-en and I know By the blood I am made

1. word. (kept His word.)
2. down. (writ-ten down.) There's a new name writ-ten down in glo-ry, And it's
3. whole. (am made whole.)

WITNESS AND TESTIMONY

mine,   O yes, it's mine!   And the white-robed an-gels sing the
And it's mine,   yes, it's mine!

sto-ry,   "A   sin - ner   has   come   home."   For there's a
has come home.

new name written down in glo-ry,   And it's mine,   O yes, it's mine!   With my
And it's mine,   yes, it's mine!

sins for-giv-en I am bound for heav-en,   Nev-er-more to roam.

WITNESS AND TESTIMONY

572 Since I Have Been Redeemed

"Christ redeemed us from the curse of the law by becoming a curse for us, for it is written: 'Cursed is everyone who is hung on a tree.' "—Galatians 3:13

C.M.wR.
OTHELLO
Edwin O. Excell

Edwin O. Excell

1 I have a song I love to sing, Since I have been re-deemed,
2 I have a Christ that sat-is-fies, Since I have been re-deemed,
3 I have a wit-ness bright and clear, Since I have been re-deemed,
4 I have a home pre-pared for me, Since I have been re-deemed,

1 Of my Re-deem-er, Sav-ior, King— Since I have been re-deemed.
2 To do His will my high-est prize— Since I have been re-deemed.
3 Dis-pell-ing ev-ery doubt and fear— Since I have been re-deemed.
4 Where I shall dwell e-ter-nal-ly— Since I have been re-deemed.

Since I have been re-deemed, Since I have been re-deemed, I will glo-ry in His name:

Since I have been re-deemed, I will glo-ry in my Sav-ior's name.

At Calvary

573

*"It is for freedom that Christ has set us free. Stand firm, then, and do not let
yourselves be burdened again by a yoke of slavery."—Galatians 5:1*

William R. Newell

9.9.9.4.wR.
CALVARY
Daniel B. Towner

1 Years I spent in van - i - ty and pride, Car - ing not my Lord was
2 By God's Word at last my sin I learned; Then I trem-bled at the
3 Now I've given to Je - sus ev - ery-thing; Now I glad - ly own Him
4 O the love that drew sal - va-tion's plan! O the grace that bro't it

1 cru - ci - fied, Know-ing not it was for me He died On Cal - va - ry.
2 law I'd spurned, 'Til my guilt-y soul im - plor-ing turned To Cal - va - ry.
3 as my King; Now my rap-tured soul can on - ly sing Of Cal - va - ry.
4 down to man! O the might-y gulf that God did span At Cal - va - ry.

Mer - cy there was great and grace was free, Par - don there was mul - ti -

plied to me, There my bur-dened soul found lib - er - ty— At Cal - va - ry.

574

Waves of Devotion

"Indeed, the water I give him will become in him a spring of water welling up to eternal life."—John 4:14b

Barney E. Warren

WAVES OF DEVOTION
Barney E. Warren

1 A glo - ri - ous bless - ing be - stowed up - on me— Sal - va - tion the
2 Sal - va - tion, O glo - ry! its rap - ture I feel— A cur - rent of
3 My path - way is bright as the cloud - less noon-day, My peace like a
4 More pre-cious, more price-less than ru - bies or gold, His full - ness of

1 joy of my heart! The theme of my song and for - ev - er shall be,
2 heav - en - ly bliss; My soul is de - light - ed, I can - not con - ceal
3 riv - er that flows; Up - on me such bless - ings are show-ered al - way,
4 in - fi - nite love; He's fill - ing my heart with its trea-sures un - told,

1 To me Thy rich grac - es im - part.
2 The deep-seat-ed joy I pos - sess.
3 Which grace in pro - fu - sion be - stows.
4 I'm feast - ing with Him from a - bove.

The waves of de - vo - tion are

flood - ing my soul, And spar - kle so bright in the sun; I drink of that

WITNESS AND TESTIMONY

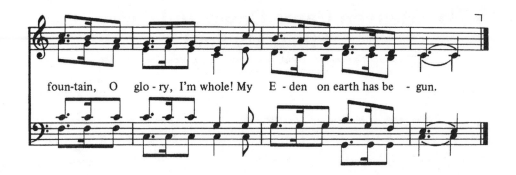

foun-tain, O glo - ry, I'm whole! My E - den on earth has be - gun.

Love Is the Greatest Witness **575**

Jesus walked with common men . . . but
there was nothing common about His
words . . . they upset every comfortable
ethic!

He upset judicial systems when He said
. . . "Love those who hate you."

He upset patterns of religion by declaring
that *real* temples of worship were in the
hearts of believers.

He refused to discuss laws and rules
governing people's actions, but zeroed in
on their thoughts and attitudes instead.

If Christ had been a warrior they could
have fought Him.

Had He been a religionist, they could
have ignored Him as an eccentric.

But Christ was Love . . . what do you
do with that?

—Gloria Gaither

From *Alleluia: A Praise Gathering For Believers*

576 Heaven Came Down and Glory Filled My Soul

*"Therefore, if anyone is in Christ, he is a new creation; the old has gone, the
new has come!"—II Corinthians 5:17*

John W. Peterson

HEAVEN CAME DOWN
John W. Peterson

1 O what a won-der-ful, won-der-ful day— Day I will nev-er for-
2 Born of the Spir-it with life from a-bove In - to God's fam-i-ly di-
3 Now I've a hope that will sure-ly en-dure Af - ter the pass-ing of

1 get; Af - ter I'd wan-dered in dark-ness a-way, Je - sus my
2 vine, Jus - ti-fied ful-ly through Cal - va-ry's love, O what a
3 time; I have a fu -ture in heav-en for sure, There in those

1 Sav - ior I met. O what a ten - der, com - pas - sion-ate friend—
2 stand-ing is mine! And the trans-ac - tion so quick-ly was made
3 man-sions sub - lime. And it's be-cause of that won-der-ful day

1 He met the need of my heart; Shad - ows dis - pel - ling, With
2 When as a sin - ner I came, Took of the of - fer Of
3 When at the cross I be - lieved; Rich - es e - ter - nal And

WITNESS AND TESTIMONY

1 joy I am tell - ing, He made all the dark - ness de - part!
2 grace He did prof - fer— He saved me, O praise His dear name!
3 bless - ings su - per - nal From His pre-cious hand I re - ceived.

Heav - en came down and glo - ry filled my soul,

When at the cross the Sav-ior made me whole; My

sins were washed a - way And my night was turned to day—

Heav-en came down and glo-ry filled my soul!

WITNESS AND TESTIMONY

577 This Is the Time I Must Sing

" 'I tell you,' he replied, 'if they keep quiet, the stones will cry out.' "
—Luke 19:40

William J. Gaither
Gloria Gaither

THIS IS THE TIME
William J. Gaither

1 I have tast - ed of free-dom, I can go where He's lead - ing, for
2 If I've seen and I've done and I've gained and I've won all the

1 shack - les can hold me no more. I have
2 good things that life ev - er brings, Still my

1 learned of life's es - sence, and I stand in His pres - ence, and
2 heart knows His touch and He's loved me so much, that for -

1 sing with my heart: "He is Lord." There are days filled with sor-row, and
2 ev - er I just have to sing. If the rocks would cry out, should His

1 plans for to - mor - row, but this is the time I must
2 prais - es die out, then the stones must keep si - lent as

WITNESS AND TESTIMONY

WITNESS AND TESTIMONY

578 The Lord Raised Me

"He lifted me out of the slimy pit, out of the mud and mire . . . "—Psalm 40:2a

James Rowe

THE LORD RAISED ME
Hamp Sewell

1 In the aw - ful sea of sin I was sink - ing fast;
2 On the peace - ful shore to - day Prais - es glad I sing;
3 Soul a - drift, the waves roll high, Break-ers are a - head;

1 There were man - y stains with - in From my sin - ful past;
2 Sin - ful days have passed a - way, To the Lord I cling;
3 To the bless - ed Sav - ior cry, Ere your hope is dead;

1 But I looked to Him a - bove, Made a dy - ing plea,
2 In His ho - ly light I dwell, Pure and sweet and free,
3 Noth-ing bet - ter you can do, Saved from death to be;

WITNESS AND TESTIMONY

1 And His might - y hand of love Reached down for me.
2 While to all the world I tell How He raised me.
3 He a - lone can res - cue you, For He raised me.

The Lord raised me, the Lord raised me, Whis-pered com-fort

to my soul and made me free; The Lord raised me, the

Lord raised me; When light had fled and hope was dead The Lord raised me.

579 All Taken Away

"If we confess our sins, he is faithful and just and will forgive us our sins and
purify us from all unrighteousness."—I John 1:9

R. Kelso Carter

ALL TAKEN AWAY
Unknown

1 Did you hear what Je - sus said to me? "They're all tak-en a-
2 O this won - drous grace so free and full, They're all tak-en a-
3 I have plunged be - neath the crim - son tide, They're all tak-en a-
4 Now the Spir - it wit - ness - es to me They're all tak-en a-
5 So I praise the Lord for sins for-giv'n, They're all tak-en a-

1 way, a - way; Your sins are par-doned and you are free, They're
2 way, a - way; Tho red like crim - son they're now as wool, They're
3 way, a - way; And now by faith I am pu - ri - fied, They're
4 way, a - way; And keeps me stand-ing in lib - er - ty, They're
5 way, a - way; While on - ward press-ing my way to heav'n, They're

all tak-en a - way." They're all tak-en a - way, a - way,

They're all tak - en a - way, a-way; They're all tak - en a -

way, a - way, My sins are all tak - en a - way.

WITNESS AND TESTIMONY

In the Light of God

"But if we walk in the light, as he is in the light, we have fellowship with one another, and the blood of Jesus, his Son, purifies us from all sin."—I John 1:7

Daniel S. Warner

IN THE LIGHT OF GOD
Joshua A. Knight

1 A - long a dark and gloom-y path I groped be-neath the shades of death,
2 My dark-ness now is passed a-way, In Je - sus all is per - fect day,
3 O Je - sus, to my heart so sweet, Your Word's a light un - to my feet;
4 All glo - ry to my Sav-ior's name! To do Your will my high - est aim;

1 No hope be-yond my dy - ing breath Till light from the Sav-ior came.
2 And peace and com-fort ev - er stay, Since Christ is my per-fect light.
3 How ho - ly, hap - py, and com-plete! I walk in the pre-cious light.
4 Your fa - vor's more than earth-ly fame, Your smile is my con-stant light.

In the light of God, Now my soul is sing-ing, All, all is bright;
In the light, the light of God,

In the light of God, I'm now in the light of God.
In the light, bless - ed light,

WITNESS AND TESTIMONY

581 Since Jesus Came into My Heart

"The fruit of the Spirit is love, joy, peace . . . "—Galatians 5:22a

Rufus H. McDaniel

12.8.12.8.wR.
McDANIEL
Charles H. Gabriel

1 What a won-der-ful change in my life has been wrought Since Je-sus came
2 I have ceased from my wan-dering and go-ing a-stray, Since Je-sus came
3 I shall go there to dwell in that Cit-y, I know, Since Je-sus came

1 in-to my heart! I have light in my soul for which long I have sought,
2 in-to my heart! And my sins, which were man-y, are all washed a-way,
3 in-to my heart! And I'm hap-py, so hap-py, as on-ward I go,

Since Je-sus came in-to my heart! Since Je-sus came in-to my

heart, Since Je-sus came in-to my heart, Floods of joy o'er my

soul like the sea bil-lows roll, Since Je-sus came in-to my heart.

WITNESS AND TESTIMONY

Saved! Saved!

582

"And everyone who calls on the name of the Lord will be saved."—Acts 2:21

8.6.8.8.wR.
SCHOLFIELD
Jack P. Scholfield

Jack P. Scholfield

Unison

1 I've found a Friend who is all to me, His
2 He saves me from ev-ery sin and harm, Se-
3 When poor and need-y and all a-lone, In

1 love is ev-er true; I love to tell how He
2 cures my soul each day; I'm lean-ing strong on His
3 love He said to me, "Come un-to Me and I'll

1 lift-ed me, And what His grace can do for you.
2 might-y arm; I know He'll guide me all the way.
3 lead you home, To live with Me e-ter-nal-ly."

Harmony

Saved by His pow'r di-vine, Saved to new life sub-lime!
Saved by His pow'r, Saved to new life,

Life now is sweet and my joy is com-plete, For I'm saved, saved, saved!

WITNESS AND TESTIMONY

583

Glory, Glory, Glory

"... Worthy is the Lamb ... to receive ... honor and glory and praise."
—Revelation 5:12b,d,e

J. S. May

GLORY
J. S. May

Glo - ry, glo - ry, glo - ry! Glo - ry to the Lamb.

Hal - le - lu - jah! I am saved, and I'm so glad I am.

O glo - ry, glo - ry, glo - ry! Glo - ry to the Lamb.

Hal - le - lu - jah! I am saved, and I'm so glad I am.

WITNESS AND TESTIMONY

No One Ever Cared for Me Like Jesus

584

"Greater love has no one than this, that one lay down his life for his friends."
—John 15:13

C. F. Weigle

12.11.12.11.wR.
WEIGLE
C. F. Weigle

1 I would love to tell you what I think of Je-sus Since I found in Him a
2 All my life was full of sin when Je-sus found me, All my heart was full of
3 Ev-ery day He comes to me with new as-sur-ance, More and more I un-der-

1 friend so strong and true; I would tell you how He changed my life com-plete-ly,
2 mis-er-y and woe; Je-sus placed His strong and lov-ing arms a-round me,
3 stand His words of love; But I'll nev-er know just why He came to save me,

1 He did some-thing that no oth-er friend could do.
2 And He led me in the way I ought to go. No one ev-er cared for
3 Till some day I see His bless-ed face a-bove.

me like Je-sus, There's no oth-er friend so kind as He; No one

else could take the sin and sad-ness from me, O how much He cared for me.

WITNESS AND TESTIMONY

585 A Child of the King

"Now if we are children, then we are heirs—heirs of God and co-heirs with Christ, if indeed we share in his sufferings in order that we may also share in his glory."—Romans 8:17

Harriett E. P. Buell

BINGHAMTON
John B. Sumner

1 My Father is rich in hous-es and lands, He hold-eth the
2 My Father's own Son, the Sav-ior in-deed, Once wan-dered on
3 I once was an out-cast stran-ger on earth, A sin-ner by
4 A tent or a cot-tage, why should I care? They're build-ing a

1 wealth of the world in His hands! Of ru-bies and dia-monds, of
2 earth as the poor-est, in need; But now He is reign-ing for-
3 choice, and an al-ien by birth; But I've been a-dopt-ed, my
4 pal-ace for me o-ver there; Though ex-iled from home, yet

1 sil-ver and gold, His cof-fers are full, He has rich-es un-told.
2 ev-er on high, And will give me a home in heav'n by and by.
3 name's writ-ten down, An heir to a man-sion, a robe, and a crown.
4 still I may sing: All glo-ry to God, I'm a child of the King.

I'm a child of the King, A child of the King:

With Je-sus my Sav-ior, I'm a child of the King.

Satisfied

586

"For he satisfies the thirsty and fills the hungry with good things."—Psalm 107:9

Clara T. Williams

8.7.8.7.wR.
SATISFIED
Ralph E. Hudson

1 All my life-long I had pant-ed For a drink from some cool spring
2 Feed-ing on the husks a - round me 'Til my strength was al - most gone,
3 Well of wa - ter, ev - er spring-ing, Bread of life, so rich and free,

1 That I hoped would quench the burn-ing Of the thirst I felt with-in.
2 Longed my soul for some-thing bet-ter, On-ly still to hun-ger on.
3 Un - told wealth that nev - er fail-eth, My Re - deem-er is to me.

Hal-le - lu - jah! I have found Him—Whom my soul so long has craved!

Je-sus sat - is-fies my long - ing; Through His blood I now am saved.

587   I Will Sing of My Redeemer

"In him we have redemption through his blood, the forgiveness of sins, in accordance with the riches of God's grace."—Ephesians 1:7

Philip P. Bliss

8.7.8.7.wR.
MY REDEEMER
James McGranahan

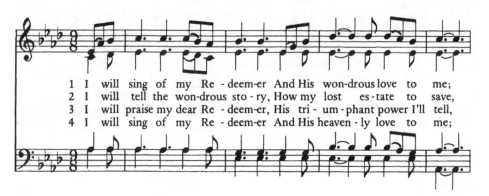

1 I will sing of my Re - deem-er And His won-drous love to me;
2 I will tell the won-drous sto - ry, How my lost es-tate to save,
3 I will praise my dear Re - deem-er, His tri - um-phant power I'll tell,
4 I will sing of my Re - deem-er And His heaven-ly love to me;

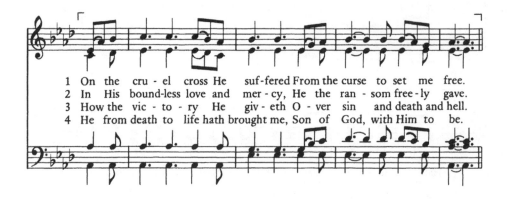

1 On the cru - el cross He suf-fered From the curse to set me free.
2 In His bound-less love and mer - cy, He the ran - som free-ly gave.
3 How the vic - to - ry He giv - eth O - ver sin and death and hell.
4 He from death to life hath brought me, Son of God, with Him to be.

Sing, O sing of my Re - deem - er, With His
sing of my Re-deem-er, Sing, O sing of my Re-deem-er,

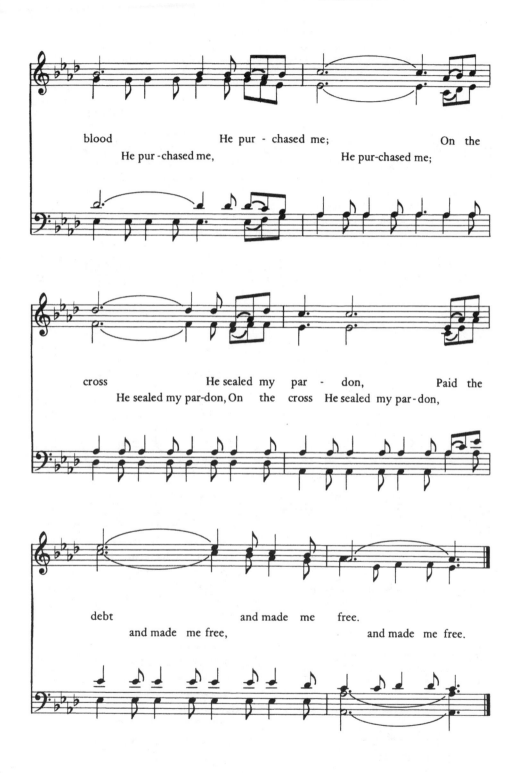

588   Redeemed

"For you know that it was not with perishable things such as silver or gold that you were redeemed from the empty way of life handed down to you from your forefathers, but with the precious blood of Christ, a lamb without blemish or defect."—I Peter 1:18-19

9.8.9.8.wR.
REDEEMED
William J. Kirkpatrick

Fanny J. Crosby

1 Redeemed—how I love to pro-claim it! Redeemed by the blood of the Lamb;
2 Redeemed and so hap-py in Je - sus, No lan-guage my rap-ture can tell;
3 I think of my bless-ed Re - deem-er, I think of Him all the day long;
4 I know I shall see in His beau-ty The King in whose law I de - light;

1 Redeemed through His in - fi-nite mer - cy, His child, and for-ev-er, I am.
2 I know that the light of His pres-ence With me shall con-tin-ual-ly dwell.
3 I sing, for I can-not be si - lent; His love is the theme of my song.
4 Who lov-ing-ly guards ev-ery foot-step, And gives me a song in the night.

Re - deemed, re - deemed, Re - deemed by the blood of the Lamb.

Re - deemed, re - deemed, His child, and for - ev - er, I am.

Redeemed

589

"For you know that it was not with perishable things such as silver or gold that you were redeemed from the empty way of life handed down to you from your forefathers, but with the precious blood of Christ, a lamb without blemish or defect."—I Peter 1:18-19

Fanny J. Crosby

9.8.9.8.wR.
ADA
A. L. Butler

1 Re - deemed, how I love to pro-claim it! Re - deemed by the
2 Re - deemed, and so hap - py in Je - sus, No lan - guage my
3 I think of my bless—ed Re - deem-er, I think of Him

1 blood of the Lamb; Re - deemed thro' His in - fi-nite mer-cy, His
2 rap - ture can tell; I know that the light of His pres-ence With
3 all the day long; I sing, for I can-not be si - lent; His

1 child, and for - ev - er, I am.
2 me doth con - tin - ual - ly dwell. Re - deemed, re -
3 love is the theme of my song.

deemed, Re - deemed by the blood of the Lamb; Re -

deemed thro' His in - fi-nite mer-cy, His child and for-ev - er I am.

WITNESS AND TESTIMONY

590 He Touched Me

"Jesus reached out his hand and touched the man. 'I am willing,' he said, 'Be clean!'" —Matthew 8:3a

William J. Gaither

HE TOUCHED ME
William J. Gaither

1 Shack-led by a heav-y bur-den, 'Neath a load of
2 Since I met this bless-ed Sav-ior, Since He cleansed and

1 guilt and shame— Then the hand of Je-sus touched me,
2 made me whole, I will nev-er cease to praise Him—

1 And now I am no long-er the same. He touched me, O He
2 I'll shout it while e-ter-ni-ty rolls.

touched me, And O the joy that floods my soul; Some-thing

hap-pened, and now I know, He touched me and made me whole.

WITNESS AND TESTIMONY

Something Worth Living For

591

"... 'he went away and sold everything he had and bought it.' "
—Matthew 13:46b

W. Dale Oldham

SOMETHING MORE
William J. Gaither

1 Life was shat-tered and hope was gone— Crush-ing the load that I
2 There, with life at its low-est ebb, Who could heal and re-
3 O the joy of sins for-given— Noth-ing's the same as be-

1 bore; Then out of the depths I cried, "O God,
2 store? Then He came and mend-ed my bro-ken heart—
3 fore; My life o-ver-flows since Je-sus came

1 Give me some-thing worth liv-ing for."
2 He gave me some-thing worth liv-ing for.
3 And gave me some-thing worth liv-ing for. Some-thing more than my

yes-ter-days, More than I had be-fore, Some-thing more than

wealth or fame— He gave me some-thing worth liv-ing for.

WITNESS AND TESTIMONY

592 He's Everything to Me

"When I consider your heavens, the work of your fingers, the moon and the stars, which you have set in place, what is man that you are mindful of him, the son of man that you care for him?"—Psalm 8:3-4

Ralph Carmichael

WOODLAND HILLS
Ralph Carmichael

1 In the stars His hand-i - work I see, On the
2 I will cel - e - brate na - tiv - i - ty, For it

1 wind He speaks with maj - es - ty; Though He rul - eth o - ver
2 has a place in his - to - ry; Sure, He came to set His

1 land and sea, What is that to me?
2 peo - ple free,

What is that to me? 'Til by faith I met Him

face to face And I felt the won-der of His grace,

WITNESS AND TESTIMONY

Then I knew that He was more than just a God who did-n't care, who lived a - way out there, And now He walks be - side me day by day, Ev - er watch-ing o'er me lest I stray, Help-ing me to find that nar - row way, He's ev - ery-thing to me. He's ev - ery - thing to me.

593 This Is Why I Love My Savior

"We love because he first loved us."—I John 4:19

Daniel S. Warner

I LOVE MY SAVIOR
Barney E. Warren

1 Shall I tell you why I ceased from fol - ly, Why I
2 Do you ask me why I seek no pleas - ure In the
3 Would you bid me give to all a rea - son For the
4 Tho the world may look on me with won - der At the

1 turned a - way from sin? 'Twas be - cause the love of my Re -
2 things I once did love? 'Tis be - cause I've tast - ed life's pure
3 hope I now pos - sess? It is Christ in me, the hope of
4 change that's tak - en place, I will walk the down-ward road no

1 deem - er Ful - ly won my heart to Him.
2 riv - er, Flow - ing from the throne a - bove.
3 glo - ry, And His per - fect ho - li - ness.
4 long - er; Bless the Lord for sav - ing grace!

This is why I love my Sav - ior, Why I
This is why, why I love my Sav-ior,

love to fol-low Him: For He died my soul to
Why I love, love to fol-low Him; For He died,

ran - som, And He washed me from my sin.
died my soul to ran-som, And He washed me from, He washed me from my sin.

594

In His Love Let Me Hide

"Therefore, since we have been justified through faith, we have peace with God through our Lord Jesus Christ."—Romans 5:1

Lucena C. Byrum

LET ME HIDE
Andrew L. Byers

1 Let me walk in the path which my Sav - ior has trod, Let me
2 Let my heart e'er be fixed on my trea - sures a - bove, Let the
3 Do you ask why I love Him the dear - est of all? Why so
4 It is bless - ed to serve Him and do His good will, For so

1 fol - low so close by His side; For by trust - ing in Him I am
2 plea-sures of earth fade a - way; For there's noth - ing so love -ly as
3 free - ly I yield un - to Him? 'Tis be - cause He has loved me and
4 pre - cious to me is His love; Let my tal - ents and time all be

1 hap - py and free, In the fold of His love let me hide.
2 Je - sus to me, Let me ne'er from His love go a - stray.
3 died on the cross, My poor soul lost in sin to re - deem.
4 giv - en to Him, Till He calls me to meet Him a - bove.

WITNESS AND TESTIMONY

In His love let me hide, In His love let me hide (let me hide); For by trust-ing in Him I am hap - py and free, In the fold of His love let me hide (let me hide).

In the fold of His love let me hide, In the fold of His love let me hide; In the fold of His love let me hide;

595 Victory in Jesus

"But thanks be to God! He gives us the victory through our Lord Jesus Christ."
—I Corinthians 15:57

HARTFORD

Eugene M. Bartlett

Eugene M. Bartlett

1 I heard an old, old sto - ry, how a Sav - ior came from glo - ry,
2 I heard a - bout His heal - ing, of His cleans - ing power re - veal - ing,
3 I heard a - bout a man - sion He has built for me in glo - ry,

1 How He gave His life on Cal - va - ry to save a wretch like me;
2 How He made the lame to walk a - gain and caused the blind to see;
3 And I heard a - bout the streets of gold be - yond the crys - tal sea;

1 I heard a - bout His groan - ing, of His pre - cious blood's a - ton - ing,
2 And then I cried, "Dear Je - sus, come and heal my bro - ken spir - it,"
3 A - bout the an - gels sing - ing and the old re - demp - tion sto - ry,

1 Then I re - pent - ed of my sins and won the vic - to - ry.
2 And some - how Je - sus came and brought to me the vic - to - ry.
3 And some sweet day I'll sing up there the song of vic - to - ry.

O vic - to - ry in Je - sus, my Sav - ior, for - ev - er! He sought me and

WITNESS AND TESTIMONY

bought me with His re-deem-ing blood; He loved me ere I knew Him, and

all my love is due Him—He plunged me to vic-to-ry be-neath the cleans-ing flood.

Victorious Living 596

God wants us to live positively, to be on the offensive, to be victorious. He desires us to be courageous, confident, serene, and without anxiety, conscious of divine help.

Our openhearted God is a fountain of power. He would have our hearts open to receive His power. He would not have us trust in self but in His sufficiency of grace and power for every need. He would have us constantly believe that in any situation that may arise there will be no lack of what is necessary to make us overcomers. By believing this, and acting as though we believe it, we will be overcomers. We will rid ourselves of many of life's question marks. Some of them will remain to eternity, but many of them need trouble us no longer. Those that cannot be removed need not darken our lives. Trusting Him we can go onward, singing the glad song that flows from the sense of His fatherhood and understanding love.

—Charles Wesley Naylor
from *The Secret of the Singing Heart*

Copyright 1954 by Warner Press, Inc. Used With Permission.

597 Victory

" . . . He gives us the victory through our Lord Jesus Christ."
—I Corinthians 15:57b

Based in I Corinthians 15:57
Barney E. Warren

VICTORY
Barney E. Warren

1 Hal - le - lu - jah, what a thought—Je - sus full sal - va - tion brought!
2 I am trust-ing in the Lord, I am an-chored on His word
3 Shout your free-dom ev - 'ry-where, His e - ter - nal peace de - clare,
4 We will sing it on that shore, When this fleet - ing life is o'er,

1 Vic - to - ry, vic-to - ry. Let the pow'rs of sin as - sail,
2 Vic - to - ry, vic-to - ry. I have peace and joy with-in,
3 Vic - to - ry, vic-to - ry. Let us sing it here be - low,
4 Vic - to - ry, vic-to - ry. Sing it here, you ransomed throng,
Vic-to - ry, vic - to - ry.

1 Heav-en's grace can nev - er fail, Vic-to - ry, vic-to - ry.
2 Since my heart is free from sin, Vic-to - ry, vic-to - ry.
3 In the face of ev - ery foe, Vic-to - ry, vic-to - ry.
4 Start the ev - er-last-ing song, Vic-to - ry, vic-to - ry.
Vic-to - ry, vic - to - ry.

WITNESS AND TESTIMONY

Vic-to - ry,   yes, vic-to - ry;   Hal-le - lu -jah! I am
Vic -to - ry,   yes, vic-to - ry;

free, Je-sus gives me vic - to - ry! Glo - ry, glo - ry, hal - le -
     Glo - ry, glo - ry,

lu - jah! He is all   in all to me.
Hal - le - lu - jah! He is all, He is all in all to me (all to me).

WITNESS AND TESTIMONY

598

He Lifted Me Out

"He lifted me out of the slimy pit, out of the mud and mire."—Psalm 40:2b

Lawrence E. Brooks
Harm. by K. Y. Plank

HE LIFTED ME OUT
Lawrence E. Brooks

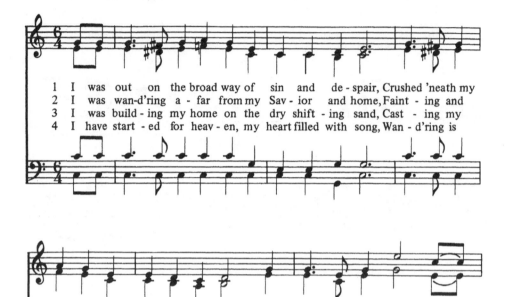

1 I was out on the broad way of sin and de-spair, Crushed 'neath my
2 I was wan-d'ring a-far from my Sav-ior and home, Faint-ing and
3 I was build-ing my home on the dry shift-ing sand, Cast-ing my
4 I have start-ed for heav-en, my heart filled with song, Wan-d'ring is

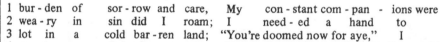

1 bur-den of sor-row and care, My con-stant com-pan-ions were
2 wea-ry in sin did I roam; I need-ed a hand to
3 lot in a cold bar-ren land; "You're doomed now for aye," I
4 o-ver, my sins all are gone; Thru Je-sus own blood cleansed with-

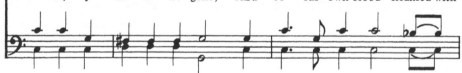

1 trou-ble and doubt, Till Je-sus reached down and lift-ed me out.
2 turn me a-bout, Then Je-sus reached down and lift-ed me out.
3 heard Sa-tan shout. But Je-sus reached down and lift-ed me out.
4 in and with-out, O praise His dear name! He lift-ed me out.

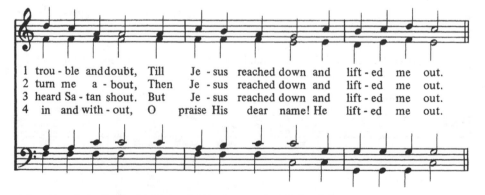

WITNESS AND TESTIMONY

He lift-ed me out of the deep mir-y clay; He set-tled my feet

in the strait, nar-row way; He lift-ed me up to a heav-en-ly place,

And flood-eth my soul each day with His grace.

WITNESS AND TESTIMONY

599

His Yoke Is Easy

"For my yoke is easy and my burden is light."—Matthew 11:30

Based on Matthew 11:28-30
Daniel S. Warner

HIS YOKE IS EASY
Barney E. Warren

1 I've found my Lord and He is mine, He won me by His love;
2 No oth-er Lord but Christ I know, I walk with Him a - lone;
3 He's dear-er to my heart than life, He found me lost in sin;
4 I've tried the road of sin, and found Its pros-pects all de - ceive;

1 I'll serve Him all my years of time And dwell with Him a - bove.
2 His streams of love for - ev - er flow With - in my heart, His throne.
3 He calmed the sea of in - ward strife And bade me come to Him.
4 I've proved the Lord, and joys a-bound, More than I could be - lieve.

His yoke is eas-y, His bur-den is light, I've found it so, I've found it so;

His serv - ice is my sweet-est de-light, His bless-ings ev - er flow.

He Lifted Me

"He lifted me out of a slimy pit . . . and gave me a firm place to stand."
—Psalm 40:2a,d

Charles H. Gabriel

HE LIFTED ME
Charles H. Gabriel

1 In loving-kindness Jesus came My soul in mercy to reclaim,
2 He called me long before I heard, Before my sinful heart was stirred,
3 His brow was pierced with many a thorn, His hands by cruel nails were torn,
4 Now on a higher plane I dwell, And with my soul I know 'tis well;

1 And from the depths of sin and shame Through grace He lifted me.
2 But when I took Him at His word, Forgiven He lifted me.
3 When from my guilt and grief, forlorn, In love He lifted me.
4 Yet how or why, I cannot tell, He should have lifted me.

From sinking sand He lifted me, With tender hand He lifted me;

From shades of night to plains of light, O praise His name, He lifted me!

WITNESS AND TESTIMONY

601

All in Jesus

"Come and share your master's happiness!"—Matthew 25:21c

ALL IN JESUS
Barney E. Warren

Barney E. Warren

1 There is peace and joy in the Lord to-day, More than
2 I am blest to-day, I am free in-deed, What a
3 Since my cross is gone and my heart is right, O how
4 All His grace is free as the air we breathe, We may

1 all in this world of sin; There's a hap-py life in the
2 plea-sure to serve the Lord! How it fills my soul with de-
3 bless-ed to do His will! Now His yoke is eas-y, His
4 each have a full sup-ply; If we will o-bey and His

1 ho-ly way, Praise the Lord, I have en-tered in!
2 light to read In His sa-cred and ho-ly Word!
3 bur-den light, And His Spir-it my soul doth fill.
4 word be-lieve, He'll pre-pare us to dwell on high.

Praise the Lord, I am free In His love and grace!
Praise the Lord, I'm free, I am free in-deed In His love, His ten-der love and grace!

WITNESS AND TESTIMONY

O His blood reach-es me! I a-bide 'neath His smil-ing face.
O His pre-cious blood reach-es e-ven me!

Something Beautiful

602

" 'For this son of mine was dead and is alive again; he was lost and is found.'
So they began to celebrate."—Luke 15:24

Gloria Gaither

SOMETHING BEAUTIFUL
William J. Gaither

Some - thing beau - ti - ful, some - thing good;

All my con - fu - sion He un - der - stood;

All I had to of - fer Him was bro - ken - ness and

strife, But He made some - thing beau - ti - ful of my life.

WITNESS AND TESTIMONY

603

The Lord Bless You
and Keep You

"The Lord bless you and keep you; the Lord make his face to shine upon you
. . . "—Numbers 6:24,25a

BENEDICTION
Peter C. Lutkin

Numbers 6:24-26

PEACE AND JOY

PEACE AND JOY

604 Love Lifted Me

"This is love: not that we loved God, but that he loved us and sent his Son as an atoning sacrifice for our sins." —I John 4:10

James Rowe

7.6.7.6.7.6.7.4.wR.
SAFETY
Howard E. Smith

1 I was sink-ing deep in sin, Far from the peace-ful shore, Ver-y deep-ly
2 All my heart to Him I give, Ev - er to Him I'll cling, In His bless-ed
3 Souls in dan - ger, look a-bove, Je - sus com-plete-ly saves; He will lift you

1 stained with-in, Sink-ing to rise no more; But the Mas-ter of the sea
2 pres - ence live, Ev - er His prais - es sing; Love so might-y and so true
3 by His love Out of the an - gry waves; He's the Mas-ter of the sea,

1 Heard my de-spair-ing cry, From the wa - ters lift - ed me, Now safe am I.
2 Mer - its my soul's best songs; Faith-ful, lov - ing ser-vice, too, To Him be-longs.
3 Bil - lows His will o - bey; He your Sav - ior wants to be, Be saved to-day.

Love lift - ed me! Love lift - ed me! When noth-ing
e - ven me! e - ven me!

1.
else could help, Love lift - ed me.

2.
Love lift - ed me.

WITNESS AND TESTIMONY

A Gaelic Blessing

605

LEADER: Deep peace of the running wave to you,

PEOPLE: *Deep peace of the flowing air to you,*

LEADER: Deep peace of the quiet earth to you,

PEOPLE: *Deep peace of the shining stars to you,*

LEADER: Deep peace of the gentle night to you,

PEOPLE: *Moon and stars pour their healing light on you;*

LEADER: Deep peace of Christ, the Light of the World, to you—

PEOPLE: *Deep peace of Christ to you.*

—An old Gaelic rune

Lord, Dismiss Us with Thy Blessing

606

"From the Lord comes deliverance. May your blessing be on your people."
—Psalm 3:8

8.7.8.7.8.7.

John Fawcett, altered

SICILIAN MARINERS
Tattersall's *Psalmody,* 1794

1 Lord, dis - miss us   with Thy bless-ing, Fill our hearts with   joy and peace;
2 Thanks we give and   ad - o - ra - tion For Thy gos - pel's   joy-ful sound;

1 Let us each, Thy   love pos-ses - sing, Tri - umph in   re - deem-ing grace.
2 May the fruits of   Thy sal - va - tion In   our hearts and   lives a - bound.

1 O re - fresh us,   O re - fresh us, Trav-eling through this wil-der-ness.
2 Ev - er faith - ful,   ev - er faith - ful To the truth may   we be found. A-men.

PEACE AND JOY

607 Wonderful Peace

"The Lord gives strength to his people; the Lord blesses his people with peace."
—Psalm 29:11

W. D. Cornell

12.9.12.9.wR.
WONDERFUL PEACE
W. G. Cooper

1. Far a - way in the depths of my spir - it to - night Rolls a
2. What a trea - sure I have in this won - der - ful peace, Bur - ied
3. I am rest - ing to - night in this won - der - ful peace, Rest - ing
4. And I think when I rise to that cit - y of peace, Where the
5. O my soul, are you here with - out com - fort or rest, March - ing

1. mel - o - dy sweet - er than psalm; In ce - les - tial - like strains it un -
2. deep in the heart of my soul, So se - cure that no pow - er can
3. sweet - ly in Je - sus' con - trol, For I'm kept from all dan - ger by
4. au - thor of peace I shall see, That one strain of the song which the
5. down the rough path - way of time? Make the Sav - ior your friend when the

1. ceas - ing - ly falls O'er my soul like an in - fi - nite calm.
2. mine it a - way While the years of e - ter - ni - ty roll.
3. night and by day, And His glo - ry is flood - ing my soul.
4. ran - somed will sing, In that heav - en - ly king - dom shall be:
5. shad - ows grow dark; O ac - cept this sweet peace so sub - lime.

Peace! peace! won - der - ful peace, Coming down from the Fa - ther a - bove, Sweep

PEACE AND JOY

o-ver my spir-it for - ev - er, I pray, In fath - om-less bil-lows of love.

In Perfect Peace 608

"Thou wilt keep him in perfect peace, whose
mind is stayed on thee."
—*Isaiah 26:3*

We need not be reminded that we live in a day
of anxieties and pressure. One need only glance
at the faces of passers-by to see etchings of
worry, fear, tension, and strain. The cause is not
too difficult to discover. The excitement, tur-
moil, rush, noise and hectic tempo of modern
living often rob us of peace of mind.

But the cause is not as important as the cure.
Jesus was not dependent on the insecure, tumul-
tuous environment of His day for peace and
poise. His secret was to be kept day by day
within the purposes of God's will and to
strengthen His contact with the Father by time
alone with God. Let us learn of Him.

O Master, let me walk with Thee
In lowly paths of service free;
Tell me Thy secret; help me bear
The strain of toil, the fret of care.
—Washington Gladden

—Marvin J. Hartman
from *He Restoreth My Soul*

609 Lead Us, O Father, in the Paths of Peace

"To shine on those living in darkness and in the shadow of death, to guide our feet into the path of peace."—Luke 1:79

Willliam H. Burleigh

10.10.10.10.

MORECAMBE
Frederick C. Atkinson

1 Lead us, O Fa - ther, in the paths of peace:
2 Lead us, O Fa - ther, in the paths of truth;
3 Lead us, O Fa - ther, in the paths of right;
4 Lead us, O Fa - ther, to Thy heav'n - ly rest,

1 With - out Thy guid - ing hand we go a - stray,
2 Un - helped by Thee, in er - ror's maze we grope,
3 Blind - ly we stum - ble when we walk a - lone,
4 How - ev - er rough and steep the path - way be,

1 And doubts ap - pall, and sor - rows still in - crease;
2 While pas - sion stains and fol - ly dims our youth,
3 In - volved in shad - ows of a dark - 'ning night;
4 Through joy or sor - row, as Thou deem - est best,

1 Lead us through Christ, the true and liv - ing Way.
2 And age comes on un - cheered by faith or hope.
3 On - ly with Thee we jour - ney safe - ly on.
4 Un - til our lives are per - fect - ed in Thee. A - men.

PEACE AND JOY

God Be with You 'Til We Meet Again

"May the grace of the Lord Jesus Christ, and the love of God and the fellowship of the Holy Spirit be with you all."—II Corinthians 13:14

Jeremiah E. Rankin

GOD BE WITH YOU
William G. Tomer

1 God be with you 'til we meet a - gain, By His coun-sels guide, up-hold you,
2 God be with you 'til we meet a - gain, 'Neath His wings protecting hide you,
3 God be with you 'til we meet a - gain, If life's tri-als should con-found you,
4 God be with you 'til we meet a - gain, Keep love's ban-ner float-ing o'er you,

1 With His sheep se - cure - ly fold you: God be with you 'til we meet a-gain.
2 Dai - ly man-na still pro - vide you: God be with you 'til we meet a-gain.
3 God will put His arms a - round you: God be with you 'til we meet a-gain.
4 Smite death's threat'ning wave before you: God be with you 'til we meet a-gain.

Take His Peace

PEOPLE: *When the whirlwinds of doubt*
Churn their way into your soul,
LEADER: Take His peace.
PEOPLE: *When your world's reduced to ashes,*
Leaving nothing firm and whole,
LEADER: Take His peace.

LEADER: There amidst the broken wreckage
In the midnight of your day,
In the apex of the stormcloud,
He's the quiet place to stay,
ALL: *Take His peace, take His peace.*

PEOPLE: *When your mind gropes for answers*
To the questions that you face,
LEADER: Take His peace.
PEOPLE: *When your past comes back to haunt*
you
And you need amazing grace,
LEADER: Take His peace.

LEADER: There's an answer beyond question,
It's the truth for which you yearn:
There's forgiveness without merit,
There's a love you needn't earn,
ALL: *Take His peace, take His peace.*

PEOPLE: *When you're weary of the struggle*
And you need a place to rest,

LEADER: Take His peace.
PEOPLE: *When you lose more than you're*
winning
And you're failing every test,
LEADER: Take His peace.

LEADER: There's no need to win a battle
That's been fought and won before;
You can lay back in the Victory,
Freely share His boundless store,
ALL: *Take His peace, take His peace.*

LEADER: When you're worried and you're
fearful
For the children you hold dear,
PEOPLE: *Take His peace.*
LEADER: Let a loving Heavenly Father
Share each joy and dry each tear,
PEOPLE: *Take His peace.*

LEADER: God has promised if we teach them
And we guide them from the start,
Then the seed of truth and peace
Shall find rich soil in their hearts,
ALL: *Claim His peace, claim His peace!*
—Gloria Gaither

PEACE AND JOY

612 It Is Well with My Soul

"He ransoms me unharmed from the battle waged against me, even though many oppose me."—Psalm 55:18

11.8.11.9.wR.
VILLE DU HAVRE

Horatio G. Spafford

Philip P. Bliss

1 When peace, like a riv-er, at-tend-eth my way, When sor-rows like
2 My sin— O the joy of this glo-ri-ous thought—My sin, not in
3 And, Lord, haste the day when my faith shall be sight, The clouds be rolled

1 sea bil-lows roll— What-ev-er my lot, Thou hast taught me to say,
2 part, but the whole, Is nailed to the cross, and I bear it no more:
3 back as a scroll: The trump shall re-sound and the Lord shall de-scend,

1 It is well, it is well with my soul. It is well
2 Praise the Lord, praise the Lord, O my soul! It is well
3 "E-ven so"— it is well with my soul. It is well

with my soul, It is well, it is well with my soul.
with my soul,

PEACE AND JOY

Like a River Glorious

613

*"If only you had paid attention to my commands, your peace would have been
like a river, your righteousness like the waves of the sea."—Isaiah 48:18*

Frances R. Havergal
Jeff Redd, alt., stanza 3

6.5.6.5.D.wR.
WYE VALLEY
James Mountain

1 Like a riv-er glo-rious Is God's per-fect peace, O-ver all vic-
2 Hid-den in the hol-low Of His bless-ed hand, Nev-er foe can
3 Ev-ery joy or test-ing Comes from God a-bove, Giv-en to His

1 to-rious In its bright in-crease; Per-fect, yet it flow-eth Full-er
2 fol-low, Nev-er trai-tor stand; Not a surge of wor-ry, Not a
3 chil-dren As an act of love; We may trust Him ful-ly All for

1 ev-ery day, Per-fect, yet it grow-eth Deep-er all the way.
2 shade of care, Not a blast of hur-ry Touch the spir-it there.
3 us to do— Those who trust Him whol-ly Find Him whol-ly true.

Trust-ing in Je-ho-vah, Hearts are ful-ly blest—

Find-ing, as He prom-ised, Per-fect peace and rest.

PEACE AND JOY

614 There Is Joy in the Service of the Master

"I have told you this so that my joy may be in you and that your joy may be complete."—John 15:11

Daniel S. Warner

JOY IN THE SERVICE
Barney E. Warren

1 There is joy in the serv-ice of the Mas-ter, Let me sing of the
2 Could you bring me the trea-sures of the o-cean, Could you of-fer the
3 Could I soar to the high-est throne of hon-or, Could I shine with the
4 Could I sing out the plea-sure in my bos-om, How my heart thrills with

1 glo-ry I have found; Since I gave all to Je-sus and His fa-vor gained,
2 gold-en stores of earth, I would sing, "Hal-le-lu-jah, I've a great-er wealth,
3 wis-dom of a sage, All this poor fad-ing glo-ry could no tho't en-gage,
4 glo-ry in the way, All the world would no long-er in the des-ert stay,

1 O won-drous streams of joy for-ev-er a-bound!
2 I have my Sav-ior's love, a heav-en-ly birth."
3 Since Je-sus is my all, my own her-i-tage.
4 But to my Je-sus come, and ev-en to-day.

Je-sus, my life and my

joy ev-er-more, Je-sus, for-ev-er my heart's deep store: Glo-ry to God

PEACE AND JOY

for re - deem-ing love! O won-drous peace of God that flows from a-bove.

A Song of Joy

615

"Speak to one another with psalms, hymns and spiritual songs. Sing and make music in your heart to the Lord."—Ephesians 5:19

D. Otis Teasley

SONG OF JOY
D. Otis Teasley

1 Sal - va-tion's free, glad joy to all Of Ad - am's fall -en race;
2 From wells of ev - er - last - ing joy Our strength by faith we bring;
3 How blest the soul that's purged as pure As gold with-out al - loy!
4 I'll live for Christ thru this dark world, And faith-ful I will be;

1 We'll tell the sto - ry far and near Of sav - ing, keep-ing grace.
2 The joy that thrills my ran-somed soul Can make the sad heart sing.
3 How peace-ful is the flow - ing stream Of deep e - ter - nal joy!
4 The joy I know that keeps my soul Shall last e - ter-nal - ly.

There's joy, glad joy Now flow - ing from a - bove;
There's joy, glad joy, there's joy, glad joy

There's joy, glad joy In the full-ness of His love.
There's joy, glad joy, there's joy, glad joy

PEACE AND JOY

616 There Is Joy in the Lord

"I have told you this so that my joy may be in you and that your joy may be complete."—John 15:11

Barney E. Warren

JOY IN THE LORD
Barney E. Warren

1 I will sing hal-le-lu-jah, for there's joy in the Lord,
2 I will live for the Sav-ior, I am His ev-er-more,
3 When I come to the por-tals of that land of the blest,
O can-tad a-le-lu-ya, pues hay go-zo en Je-sús,

1 And He fills my heart with rap-ture as I rest on His Word;
2 I am rest-ing in His fa-vor, I am safe and se-cure;
3 I shall sing with ho-ly an-gels of this rest, hap-py rest;
Yal con-fiar el al-ma en su Pa-la-bra go-za de luz;

1 I will trust in His prom-ise, I will shout I am free,
2 For the light shin-ing bright-er on my path ev-'ry day
3 I shall dwell there for-ev-er with my Lord and my King,
Ya por su gran pro-me-sa go-zo de li-ber-tad,

1 In my bless-ed lov-ing Sav-ior I have sweet vic-to-ry.
2 Cheers my hap-py soul with rap-ture as I walk in the way.
3 And with ev-er-last-ing prais-es make those high arch-es ring.
La vic-to-ria Cris-to ya me ha da-do en su gran bon-dad.

PEACE AND JOY

There is joy in the Lord, there is joy in the Lord; Hal - le - lu -jah, glo - ry,
Go - zo hay en Je - sús, ple - no go - zo en Je - sús, ¡A - le - lu - ya, glo - ria,

glo - ry! There is joy in the Lord, There is joy in the Lord, There is
glo - ria! Go - zo hay en Je - sús; Go - zo hay en Je - sús, ple - no

joy in the Lord; Hal - le - lu - jah, glo - ry, glo - ry! There is joy in the Lord.
go - zo en Je - sús, ¡A - le - lu - ya, glo - ria, glo - ria! Go - zo hay en Je - sús.

A Place for the Singing of Angels 617

There must be always remaining in everyone's life some place for the
singing of angels—some place for that which in itself is breathlessly beautiful and by an inherent prerogative, throwing all the rest of life into a new
and creative relatedness—something that gathers up in itself all the freshets
of experience from drab and commonplace areas of living and glows in one
bright light of penetrating beauty and meaning—then passes. The commonplace is shot through with new glory—old burdens become lighter, deep and
ancient wounds lose much of their old, old hurting. A crown is placed over
our heads that for the rest of our lives we are trying to grow tall enough to
wear. Despite all the crassness of life, despite all the hardness of life,
despite all the harsh discords of life, life is saved by the singing of angels.

—Howard Thurman
From *Deep Is the Hunger*

618 There's Music in My Soul

"Praise the Lord! Sing to the Lord a new song . . . "—Psalm 149:1a,b

Daniel S. Warner

MUSIC IN MY SOUL
Barney E. Warren

1 Since I have found my Sav - ior, Bowed to His con - trol,
2 I sing of my Re - deem - er, Hap - py in the way,
3 Since I have been for - giv - en, Heav - en's an - thems roll
4 The an - gels sing in heav - en, Let the prais - es roll:

1 There's ev - er - last - ing mu - sic Ring - ing in my soul.
2 He sweet - ly tunes the spir - it, Sing - ing all the day.
3 In sweet ac - cord, with joy - ful Mu - sic in my soul.
4 There's mu - sic in cre - a - tion, Mu - sic in my soul.

There is mu - sic in my soul, O there is mu - sic in my soul;

'Tis my glo - ry ev - er sing - ing, "Heav - en's balm has made me whole."

There is mu - sic in my soul, O let the hap - py ti - dings roll!

PEACE AND JOY

Let it roll,   let it roll,   O there's mu-sic in my soul.
Let it roll,   let it roll,

There Is Sunshine in My Soul 619

"The prospect of the righteous is joy . . . "—Proverbs 10:28a

9.6.8.6.wR.
SUNSHINE

Eliza E. Hewitt

John R. Sweney

1 There is   sun-shine in my soul to-day,   More glo-ri-ous and bright
2 There is   mu-sic in my soul to-day,   A   car-ol to my King,
3 There is   spring-time in my soul to-day,   For when the Lord is near
4 There is   glad-ness in my soul to-day,   And hope and praise and love,

1 Than   glows in an-y earth-ly sky,   For Je-sus is my light.
2 And   Je-sus, lis-ten-ing can hear   The songs I can-not sing.
3 The   dove of peace sings in my heart,   The flowers of grace ap-pear.
4 For   bless-ings which He gives me now,   For joys laid up a-bove.

O there's sun-shine, bless-ed sun-shine, When the peace-ful, hap-py mo-ments

roll;   When Je-sus shows His smil-ing face, There is sun-shine in my soul.

PEACE AND JOY

620 Joy Unspeakable

" . . . you believe in him and are filled with an inexpressible and glorious joy."
—I Peter 1:8b

Barney E. Warren

JOY UNSPEAKABLE
Barney E. Warren

1 I have found His grace is all com-plete, He sup-pli-eth ev-'ry need;
2 I have found the plea-sure I once craved, It is joy and peace with-in;
3 I have found a hope so bright and clear, Liv-ing in the realm of grace;
4 I have found the joy no tongue can tell; How its waves of glo-ry roll!

1 While I sit and learn at Je-sus' feet I am free, yes, free in-deed.
2 What a won-drous bless-ing! I am saved From the aw-ful gulf of sin.
3 O the Sav-ior's pres-ence is so near I can see His smil-ing face.
4 It is like a great o'er-flow-ing well Spring-ing up with-in my soul.

It is joy un-speak-a-ble and full of glo-ry, Full of glo-ry, full of glo-ry; It is joy un-speak-a-ble and full of glo-ry, O the half has nev-er yet been told!

In My Heart There Rings a Melody

621

"Let the word of Christ dwell in you richly as you teach and admonish one another with all wisdom, and as you sing psalms, hymns and spiritual songs with gratitude in your hearts to God."—Colossians 3:16

Elton M. Roth

Irreg.
HEART MELODY
Elton M. Roth

1 I have a song that Je - sus gave me, It was sent from
2 I love the Christ who died on Cal - vary, For He washed my
3 'Twill be my end - less theme in glo - ry, With the an - gels

1 heaven a - bove; There nev - er was a sweet - er mel - o - dy, 'Tis a
2 sins a - way; He put with - in my heart a mel - o - dy, And I
3 I will sing; 'Twill be a song with glo - rious har - mo - ny, When the

1 mel - o - dy of love.
2 know it's there to stay. In my heart there rings a mel - o - dy, There
3 courts of heav - en ring.

rings a mel - o - dy with heav - en's har - mo - ny; In my heart there

rings a mel - o - dy, There rings a mel - o - dy of love.

PEACE AND JOY

622

The Trees of the Field

"You will go out in joy and be led forth in peace; the mountains and hills will burst into song before you, and all the trees of the field will clap their hands."
—Isaiah 55:12

Based on Isaiah 55:12
Steffi Geiser Rubin

THE TREES OF THE FIELD
Stuart Dauermann

You shall go out with joy and be led forth with peace; The moun-tains and the hills will break forth be-fore you. There'll be shouts of joy, and all the trees of the field Will clap, will clap their hands.

PEACE AND JOY

PEACE AND JOY

623 Come, We That Love the Lord

"Let Israel rejoice in their Maker; let the people of Zion be glad in their King."
—Psalm 149:2

6.6.8.8.6.6.wR.
MARCHING TO ZION
Robert Lowry

Isaac Watts
Robert Lowry

1 Come, we that love the Lord, And let our joys be known; Join
2 Let those re - fuse to sing Who nev - er knew our God; But
3 Then let our songs a - bound And ev - ery tear be dry; We're

1 in a song with sweet ac - cord, Join in a song with sweet ac-cord
2 chil - dren of the heaven - ly King, But chil-dren of the heaven-ly King
3 march-ing thru Em - man - uel's ground, We're march-ing thru Em-man-uel's ground

1 And thus sur - round the throne, And thus sur-round the throne.
2 May speak their joys a - broad, May speak their joys a - broad.
3 To fair - er worlds on high, To fair - er worlds on high.

We're march - ing to Zi - on, Beau - ti - ful, beau-ti-ful Zi - on; We're

march - ing up-ward to Zi - on, The beau-ti-ful cit - y of God.

PEACE AND JOY

He Keeps Me Singing

624

"Sing to the Lord, for he has done glorious things; let this be known to all the world."—Isaiah 12:5

Luther B. Bridgers

SWEETEST NAME I KNOW
Luther B. Bridgers

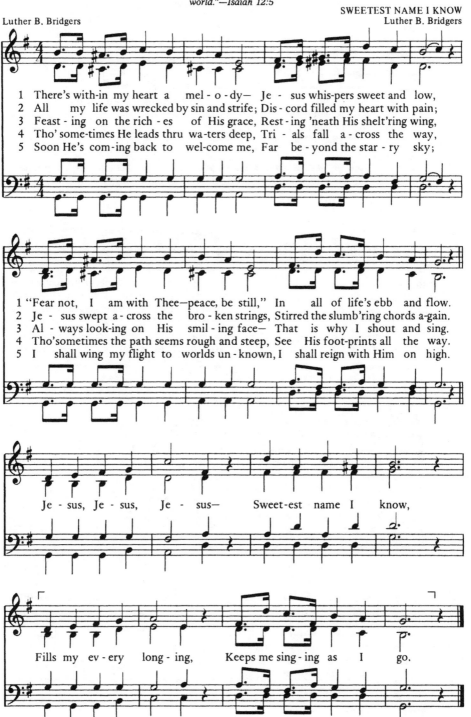

1 There's with-in my heart a mel - o - dy— Je - sus whis-pers sweet and low,
2 All my life was wrecked by sin and strife; Dis - cord filled my heart with pain;
3 Feast - ing on the rich - es of His grace, Rest - ing 'neath His shelt'ring wing,
4 Tho' some-times He leads thru wa-ters deep, Tri - als fall a - cross the way,
5 Soon He's com-ing back to wel-come me, Far be - yond the star - ry sky;

1 "Fear not, I am with Thee—peace, be still," In all of life's ebb and flow.
2 Je - sus swept a - cross the bro - ken strings, Stirred the slumb'ring chords a-gain.
3 Al - ways look-ing on His smil - ing face, That is why I shout and sing.
4 Tho' sometimes the path seems rough and steep, See His foot-prints all the way.
5 I shall wing my flight to worlds un - known, I shall reign with Him on high.

Je - sus, Je - sus, Je - sus— Sweet-est name I know,

Fills my ev - ery long - ing, Keeps me sing-ing as I go.

PEACE AND JOY

625 It Is Glory Just to Walk with Him

"They asked each other, 'Were not our hearts burning wthin us while he talked with us on the road and opened the Scriptures to us?' "—Luke 24:32

Avis M. Burgeson

GLORY JUST TO WALK
Haldor Lillenas

1 It is glo-ry just to walk with Him whose blood has ran-somed me; It is
2 It is glo-ry when the shad-ows fall to know that He is near; O what
3 'Twill be glo-ry when I walk with Him on heav-en's gold-en shore, Nev-er

1 rap-ture for my soul each day. It is joy di-vine to feel Him near where-
2 joy to sim-ply trust and pray! It is glo-ry to a-bide in Him when
3 from His side a-gain to stray. 'Twill be glo-ry, wondrous glo-ry with the

1 e'er my path may be; Bless the Lord, it's glo-ry all the way!
2 skies a-bove are clear; Yes, with Him, it's glo-ry all the way!
3 Sav-ior ev-er-more, Ev-er-last-ing glo-ry all the way!

It is glo-ry just to walk with Him,
walk with Him,
It is

PEACE AND JOY

glo - ry just to walk with Him. He will guide my steps a-right, Thru the
walk with Him.

vale and o'er the height; It is glo - ry just to walk with Him.
walk with Him.

Rules for Living   **626**

LEADER: Rejoice in the Lord always. I will say it again: Rejoice!
Let your gentleness be evident to all. The Lord is near.

PEOPLE: *Do not be anxious about anything, but in*
everything, by prayer and petition, with
thanksgiving, present your requests to God.

LEADER: And the peace of God, which transcends all
understanding, will guard your hearts and your minds in
Christ Jesus.

PEOPLE: *Finally, brothers, whatever is true, whatever is*
noble, whatever
is right, whatever is pure, whatever is lovely,
whatever is admirable—if anything is excellent or
praiseworthy—think about such things.

LEADER: Whatever you have learned or received or heard from
me, or seen in me—put it into practice.

PEOPLE: *And the God of peace will be with you.*

—Philippians 4:4–9 (NIV)

627 Heavenly Sunlight

"This is the message we have heard from him and declare to you: God is light;
in him there is no darkness at all."—I John 1:5

H. J. Zelley

HEAVENLY SUNLIGHT
George H. Cook

1 Walk-ing in sun-light all of my jour-ney, O-ver the moun-tains,
2 Shad-ows a-round me, shad-ows a-bove me, Nev-er con-ceal my
3 In the bright sun-light, ev-er re-joic-ing, Press-ing my way to

1 thru the deep vale; Je-sus has said, "I'll nev-er for-sake thee,"
2 Sav-ior and guide; He is the light, in Him is no dark-ness,
3 man-sions a-bove, Sing-ing His prais-es, glad-ly I'm walk-ing,

1 Prom-ise di-vine that nev-er can fail.
2 Ev-er I'm walk-ing close to His side. Heav-en-ly sun-light,
3 Walk-ing in sun-light, sun-light of love.

heav-en-ly sun-light, Flood-ing my soul with glo-ry di-vine; Hal-le-

lu-jah! I am re-joic-ing, Sing-ing His prais-es, Je-sus is mine.

PEACE AND JOY

Under His Wings

628

"He will cover you with his feathers, and under his wings you will find refuge;
his faithfulness will be your shield and rampart."—Psalm 91:4

11.10.11.10.wR.

HINGHAM
Ira D. Sankey

William O. Cushing

1 Un - der His wings I am safe-ly a - bid - ing, Though the night
2 Un - der His wings, what a ref - uge in sor - row! How the heart
3 Un - der His wings, O what pre-cious en - joy - ment! There will I

1 deep - ens and tem - pests are wild; Still I can trust Him— I
2 yearn - ing - ly turns to His rest! Of - ten when earth has no
3 hide 'til life's tri - als are o'er! Shel - tered, pro - tect - ed, no

1 know He will keep me, He has re - deemed me and I am His child.
2 balm for my heal - ing, There I find com - fort and there I am blest.
3 e - vil can harm me, Rest - ing in Je - sus I'm safe ev - er-more.

Un - der His wings, un - der His wings, Who from His love can sev - er?

Un - der His wings my soul shall a - bide, Safe - ly a - bide for - ev - er.

TRUST AND ASSURANCE

629 He Hideth My Soul

"For in the day of trouble he will keep me safe in his dwelling; he will hide me in the shelter of his tabernacle and set me high upon a rock."—Psalm 27:5

Fanny J. Crosby

HE HIDETH MY SOUL
William J. Kirkpatrick

1 A won-der-ful Sav-ior is Je-sus my Lord, A
2 A won-der-ful Sav-ior is Je-sus my Lord, He
3 With num-ber-less bless-ings each mo-ment He crowns, And,
4 When clothed in His bright-ness trans-port-ed I rise To

1 won-der-ful Sav-ior to me; He hid-eth my soul in the
2 tak-eth my bur-den a-way; He hold-eth me up, and I
3 filled with His full-ness di-vine, I sing in my rap-ture, "O
4 meet Him in clouds of the sky, His per-fect sal-va-tion, His

1 cleft of the rock, Where riv-ers of pleas-ure I see.
2 shall not be moved, He giv-eth me strength for each day.
3 glo-ry to God For such a Re-deem-er as mine!"
4 won-der-ful love, I'll shout with the mil-lions on high.

He hid-eth my soul in the cleft of the rock That shad-ows a

TRUST AND ASSURANCE

dry, thirst-y land; He hid-eth my life in the depths of His love,

And cov-ers me there with His hand, And cov-ers me there with His hand.

Rock of Ages, Cleft for Me 630

" . . . and drank the same spiritual drink; for they drank from the spiritual rock that accompanied them, and that rock was Christ."—I Corinthians 10:4

7.7.7.7.7.7.
TOPLADY

Augustus M. Toplady

Thomas Hastings

1 Rock of A - ges, cleft for me, Let me hide my-self in Thee;
2 Could my tears for - ev - er flow, Could my zeal no weak-ness know,
3 While I draw this fi - nal breath, When my eyes shall close in death,

1 Let the wa - ter and the blood, From Thy wound-ed side which flowed,
2 These for sin could not a - tone— Thou must save, and Thou a - lone:
3 When I rise to worlds un - known, And be - hold Thee on Thy throne,

1 Be of sin the dou-ble cure, Save from wrath and make me pure.
2 In my hand no price I bring, Sim-ply to Thy cross I cling.
3 Rock of A - ges, cleft for me, Let me hide my-self in Thee. A - men.

TRUST AND ASSURANCE

631 Let Not Your Heart Be Troubled

"Do not let your hearts be troubled. Trust in God; trust also in me."—John 14:1

Based on John 14:1-3
Barney E. Warren

HEART
Barney E. Warren

1 Let not your wea-ry heart be troub-led, Be-lieve in
2 Let not your peace and calm as-sur-ance Be ruf-fled
3 Let not your hope be dimmed with doubt-ing, Let not life's

1 God, be-lieve in Me; In Fa-ther's house are man-y man-sions, I
2 by the storms of life, But strong and sure with firm en-dur-ance, Just
3 bur-dens foil your grace, But in each con-flict vic-t'ry shout-ing, As

1 will pre--pare a place for thee.
2 glo-ry in the ho-ly strife. Let not your heart be
3 one who runs to win a race. Let not your heart be

troub-led, Let not your heart be troub-led, Let
troub-led, Let not your heart be troub-led,

not your heart be troub-led, Nor let it be a-fraid.
Let not your heart be troub-led,

TRUST AND ASSURANCE

Hiding in Thee

632

"From the ends of the earth I call to you, I call as my heart grows faint; lead me to the rock that is higher than I."—Psalm 61:2

11.11.11.11.wR.
HIDING IN THEE
Ira D. Sankey

William O. Cushing

1 O safe to the Rock that is high - er than I My
2 In the calm of the noon - tide, in sor - row's lone hour, In
3 How of - ten in con - flict, when pressed by the foe, I have

1 soul in its con - flicts and sor - rows would fly; So sin - ful, so
2 times when temp - ta - tion casts o'er me its power, In the tem - pests of
3 fled to my Ref - uge and breathed out my woe; How of - ten, when

1 wea - ry—Thine, Thine would I be: Thou blest "Rock of A - ges," I'm
2 life, on its wide, heav-ing sea, Thou blest "Rock of A - ges," I'm
3 tri - als like sea bil - lows roll, Have I hid - den in Thee, O Thou

1 hid - ing in Thee.
2 hid - ing in Thee. Hid - ing in Thee, Hid - ing in
3 Rock of my soul.

Thee, Thou blest "Rock of A - ges," I'm hid - ing in Thee.

TRUST AND ASSURANCE

633 A Shelter in the Time of Storm

"My salvation and my honor depend on God; he is my mighty rock, my refuge."
—Psalm 62:7

Vernon J. Charlesworth
Adapted by Ira D. Sankey

L.M.wR.
SHELTER
Ira D. Sankey

1 The Lord's our rock, in Him we hide, A shel-ter in the time of storm;
2 A shade by day, de - fense by night, A shel-ter in the time of storm;
3 The rag-ing storms may 'round us beat, A shel-ter in the time of storm;
4 O Rock di-vine, O Ref-uge dear, A shel-ter in the time of storm;

1 Se - cure what-ev - er ill be-tide, A shel-ter in the time of storm.
2 No fears a - larm, no fears af-fright, A shel-ter in the time of storm.
3 We'll nev - er leave our safe re-treat, A shel-ter in the time of storm.
4 Be Thou our help - er ev - er near, A shel-ter in the time of storm.

O Je - sus is a rock in a wea - ry land, A

wea - ry land, a wea - ry land; O Je - sus is a

rock in a wea - ry land, A shel - ter in the time of storm.

TRUST AND ASSURANCE

God Will Take Care of You 634

"Humble yourselves, therefore, under God's mighty hand, that he may lift you up in due time. Cast all your anxiety on him because he cares for you."
—I Peter 5:6-7

Civilla D. Martin, alt.

GOD CARES
W. Stillman Martin

1 Be not dis-mayed what-e'er be-tide, God will take care of you;
2 Through days of toil when your heart doth fail, God will take care of you;
3 All you may need He will pro-vide, God will take care of you;
4 No mat-ter what may be the test, God will take care of you;

1 Be-neath His wings of love a-bide, God will take care of you.
2 When dan-gers fierce your path as-sail, God will take care of you.
3 Noth-ing you ask will be de-nied, God will take care of you.
4 Lean, wea-ry one, up-on His breast, God will take care of you.

God will take care of you, Through ev-'ry day, o'er all the way;

He will take care of you, God will take care of you.

TRUST AND ASSURANCE

635 Day by Day

"But he said to me, 'My grace is sufficient for you, for my power is made perfect in weakness.' "—II Corinthians 12:9

Lina Sandell
Tr. by A. L. Skoog

BLOTT EN DAG
Oscar Ahnfelt

1 Day by day and with each pass-ing mo-ment, Strength I find to meet my tri-als here; Trust-ing in my Fa-ther's wise be-stow-ment, I've no cause for wor-ry or for fear. He whose heart is kind be-yond all meas-ure Gives un-to each

2 Ev-ery day the Lord Him-self is near me With a spe-cial mer-cy for each hour; All my cares He fain would bear, and cheer me, He whose name is Coun-sel-lor and Power. The pro-tec-tion of His child and treas-ure Is a charge that

3 Help me then in ev-ery trib-u-la-tion So to trust Thy prom-is-es, O Lord, That I lose not faith's sweet con-so-la-tion Of-fered me with-in Thy ho-ly word. Help me, Lord, when toil and trou-ble meet-ing, E'er to take, as

TRUST AND ASSURANCE

1 day what He deems best— Lov - ing - ly, its part of pain and
2 on Him - self He laid; "As thy days, thy strength shall be in
3 from a fa - ther's hand, One by one, the days, the mo-ments

1 pleas - ure, Min - gling toil with peace and rest.
2 meas - ure," This the pledge to me He made.
3 fleet - ing, 'Til I reach the prom - ised land. A - men.

I Lift Up My Eyes to the Hills **636**

If I lift up my eyes to the hills, where shall I find help?

Help comes only from the Lord, maker of heaven and earth.

How could He let your foot stumble?
How could He, your guardian, sleep?

The guardian of Israel never slumbers, never sleeps.

The Lord is your guardian, your defense at your right hand;
the sun will not strike you by day nor the moon by night.

The Lord will guard you against all evil;
He will guard you, body and soul.

The Lord will guard your going and your coming, now and for
evermore.

For God alone my soul waits in silence; from Him comes my
salvation.
He only is my Rock and my Salvation, my Fortress;
I shall not be greatly moved.

How long will you set upon a man to shatter him, all of you, like a
wall, a tottering fence?
They only plan to thrust him down from his eminence.
They take pleasure in falsehood.
They bless with their mouths, but inwardly they curse.

For God alone my soul waits in silence, for my hope is from Him.
He only is my Rock and my Salvation, my Fortress; I shall not be
shaken.
On God rests my deliverance and my honor;
my mighty rock, my refuge is God.

—Psalm 121 and Psalm 62

TRUST AND ASSURANCE

637 Through It All

"In this you greatly rejoice, though now for a little while you may have had to suffer grief in all kinds of trials. These have come so that your faith—of greater worth than gold, which perishes even though refined by fire—may be proved genuine and may result in praise, glory and honor when Jesus Christ is revealed."—I Peter 1:6-7

Andraé Crouch

THROUGH IT ALL
Andraé Crouch

Through it all, Through it all, I've learned to trust in Je - sus, I've learned to trust in God; Through it all, Through it all, I've learned to de - pend up-on His Word.

©Copyright 1971 by Manna Music Inc. International Copyright Secured. All Rights Reserved. Used By Permission.

638 *Assurances from God*

"Where two or three meet in
    My name,
I shall be there with them."

*"The hour will come—in fact it is
    here already—
when true worshipers will worship
    the Father in spirit and in truth:*

"That is the kind of worshiper
    the Father wants.
God is spirit,
    and those who worship
must worship in spirit and truth."

"Come to Me, all you who labor and
    are overburdened,
and I will give you rest.
Shoulder my yoke and learn
    from Me,
for I am gentle and humble in heart
and you will find rest for your soul.
Yes, My yoke is easy and My
    burden light."

—Matthew 18:20; John 4:23, 24
Matthew 11:28-30 (TJB)

TRUST AND ASSURANCE

I Am the Lord's, I Know

"Who shall separate us from the love of Christ? Shall trouble or hardship or
persecution or famine or nakedness or danger or sword?"—Romans 8:35

Based on Romans 8:35-39
Charles W. Naylor

I AM THE LORD'S
D. Otis Teasley

1 Wheth-er I live or die, Wheth-er I wake or sleep,
2 When with a-bun-dant store Or in deep pov-er-ty,
3 When I am safe at home Or in a for-eign land,
4 Noth-ing shall sep-a-rate From His un-bound-ed love,

1 Wheth-er up-on the land Or on the storm-y deep;
2 And when the world may smile Or it may frown on me;
3 When on an ice-bound shore Or on a sun-lit strand;
4 Nei-ther in depths be-low Nor in the heights a-bove;

1 When 'tis se-rene and calm Or when the wild winds blow,
2 When it shall help me on Or shall ob-struct my way,
3 When on the moun-tain height Or in the val-ley low,
4 And in the years to come He will a-bide with me;

rit.

1 I shall not be a-fraid— I am the Lord's, I know.
2 Still shall my heart re-joice— I am the Lord's to-day.
3 Still doth He care for me— I am the Lord's, I know.
4 I am the Lord's, I know, For all e-ter-ni-ty.

TRUST AND ASSURANCE

640 Leaning on the Everlasting Arms

"The eternal God is your refuge, and underneath are the everlasting arms. He will drive out your enemy before you saying, 'Destroy him!' "
—Deuteronomy 33:27

10.9.10.9.wR.
SHOWALTER
Anthony J. Showalter

Elisha A. Hoffman

1 What a fel-low-ship, what a joy di-vine, Lean-ing on the ev-er-
2 O how sweet to walk in this pil-grim way, Lean-ing on the ev-er-
3 What have I to dread, what have I to fear, Lean-ing on the ev-er-

1 last-ing arms; What a bless-ed-ness, what a peace is mine,
2 last-ing arms; O how bright the path grows from day to day,
3 last-ing arms? I have bless-ed peace with my Lord so near,

1 Lean-ing on the ev-er-last-ing arms. Lean - ing,
2 Lean-ing on the ev-er-last-ing arms. Lean-ing on Je-sus,
3 Lean-ing on the ev-er-last-ing arms.

lean - ing, Safe and se-cure from all a-larms; Lean-
lean-ing on Je-sus, Lean-ing on

ing, lean - ing, Lean-ing on the ev-er-last-ing arms.
Je-sus, lean-ing on Je-sus,

TRUST AND ASSURANCE

Let not your heart be troubled; believe in God, believe also in Me.

In My Father's house are many rooms; if it were not so, would I have told you that I go to prepare a place for you?

And when I go and prepare a place for you, I will come again and will take you to Myself, that where I am you may be also.

If you love Me, you will keep My commandments.

And I will pray the Father, and He will give you another Counselor, to be with you forever.

Peace I leave with you; My peace I give to you; not as the world gives do I give to you. Let not your hearts be troubled, neither let them be afraid.

Blessed be the God and Father of our Lord Jesus Christ, the Father of mercies and God of all comfort, who comforts us in all our affliction, so that we may be able to comfort those who are in any affliction, with the comfort with which we ourselves are comforted by God.

For as we share abundantly in Christ's sufferings, so through Christ we share abundantly in comfort, too.

If we are afflicted, it is for your comfort and salvation; and if we are comforted, it is for your comfort, which you experience when you patiently endure the same sufferings that we suffer.

Our hope for you is unshaken; for we know that as you share in our sufferings, you will also share in our comfort.

—John 14:1-3, 15-16,27; II Cor. 1:3-7

642 Because He Loves Me

"I would hurry to my place of shelter, far from the tempest and storm."
—Psalm 55:8

Charles W. Naylor

BECAUSE HE LOVES ME
Andrew L. Byers

1 When the storm winds rage and the rain falls fast, And the clouds hang
2 It was not that I was so good or great, For my heart was
3 If He loved me so when I grieved Him sore That He sought me
4 I will trust His love, for it e'er will last, It is rich and

1 low a - bove, I shall be se - cure till the storm is past,
2 vile with sin; I had turned my back on the nar - row gate,
3 ten - der - ly, Till He won my heart and my sins He bore,
4 warm and free; Thru the years of life it will hold me fast,

1 For I trust my Sav - ior's love. And He knows the way and He
2 Nei - ther cared nor lived for Him. But I pleased my - self and I
3 So that I His child might be, Will He love me less since I
4 And my help and com - fort be. To my wait - ing heart all its

1 holds my hand, And He will not let it go; He will lead me
2 chose my way, For His grace I did not know; But He sought me
3 love Him, too, So my heart with fer - vor glows, And I haste each
4 trea - sures rare As a spar - kling stream shall flow; In the joy of

TRUST AND ASSURANCE

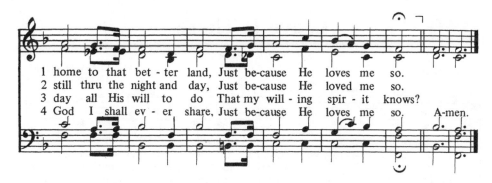

1 home to that bet - ter land, Just be-cause He loves me so.
2 still thru the night and day, Just be-cause He loved me so.
3 day all His will to do That my will - ing spir - it knows?
4 God I shall ev - er share, Just be-cause He loves me so. A-men.

Learning to Lean
643

"Trust in the Lord with all your heart and lean not on your own understanding."—Proverbs 3:5

John Stallings

LEARNING TO LEAN
John Stallings

Learn - ing to lean, learn - ing to lean, I'm

learn - ing to lean on Je - sus.

Find - ing more pow - er than I'd ev - er dreamed, I'm

learn - ing to lean on Je - sus.

TRUST AND ASSURANCE

644 Leave It There

"Cast your cares on the Lord and he will sustain you; he will never let the righteous fall."—Psalm 55:22

Charles A. Tindley

LEAVE IT THERE
Charles A. Tindley

1 If the world from you with-hold of its sil - ver and its gold,
2 If your bod - y suf - fers pain, and your health you can't re - gain,
3 When your en - e - mies as - sail, and your heart be - gins to fail,
4 When your youth-ful days are gone, and old age is steal-ing on,

1 And you have to get a - long with mea - ger fare,
2 And your soul is al - most sink - ing in de - spair,
3 Don't for - get that God in heav - en an - swers prayer;
4 And your bod - y bends be - neath the weight of care,

1 Just re - mem-ber in His Word, how He feeds the lit - tle bird,
2 Je - sus knows the pain you feel, He can save and He can heal,
3 He will make a way for you, and will lead you safe - ly through,
4 He will nev - er leave you then, He'll go with you to the end,

1 Take your bur - den to the Lord and leave it there.
2 Take your bur - den to the Lord and leave it there.
3 Take your bur - den to the Lord and leave it there.
4 Take your bur - den to the Lord and leave it there. (leave it there.)

TRUST AND ASSURANCE

Leave it there, leave it there, leave it there, leave it there,

Take your bur-den to the Lord and leave it there. leave it there.

If you trust and nev-er doubt, He will sure-ly bring you out—

Take your bur-den to the Lord and leave it there.

Sensing God's Presence 645

God promised, "My presence shall go with thee." That promise has been a comfort and consolation to God's people for three thousand years. We need to cultivate a sense of God's presence. He has said, "I will never leave thee nor forsake thee." His presence with us is real whether or not we can realize it. We need not try to create a sense of its reality in our imagination. It is a fact, not a fancy. We have only to sense the fact and to treat it as a fact. We may say that God is everywhere. True, but it is not His presence everywhere that counts for us; it is only that part of everywhere where we are. God is just as real in that little part of everywhere where you and I now are as He is in heaven on His throne. It is His presence where we are the really counts for us. Therefore it is the sense of the reality of His presence with us that makes Him real to us.

—Charles Wesley Naylor
(*The Secret of the Singing Heart* Pg. 121)

TRUST AND ASSURANCE

646 My Shepherd Will Supply My Need

"The Lord is my shepherd, I shall lack nothing."—Psalm 23:1

Based on Psalm 23
Isaac Watts

C.M.
RESIGNATION
Traditional American Melody
Arranged by Fred Bock

1 My Shep - herd will sup - ply my need; Je - ho - vah is His
2 When I walk through the shades of death, His pres - ence is my
3 The sure pro - vi - sions of my God At - tend me all my

1 name: In pas - tures fresh He makes me feed, Be - side the
2 stay: One word of His sup - port - ing grace Drives all my
3 days: O may Thy house be my a - bode, And all my

1 liv - ing stream. He brings my wan - dering spir - it back
2 fears a - way. His hand, in sight of all my foes,
3 work be praise. There would I find a set - tled rest,

1 When I for - sake His ways, And leads me, for His
2 Doth still my ta - ble spread; My cup with bless - ings
3 While oth - ers go and come; No more a stran - ger,

TRUST AND ASSURANCE

1 mer - cy's sake, In paths of truth and grace.
2 o - ver - flows, His oil a - noints my head.
3 nor a guest, But like a child at home. A - men.

'Tis So Sweet to Trust in Jesus 647

"Do not let your hearts be troubled. Trust in God; trust also in me."—John 14:1

Louisa M. R. Stead

8.7.8.7.wR.
TRUST IN JESUS
William J. Kirkpatrick

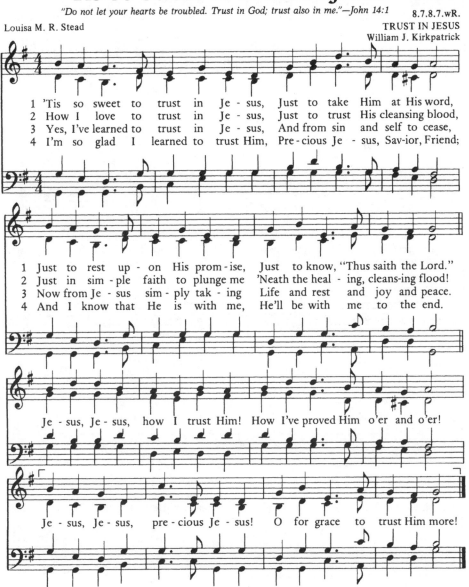

1 'Tis so sweet to trust in Je - sus, Just to take Him at His word,
2 How I love to trust in Je - sus, Just to trust His cleansing blood,
3 Yes, I've learned to trust in Je - sus, And from sin and self to cease,
4 I'm so glad I learned to trust Him, Pre - cious Je - sus, Sav-ior, Friend;

1 Just to rest up - on His prom - ise, Just to know, "Thus saith the Lord."
2 Just in sim - ple faith to plunge me 'Neath the heal - ing, cleans-ing flood!
3 Now from Je - sus sim - ply tak - ing Life and rest and joy and peace.
4 And I know that He is with me, He'll be with me to the end.

Je - sus, Je - sus, how I trust Him! How I've proved Him o'er and o'er!

Je - sus, Je - sus, pre - cious Je - sus! O for grace to trust Him more!

TRUST AND ASSURANCE

648 His Eye Is on the Sparrow

"Are not five sparrows sold for two pennies? Yet not one of them is forgotten by God."—Luke 12:6

Civilla D. Martin

SPARROW
Charles H. Gabriel

1 Why should I feel dis - cour-aged, Why should the shad - ows come,
2 "Let not your heart be trou-bled," His ten - der word I hear,
3 When-ev - er I am temp-ted, When - ev - er clouds a - rise,

1 Why should my heart be lone-ly And long for heav'n and home When
2 And rest-ing on His good-ness I lose my doubt and fears; Though
3 When songs give place to sigh-ing, When hope with-in me dies, I

1 Je - sus is my por-tion? My con-stant friend is He: His
2 by the path He lead-eth But one step I may see: His
3 draw the clos - er to Him, From care He sets me free; His

TRUST AND ASSURANCE

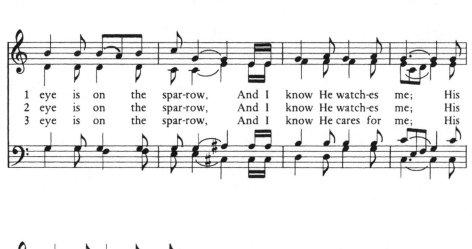

1 eye is on the spar-row, And I know He watch-es me; His
2 eye is on the spar-row, And I know He watch-es me; His
3 eye is on the spar-row, And I know He cares for me; His

1 eye is on the spar-row, And I know He watch-es me.
2 eye is on the spar-row, And I know He watch-es me.
3 eye is on the spar-row, And I know He cares for me.

I sing be-cause I'm hap-py, I sing be-cause I'm free,
I'm hap-py, I'm free,

For His eye is on the spar-row, And I know He watch-es me.

TRUST AND ASSURANCE

649

My Soul Is Satisfied

"I pray that out of his glorious riches he may strengthen you with power through his Spirit in your inner being."—Ephesians 3:16

Daniel S. Warner

MY SOUL IS SATISFIED
Barney E. Warren

1 All this world, its wealth and hon-or, Can-not soothe the hu-man soul;
2 All my soul can wish for-ev-er I now find in Christ com-plete;
3 Is your life de-void of com-fort And your heart a cheer-less place?
4 Can a bird drink up the o-cean, Thirst-ing still from shore to shore?
5 Would my soul could more en-com-pass Heav-en's glo-ry, willed to me;

1 But when filled with God, our Fa-ther, Ev-'ry want is then made whole.
2 Ev-'ry bless-ing, and the Giv-er, In my peace-ful heart now meet.
3 Say not Christ is in your des-ert While you are de-void of grace.
4 Or the God of all cre-a-tion Leave your heart yet crav-ing more?
5 O the love of God so pre-cious! It's a deep and shore-less sea!

My soul is sat-is-fied, My soul is sat-is-fied; I am com-

plete in Je-sus' love, And my soul is sat-is-fied.

TRUST AND ASSURANCE

Blessed Assurance

650

"Is any one of you in trouble? He should pray. Is anyone happy? Let him sing songs of praise."—James 5:13

9.10.9.9.wR.

ASSURANCE

Fanny J. Crosby

Phoebe P. Knapp

1 Bless-ed as - sur - ance, Je - sus is mine! O what a fore-taste of
2 Per - fect sub - mis - sion, per-fect de - light, Vi-sions of rap - ture now
3 Per - fect sub - mis - sion, all is at rest, I in my Sav - ior am

1 glo - ry di - vine! Heir of sal - va - tion, pur-chase of God,
2 burst on my sight; An - gels de - scend-ing bring from a - bove
3 hap - py and blest; Watch-ing and wait - ing, look - ing a - bove,

1 Born of His Spir - it, washed in His blood.
2 Ech - oes of mer - cy, whis - pers of love. This is my sto - ry, this is my
3 Filled with His good-ness, lost in His love.

song, Prais-ing my Sav - ior all the day long; This is my sto - ry,

this is my song, Prais-ing my Sav - ior all the day long.

TRUST AND ASSURANCE

651 The Faithfulness of God

"They are new every morning; great is your faithfulness."—Lamentations 3:23

Barney E. Warren

THE FAITHFULNESS OF GOD
Barney E. Warren

1 O look at the faith-ful-ness of Christ our Lord, How He
2 The Lord in His faith-ful-ness be-stows on us Life and
3 Be-hold all the u - ni-verse that He has made, See the
4 His Word is e - ter-nal and shall ev - er stand, It can

1 saves and keeps the soul! Who trusts in His maj-es-ty and
2 breath, yea, and all things; But great-er His sav-ing grace and
3 twin-kling worlds on high; A - lone, by His pow-er are these
4 nev - er pass a - way; By it were the heav-ens made, the

1 stands up-on His word Shall be safe while the bil-lows roll.
2 gift of right-eous-ness, O what peace, love and joy it brings!
3 star - ry heav-ens stayed, Then we know He can nev-er lie.
4 sea and all the land, And its pow'r is the same to - day.

TRUST AND ASSURANCE

O trust in God,
Trust in the faith - ful - ness and love of God,

O trust in God,
Trust in the faith - ful - ness and love of God,

O trust in God, O trust in the faith-ful God!
Trust in the faith-ful-ness and love of God,

TRUST AND ASSURANCE

652 God's Way Is Best

"And we know that in all things God works for the good of those who love him, who have been called according to his purpose."—Romans 8:28

Charles W. Naylor

GOD'S WAY IS BEST
Clarence E. Hunter

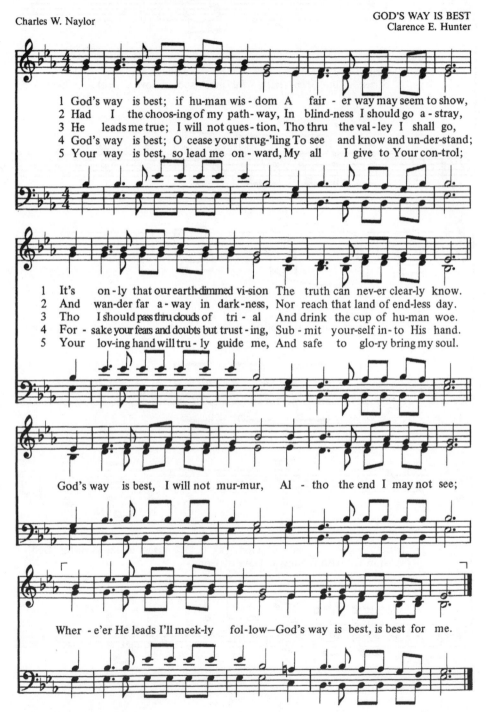

1 God's way is best; if hu-man wis-dom A fair-er way may seem to show,
2 Had I the choos-ing of my path-way, In blind-ness I should go a-stray,
3 He leads me true; I will not ques-tion, Tho thru the val-ley I shall go,
4 God's way is best; O cease your strug-'ling To see and know and un-der-stand;
5 Your way is best, so lead me on-ward, My all I give to Your con-trol;

1 It's on-ly that our earth-dimmed vi-sion The truth can nev-er clear-ly know.
2 And wan-der far a-way in dark-ness, Nor reach that land of end-less day.
3 Tho I should pass thru clouds of tri-al And drink the cup of hu-man woe.
4 For-sake your fears and doubts but trust-ing, Sub-mit your-self in-to His hand.
5 Your lov-ing hand will tru-ly guide me, And safe to glo-ry bring my soul.

God's way is best, I will not mur-mur, Al-tho the end I may not see;

Wher-e'er He leads I'll meek-ly fol-low—God's way is best, is best for me.

He Leadeth Me, O Blessed Thought

653

"When he has brought out all his own, he goes on ahead of them, and his sheep follow him because they know his voice."—John 10:4

8.8.8.8.wR.

Joseph H. Gilmore

HE LEADETH ME
William B. Bradbury
Descant by Tom Fettke

1 He leadeth me, O blessed thought! O words with heav'nly comfort fraught!
2 Lord, I would clasp Thy hand in mine, Nor ever murmur nor repine;
3 And when my task on earth is done, When by Thy grace the vict'ry's won,

1 What-e'er I do, where-e'er I be, Still 'tis God's hand that leadeth me.
2 Content whatever lot I see, Since 'tis my God that leadeth me.
3 E'en death's cold wave I will not flee, Still God through Jordan leadeth me.

Descant

He leadeth, leadeth me, By His own hand He leadeth me;

He leadeth me, He leadeth me, By His own hand He leadeth me;

His faithful follower I would be, For by His hand He leadeth me.

His faithful follower I would be, For by His hand He leadeth me.

GUIDANCE AND KEEPING

654

Lead Me, Lord

"Lead me, O Lord, in your righteousness because of my enemies—make straight your way before me."—Psalm 5:8

Psalm 4:8, 5:8
Adapted by Fred Bock

LEAD ME, LORD
Samuel Sebastian Wesley

1 Lead me, Lord; lead me in Thy right-eous-ness.
2 Teach me, Lord; teach me of Thy right-eous-ness.
3 Keep me, Lord; keep me in Thy right-eous-ness.

1 Make Thy way plain be - fore my face. For it is
2 Make Thy way plain be - fore my face. For it is
3 Make Thy way plain be - fore my face. For it is

1 Thou, Lord; Thou, O Lord, on - ly that mak-est me to
2 Thou, Lord; Thou, O Lord, on - ly that mak-est me to
3 Thou, Lord; Thou, O Lord, on - ly that mak-est me to

1 dwell in safe - ty.
2 dwell in safe - ty.
3 dwell in safe - ty. A - men.

GUIDANCE AND KEEPING

Guide Me, O Thou Great Jehovah 655

*"The Lord will guide you always; he will satisfy your needs in a sun-scorched
land and will strengthen your frame."—Isaiah 58:11*

William Williams
Tr. by Peter Williams

8.7.8.7.8.7.7.
CWM RHONDDA
John Hughes

1 Guide me, O Thou great Je - ho - vah, Pil - grim through this
2 O - pen now the crys - tal foun - tain, Whence the heal - ing
3 When I reach the riv - er Jor - dan, Bid my anx - ious

1 bar - ren land; I am weak, but Thou art might - y— Hold me with Thy
2 stream doth flow; Let the fire and cloud - y pil - lar Lead me all my
3 fears sub - side; Bear me through the swell - ing cur - rent, Land me safe on

1 power - ful hand: Bread of heav - en, Bread of heav - en,
2 jour - ney through: Strong De - liv - erer, strong De - liv - erer,
3 Ca - naan's side: Songs of prais - es, songs of prais - es

1 Feed me 'til I want no more, Feed me 'til I want no more.
2 Be Thou still my strength and shield, Be Thou still my strength and shield.
3 I will ev - er give to Thee, I will ev - er give to Thee. A-men.

GUIDANCE AND KEEPING

656 Like a Lamb Who Needs the Shepherd

"He tends his flock like a shepherd; He gathers the lambs in his arms and carries them close to his heart; he gently leads those that have young."
—Isaiah 40:11

Ralph Carmichael

LIKE A LAMB
Ralph Carmichael

1 Where He leads me I must fol - low, With - out Him I'd lose my way. I will see a bright to - mor - row If I fol - low Him to - day. Like a lamb who needs the Shep - herd, At His side I'll al - ways stay. Thro' the night His strength I'll bor - row, Then I'll see an - oth - er day.

2 Life is like a wind - ing path - way, Who can tell what lies a - head? Will it lead to shad - y pas - tures, Or to wil - der - ness in - stead? Like a lamb who needs the Shep - herd, When in - to the night I go Help me find the path that's nar - row, While I trav - el here be - low.

3 Tho' you walk thro' dark - est val - leys And the sky is cold and gray, Tho' you climb the steep - est moun - tains He will nev - er let you stray. Like a lamb who needs the Shep - herd, By your side He'll al - ways stay. Till the end of life's long jour - ney He will lead you all the way.

GUIDANCE AND KEEPING

The Lord's My Shepherd

657

"He restores my soul. He guides me in paths of righteousness for his name's sake."—Psalm 23:3

C.M.
CRIMOND
Jessie S. Irvine

Based on Psalm 23
Scottish Psalter

1 The Lord's my shep-herd, I'll not want; He makes me down to lie
2 My soul He doth re - store a - gain, And me to walk doth make
3 Yea, though I walk in death's dark vale, Yet will I fear no ill,
4 My ta - ble Thou hast fur - nish - ed In pres - ence of my foes;
5 Good-ness and mer - cy all my life Shall sure - ly fol - low me,

1 In pas - tures green; He lead - eth me The qui - et wa - ters by.
2 With-in the paths of right-eous - ness, E'en for His own name's sake.
3 For Thou art with me, and Thy rod And staff me com - fort still.
4 My head Thou dost with oil a - noint, And my cup o - ver - flows.
5 And in God's house for - ev - er - more My dwell - ing place shall be. A - men.

God's Will

658

Why does He not reveal Himself?
Why does He not speak so that the soul may hear?
If He is silent, let us be assured . . .
There is good reason for His silence . . .
Sometimes it is necessary for God to leave us in
     ignorance of His will, in order that He might
     work it out, and accomplish His designed
     purpose.
Many times our unsatisfied longings, our thwarted
     purposes, our sufferings of anguish, all work
     together to accomplish His purpose.

—Charles Wesley Naylor
from God's Will and How to Know It
© Copyright 1925 Gospel Trumpet.

GUIDANCE AND KEEPING

659 All the Way My Savior Leads Me

"For this God is our God for ever and ever; he will be our guide even to the end."—Psalm 48:14

Fanny J. Crosby

8.7.8.7.D.
ALL THE WAY
Robert Lowry

1 All the way my Sav-ior leads me— What have I to ask be-side?
2 All the way my Sav-ior leads me— Cheers each wind-ing path I tread,
3 All the way my Sav-ior leads me— O the full-ness of His love!

1 Can I doubt His ten-der mer-cy, Who through life has been my guide?
2 Gives me grace for ev-ery tri-al, Feeds me with the liv-ing bread.
3 Per-fect rest to me is prom-ised In my Fa-ther's house a-bove.

1 Heaven-ly peace, di-vin-est com-fort, Here by faith in Him to dwell!
2 Though my wea-ry steps may fal-ter And my soul a-thirst may be,
3 When my spir-it, clothed im-mor-tal, Wings its flight to realms of day,

1 For I know, what-e'er be-fall me, Je-sus do-eth all things well;
2 Gush-ing from the Rock be-fore me, Lo! a spring of joy I see;
3 This my song through end-less a-ges: Je-sus led me all the way;

1 For I know, what-e'er be-fall me, Je-sus do-eth all things well.
2 Gush-ing from the Rock be-fore me, Lo! a spring of joy I see.
3 This my song through end-less a-ges: Je-sus led me all the way.

GUIDANCE AND KEEPING

Savior, Like a Shepherd Lead Us 660

"The watchman opens the gate for him, and the sheep listen to his voice. He calls his own sheep by name and leads them out."—John 10:3

8.7.8.7.D.
BRADBURY
William B. Bradbury

Attributed to Dorothy A. Thrupp

1 Sav - ior, like a Shep-herd lead us, Much we need Thy ten-der care;
2 We are Thine; do Thou be - friend us; Be the guard-ian of our way;
3 Ear - ly let us seek Thy fa - vor; Ear - ly let us do Thy will;

1 In Thy pleas-ant pas-tures feed us; For our use Thy folds pre - pare.
2 Keep Thy flock; from sin de - fend us; Seek us when we go a - stray.
3 Bless-ed Lord and on - ly Sav - ior, With Thy love our bos-oms fill.

1 Bless-ed Je - sus, Bless-ed Je - sus, Thou hast bought us, Thine we are;
2 Bless-ed Je - sus, Bless-ed Je - sus, Hear Thy chil - dren when they pray;
3 Bless-ed Je - sus, Bless-ed Je - sus, Thou hast loved us, love us still;

1 Bless-ed Je - sus, Bless-ed Je - sus, Thou hast bought us, Thine we are.
2 Bless-ed Je - sus, Bless-ed Je - sus, Hear Thy chil - dren when they pray.
3 Bless-ed Je - sus, Bless-ed Je - sus, Thou hast loved us, love us still.

GUIDANCE AND KEEPING

661 The Lord Our Shepherd

"When he has brought out all his own, he goes on ahead of them, and his sheep follow him because they know his voice."—John 10:4

Daniel S. Warner

THE LORD OUR SHEPHERD
Uriah E. Hallman

1 We'll fol - low the Lord all the way, (all the way,)
2 The sheep of His pas - ture are one, (all are one,)
3 There's joy in the fold of the Lord, (of the Lord,)
4 By riv - ers of peace we are led, (we are led,)

1 And close to our Shep - herd we'll stay; How bless - ed to know,
2 Yea, one as the Fa - ther and Son; They're all of one mind,
3 We walk in the light of His Word; We love to o - bey
4 In pas - tures of love we are fed; We ev - er re - joice

1 as we jour - ney be - low, He's with us by night and by day!
2 as their Shep - herd de - signed, They fol - low and serve Him a - lone.
3 all the Sav - ior doth say, Thus liv - ing in ho - ly ac - cord.
4 at the sound of His voice, Re - deemed by the blood He has shed.

We will fol - low, ev - er fol - low In the
We will fol - low on, fol - low on In

GUIDANCE AND KEEPING

foot - steps   of the Sav - ior;   We will fol - low,
Je - sus' steps, the   Sav - ior's steps;   Fol - low   on,

ev - er fol - low   In His path - way bright and clear.
we'll   fol - low   on

Children of the Heavenly Father 662

"He will not let your foot slip—he who watches over you will not slumber."
—Psalm 121:3

L.M.

Carolina Sandell Berg
Tr. by Ernst W. Olson

TRYGGARE KAN INGEN VARA
Swedish Folk Melody

1 Chil - dren of the heaven-ly Fa - ther Safe - ly in His bos - om gath - er;
2 God His own doth tend and nour-ish, In His ho - ly courts they flour-ish;
3 Nei - ther life nor death shall ev - er From the Lord His chil - dren sev - er;
4 Though He giv - eth or He   tak - eth, God His chil - dren ne'er for - sak - eth;

1 Nest-ling bird nor star in heav - en Such a   ref - uge e'er was giv - en.
2 From all e - vil things He spares them, In His   might - y arms He bears them.
3 Un - to them His grace He show - eth, And their sor - rows all He know - eth.
4 His the lov - ing pur - pose sole - ly To pre - serve them pure and ho - ly.

663 He Will Care for Me

"Cast all your care on him because he cares for you." —I Peter 5:7

Charles W. Naylor

HE WILL CARE FOR ME
Andrew L. Byers

1 I walk to-day in the Chris-tian way, Tho dan-gers I may see;
2 No test I face, but suf-fi-cient grace Is read-y for my need;
3 He will not fail in the strong-est gale That storm-y winds can blow;
4 I trust in Him, tho dis-as-ters grim Be-fore me seem to be;

1 I will not fear, for the Lord is near, And He will care for me.
2 When sor-rows rise to ob-scure my skies, He proves a friend in-deed.
3 And in His grace is a hid-ing place, Un-known to an-y foe.
4 He calms my fears and He dries my tears And faith-ful is to me.

No mat-ter what hap-pens, He will care for me, He will care for me, He will care for me; And His might-y hand will en-

a-ble me to stand, No mat-ter what hap-pens to me.
what hap-pens to me.

Precious Lord, Take My Hand 664

"For I am the Lord, your God, who takes hold of your right hand and says to you, Do not fear; I will help you."—Isaiah 41:13

6.6.9.6.6.9.

PRECIOUS LORD
Arranged by Thomas A. Dorsey

Thomas A. Dorsey

1 Pre-cious Lord, take my hand, Lead me on, help me stand; I am
2 When my way grows drear, Pre-cious Lord, lin-ger near; When my

1 tired, I am weak, I am worn; Thru the storm, thru the night, Lead me
2 life is al-most gone, Hear my cry, hear my call, Hold my

1 on to the light, Take my hand, pre-cious Lord, lead me home.
2 hand lest I fall; Take my hand, pre-cious Lord, lead me home.

GUIDANCE AND KEEPING

665 Beams of Heaven As I Go

"Be strong and take heart, all you who hope in the Lord."—Psalm 31:24

Charles A. Tindley

SOME DAY
Charles A. Tindley

1 Beams of heav - en, as I go through this wil - der - ness be - low,
2 Of - ten - times my sky is clear, joy a - bounds with-out a tear;
3 Hard - er yet may be the fight, fight may of - ten yield to might;
4 Bur - dens now may crush me down, dis - ap - point-ments all a - round;

1 Guide my feet in peace-ful ways, turn my mid - nights in - to days.
2 Though a day so bright be - gun, clouds may hide to - mor-row's sun.
3 Wick - ed - ness a - while may reign, Sa - tan's cause may seem to gain.
4 Trou - bles speak in mourn-ful sigh, sor - row through a tear-stained eye.

1 When in the dark - ness I would grope, faith al - ways sees a star of hope,
2 There'll be a day that's al - ways bright, a day that nev - er yields to night,
3 There is a God that rules a - bove, with hand of pow'r and heart of love;
4 There is a world where plea-sure reigns, no mourn-ing soul shall roam its plains,

1 And seen from all life's grief and dan - ger, I shall be free some-day.
2 And in its light the streets of glo - ry, I shall be - hold some-day.
3 If I am right, He'll fight my bat - tle, I shall have peace some-day.
4 And to that land of peace and glo - ry, I want to go some-day.

GUIDANCE AND KEEPING

I do not know how long 'twill be, nor what the fu-ture holds for me;

But this I know: if Je-sus leads me, I shall get home some-day.

I Am Trusting Thee, Lord Jesus 666

"Such confidence as this is ours through Christ before God."—II Corinthians 3:4

8.5.8.3.
BULLINGER
Ethelbert W. Bullinger

Frances Ridley Havergal

1 I am trust-ing Thee, Lord Je - sus— Trust-ing on - ly Thee;
2 I am trust-ing Thee to guide me— Thou a - lone shalt lead,
3 I am trust-ing Thee for pow - er— Thine can nev - er fail;
4 I am trust-ing Thee, Lord Je - sus— Nev - er let me fall;

1 Trust - ing Thee for full sal - va - tion, Great and free.
2 Ev - ery day and hour sup - ply-ing All my need.
3 Words which Thou Thy-self shalt give me Must pre - vail.
4 I am trust-ing Thee for - ev - er, And for all. A - men.

GUIDANCE AND KEEPING

667

Gentle Shepherd

" 'I am the good shepherd; I know my sheep and my sheep know me—' "
—John 10:14

Gloria Gaither
William J. Gaither

GENTLE SHEPHERD
William J. Gaither

Gen-tle Shep-herd, come and lead us, For we need You to help us find our way. Gen-tle Shep-herd, come and feed us, For we need Your strength from day to day. There's no oth-er we can turn to Who can help us face an-oth-er day; Gen-tle Shep-herd, come and lead us, For we need You to help us find our way.

GUIDANCE AND KEEPING

Be Thou My Vision

"Your word is a lamp to my feet and a light for my path."—Psalm 119:105

668

Ancient Irish
Tr. by Mary Byrne
Versified by Eleanor Hull

10.10.10.10.
SLANE
Traditional Irish Melody
Arranged by Norman Johnson

1 Be Thou my Vi - sion, O Lord of my heart;
2 Be Thou my Wis - dom, and Thou my true Word;
3 Rich - es I heed not, nor vain emp - ty praise,
4 High King of heav - en, my vic - to - ry won,

1 Nought be all else to me, save that Thou art—
2 I ev - er with Thee and Thou with me, Lord;
3 Thou mine in - her - i - tance, now and al - ways:
4 May I reach heav - en's joys, O bright heav'n's Sun!

1 Thou my best thought, by day or by night,
2 Thou my great Fa - ther and true Friend to me;
3 Thou and Thou on - ly, first in my heart,
4 Heart of my own heart, what - ev - er be - fall,

1 Wak - ing or sleep - ing, Thy pres - ence my light.
2 Thou in me dwell - ing, and I join with Thee.
3 High King of heav - en, my Treas - ure Thou art.
4 Still be my Vi - sion, O Rul - er of all.

GUIDANCE AND KEEPING

669 Stepping in the Light

"To this were you called, because Christ suffered for you, leaving you an example, that you should follow in his steps."—I Peter 2:21

Eliza E. Hewitt

BEAUTIFUL TO WALK
William J. Kirkpatrick

1 Try - ing to walk in the steps of the Sav-ior, Try - ing to fol-low our
2 Press-ing more close-ly to Him who is lead-ing, When we are tempt-ed to
3 Walk - ing in foot-steps of gen-tle for-bear-ance, Foot-steps of faith-ful-ness,
4 Try - ing to walk in the steps of the Sav-ior, Up-ward, still up-ward we'll

1 Sav - ior and King; Shap - ing our lives by His bless - ed ex - am - ple,
2 turn from the way; Trust - ing the arm that is strong to de-fend us,
3 mer - cy and love, Look - ing to Him for the grace free-ly prom-ised,
4 fol - low our Guide; When we shall see Him, "the King in His beau-ty,"

1 Hap-py, how hap-py, the songs that we bring.
2 Hap-py, how hap-py, our prais - es each day.
3 Hap-py, how hap-py, our jour - ney a- bove.
4 Hap-py, how hap-py, our place at His side.

How beau-ti-ful to walk in the

steps of the Sav - ior, Step-ping in the light, step-ping in the light; How

beau-ti - ful to walk in the steps of the Sav - ior, Led in paths of light.

GUIDANCE AND KEEPING

My Faith Looks Up to Thee 670

"In him and through faith in him we may approach God with freedom and confidence."—Ephesians 3:12

Ray Palmer

6.6.4.6.6.6.6.4.
OLIVET
Lowell Mason

1 My faith looks up to Thee, Thou Lamb of Cal - va - ry,
2 May Thy rich grace im - part Strength to my faint - ing heart,
3 While life's dark maze I tread And griefs a - round me spread,
4 When ends life's pass - ing dream, When death's cold, threat-ening stream

1 Sav - ior di - vine! Now hear me while I pray, Take all my
2 My zeal in - spire; As Thou hast died for me, O may my
3 Be Thou my guide; Bid dark-ness turn to day, Wipe sor-row's
4 Shall o'er me roll, Blest Sav - ior, then, in love, Fear and dis -

1 guilt a - way, O let me from this day Be whol - ly Thine!
2 love to Thee Pure, warm, and change-less be, A liv - ing fire!
3 tears a - way, Nor let me ev - er stray From Thee a - side.
4 trust re-move; O lift me safe a - bove. A ran-somed soul. A-men.

Our Faith Still Holds 671

LEADER: I confess that You are not always the center of my thoughts, the focus of my attention. Where is that faith that can hold my life together?

PEOPLE: *"I shall never leave you nor forsake you." Such is the promise of our Lord even when we remember Him not. But, when our problems seem overwhelming and the parade of things undone chases sleep away, where is that faith which can free us from our anxieties and fear?*

LEADER: "Peace I leave with you; My peace I give to you. Let not your heart be troubled, neither let it be afraid."

Peace is the gift of our Lord to calm our fears. But, when the evil of the world seems everywhere, is God able? Will my faith in Him hold?

PEOPLE: *"Greater is He who is in you than he who is in the world." This is the bold promise of God.*

ALL: *Thank you, Lord, that Your Word is faithful and true. You have never abandoned us to our own foolishness, nor has our trust in You ever led us astray. In this assurance, therefore, we dare to say, "Our faith, indeed, still holds!"*

—Ralph Osborne

GUIDANCE AND KEEPING

672 In Heavenly Love Abiding

"The Lord himself goes before you and will be with you; he will never leave you nor forsake you. Do not be afraid; do not be discouraged."—Deuteronomy 31:8

7.6.7.6.D.

Based on Psalm 23
Anna L. Waring

ANGELS' STORY
Arthur H. Mann

1 In heav'n-ly love a-bid-ing, No change my heart shall fear;
2 Wher-ev-er He may guide me, No want shall turn me back;
3 Green pas-tures are be-fore me, Which yet I have not seen;

1 And safe is such con-fid-ing, For noth-ing chang-es here.
2 My Shep-herd is be-side me, And noth-ing can I lack.
3 Bright skies will soon be o'er me, Where the dark clouds have been.

1 The storm may roar with-out me, My heart may low be laid;
2 His wis-dom ev-er wak-eth, His sight is nev-er dim;
3 My hope I can-not mea-sure, My path to life is free;

1 But God is round a-bout me, And can I be dis-mayed?
2 He knows the way He tak-eth, And I will walk with Him.
3 My Sav-ior has my trea-sure, And He will walk with me.

673 *May the Lord, Mighty God*

May the Lord, mighty God, bless and keep you forever.
Grant you peace, perfect peace, courage in every endeavor.
Lift up your eyes and see His face, and His grace forever.
May the Lord, mighty God, bless and keep you forever.

—Traditional

GUIDANCE AND KEEPING

The Shield of Faith

" . . . take up the shield of faith . . . "—Ephesians 6:16a

674

Based on Ephesians 6:10-17
Daniel S. Warner

THE SHIELD OF FAITH
Barney E. Warren

1 Take the shield of faith and march on, Hold it bold-ly in the light:
2 Faith is might-y and will con-quer, Bind it firm-ly on your heart;
3 Then put on the ho-ly ar-mor And de-fy the tempt-ing throng;

1 And its aw-ful burn-ished glo-ry Will put ev-'ry foe to flight.
2 On the hot-test field of bat-tle You will quench the vil-est dart.
3 O-ver all the foes that gath-er Shout and sing the vic-tor's song.

In the might-y name of Je-sus, Ev-er lift up the shield of faith;

Wield the sword of truth and march on, Heav'n will crown your fight of faith.

LOYALTY AND COURAGE

675 A Mighty Fortress Is Our God

"The Lord Almighty is with us; the God of Jacob is our fortress."—Psalm 46:7

Based on Psalm 46
Martin Luther
Tr. by Frederick H. Hedge

8.7.8.7.6.6.6.7.
EIN' FESTE BURG
Martin Luther

1 A might-y for-tress is our God, A bul-wark nev-er fail - ing;
2 Did we in our own strength con-fide, Our striv-ing would be los - ing,
3 And though this world, with ev - il filled, Should threat-en to un-do us,
4 That word a - bove all earth - ly powers, No thanks to them, a - bid - eth;

1 Our help-er He a - mid the flood Of mor-tal ills pre-vail - ing.
2 Were not the right man on our side, The man of God's own choos - ing.
3 We will not fear, for God hath willed His truth to tri-umph through us.
4 The Spir - it and the gifts are ours Through Him who with us sid - eth.

1 For still our an - cient foe Doth seek to work us woe—His craft and power are
2 Dost ask who that may be? Christ Je - sus, it is He— Lord Sab-a-oth His
3 The prince of dark-ness grim, We trem-ble not for him— His rage we can en-
4 Let goods and kin - dred go, This mor-tal life al - so— The bod - y they may

1 great, And, armed with cru - el hate, On earth is not his e - qual.
2 name, From age to age the same, And He must win the bat - tle.
3 dure, For lo, his doom is sure: One lit - tle word shall fell him.
4 kill; God's truth a - bid-eth still: His king-dom is for - ev - er. A-men.

LOYALTY AND COURAGE

Am I a Soldier of the Cross? 676

"Endure hardship with us like a good soldier of Christ Jesus."—II Timothy 2:3

C.M.
ARLINGTON
Thomas A. Arne

Isaac Watts

1 Am I a sol-dier of the cross, A fol-lower of the Lamb?
2 Must I be car-ried to the skies On flow-ery beds of ease,
3 Are there no foes for me to face? Must I not stem the flood?
4 Sure I must fight if I would reign: In-crease my cour-age, Lord;

1 And shall I fear to own His cause Or blush to speak His name?
2 While oth-ers fought to win the prize And sailed thru blood-y seas?
3 Is this vile world a friend to grace, To help me on to God?
4 I'll bear the toil, en-dure the pain, Sup-port-ed by Thy word.

Priority 677

The Lord is my light and my
  salvation;
Whom shall I fear?
The Lord is the strength of my life;
Of whom shall I be afraid?

When the wicked came against me
  To eat up my flesh,
My enemies and foes,
They stumbled and fell.

Though an army should camp
  against me,
My heart shall not fear;
Though war should rise against me,
  In this I will be confident.

One thing I have desired of
  the Lord,
That will I seek:
That I may dwell in the house
  of the Lord
All the days of my life,
To behold the beauty of the Lord,
And to inquire in His temple.

For in the time of trouble
He shall hide me in His pavilion;
In the secret place of His tabernacle
  He shall hide me;
He shall set me high upon a rock.

And now my head shall be lifted up
  above my enemies all
  around me;
Therefore I will offer sacrifices of
  joy in His tabernacle;
I will sing, yes, I will sing praises to
  the Lord.

When my father and my mother
  forsake me,
Then the Lord will take care of me.

Teach me Your way, O Lord,
And lead me in a smooth path,
  because of my enemies.

Wait on the Lord;
Be of good courage,
And He shall strengthen your heart;
Wait, I say, on the Lord!

—*From Psalm 27* **(NKJV)**

LOYALTY AND COURAGE

678 Faith Is the Victory

"This is the victory that has overcome the world, even our faith."—I John 5:4b

John H. Yates

FAITH IS THE VICTORY
Ira D. Sankey

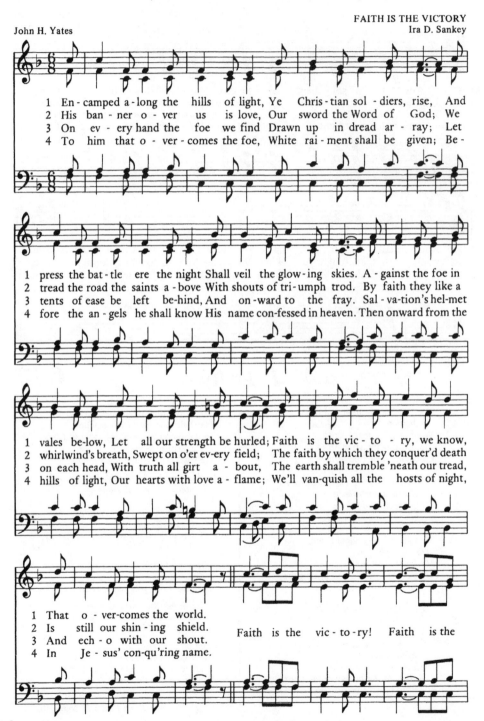

1 En-camped a-long the hills of light, Ye Chris-tian sol-diers, rise, And
2 His ban-ner o-ver us is love, Our sword the Word of God; We
3 On ev-ery hand the foe we find Drawn up in dread ar-ray; Let
4 To him that o-ver-comes the foe, White rai-ment shall be given; Be-

1 press the bat-tle ere the night Shall veil the glow-ing skies. A-gainst the foe in
2 tread the road the saints a-bove With shouts of tri-umph trod. By faith they like a
3 tents of ease be left be-hind, And on-ward to the fray. Sal-va-tion's hel-met
4 fore the an-gels he shall know His name con-fessed in heaven. Then onward from the

1 vales be-low, Let all our strength be hurled; Faith is the vic-to-ry, we know,
2 whirlwind's breath, Swept on o'er ev-ery field; The faith by which they conquer'd death
3 on each head, With truth all girt a-bout, The earth shall tremble 'neath our tread,
4 hills of light, Our hearts with love a-flame; We'll van-quish all the hosts of night,

1 That o-ver-comes the world.
2 Is still our shin-ing shield.
3 And ech-o with our shout.   Faith is the vic-to-ry! Faith is the
4 In Je-sus' con-qu'ring name.

LOYALTY AND COURAGE

vic - to - ry! O glo - ri - ous vic - to - ry, That o - ver - comes the world.

Be Strong in the Lord 679

Finally, my brethren, be strong in the Lord, and in the power of His might. Put on the whole armor of God, that ye may be able to stand against the wiles of the devil.

For we wrestle not against flesh and blood, but against principalities, against powers, against the rulers of the darkness of this world, against spiritual wickedness in high places.

Wherefore take unto you the whole armor of God, that ye may be able to withstand in the evil day, and having done all, to stand.

Stand therefore, having your loins girded about with truth, and having on the breastplate of righteousness;

And your feet shod with the preparation of the gospel of peace;

Above all, taking the shield of faith, wherewith ye shall be able to quench all the fiery darts of the wicked.

And take the helmet of salvation, and the sword of the Spirit, which is the word of God:

Praying always with all prayer and supplication in the Spirit, and watching thereunto with all perseverance and supplication for all saints.

—*Ephesians 6:10–18 (KJV)*

680 Be an Overcomer

"But take heart! I have overcome the world."—John 16:33b

Charles W. Naylor

BE AN OVERCOMER
Andrew L. Byers

1 Be an o - ver - com-er, we must nev - er yield When the foe we
2 Be an o - ver - com-er, He who stands with you Is a Might - y
3 Be an o - ver - com-er, you are heav - en's heir, And a crown of
4 Be an o - ver - com-er, for-ward bold - ly go, You are strong e -

1 meet on the bat - tle - field; We are blood-bought chil-dren of the
2 One who is al - ways true; In the sor - est con-flict you shall
3 life you may ev - er wear; So with cour - age press the bat - tle
4 nough if you trust God so— Strong e - nough to con-quer thru sus -

1 roy - al host, And must fal - ter not, nor de - sert our post.
2 win the day, Face the le - gions dark till they flee a - way.
3 to the gates, Till you gain the prize which in heav - en waits.
4 tain - ing grace And to o - ver - come ev - 'ry foe you face.

LOYALTY AND COURAGE

O - ver - come,   O - ver-
Nev - er yield a step in the hot - test fight, God will

come;   In Je - ho - vah's might put the
send you help from the realms of light;

foe to flight, And the vic - tor's crown you shall wear at last.

Perseverance   **681**

Therefore, since we are surrounded by such a
great cloud of witnesses, let us throw off
everything that hinders and the sin that so easily
entangles, and let us run with perseverance the
race marked out for us. Let us fix our eyes on
Jesus, the author and perfecter of our faith, who
for the joy set before him endured the cross,
scorning its shame, and sat down at the right
hand of the throne of God. Consider him who
endured such opposition from sinful men, so that
you will not grow weary and lose heart.

—Hebrews 12:1–3 (NIV)

682 Lead On, O King Eternal

"So they pulled their boats up on shore, left everything and followed him."
—Luke 5:11

Ernest W. Shurtleff

7.6.7.6.D.
LANCASHIRE
Henry T. Smart

1 Lead on, O King e - ter - nal, The day of march has come;
2 Lead on, O King e - ter - nal, Till sin's fierce war shall cease,
3 Lead on, O King e - ter - nal, We fol - low, not with fears,

1 Hence - forth in fields of con - quest Thy tents shall be our home.
2 And ho - li - ness shall whis - per The sweet a - men of peace.
3 For glad - ness breaks like morn - ing Wher - e'er Thy face ap - pears.

1 Through days of prep - a - ra - tion Thy grace has made us strong, And
2 For not with swords' loud clash - ing, Nor roll of stir - ring drums— With
3 Thy cross is lift - ed o'er us, We jour - ney in its light; The

1 now, O King e - ter - nal, We lift our bat - tle song.
2 deeds of love and mer - cy The heaven-ly king-dom comes.
3 crown a - waits the con - quest: Lead on, O God of might. A - men.

LOYALTY AND COURAGE

Stand Up, Stand Up for Jesus 683

"Be on your guard; stand firm in the faith; be of courage; be strong."
—1 Corinthians 16:13

7.6.7.6.D.
WEBB
George J. Webb

George Duffield

1 Stand up, stand up for Je - sus, You sol - diers of the cross;
2 Stand up, stand up for Je - sus, The trum-pet call o - bey;
3 Stand up, stand up for Je - sus, Stand in His strength a - lone;
4 Stand up, stand up for Je - sus, The strife will not be long;

1 Lift high His roy - al ban - ner, It must not suf - fer loss.
2 Forth to the might - y con - flict, In this His glo - rious day.
3 The arm of flesh will fail you, You dare not trust your own.
4 This day the noise of bat - tle, The next the vic - tor's song.

1 From vic - t'ry un - to vic - t'ry His ar - my shall He lead,
2 You that are brave now serve Him A - gainst un - num-bered foes;
3 Put on the gos - pel ar - mor, Each piece put on with prayer;
4 To those who con - quer e - vil A crown of life shall be:

1 'Til ev - 'ry foe is con-quered And Christ is Lord in - deed.
2 Let cour - age rise with dan - ger And strength to strength op - pose.
3 Where du - ty calls, or dan - ger, Be nev - er want - ing there.
4 They with the King of glo - ry Shall reign e - ter - nal - ly.

LOYALTY AND COURAGE

684 I'm on the Winning Side

"No, in all these things we are more than conquerors through him who loved us."—Romans 8:37

Charles W. Naylor

THE WINNING SIDE
Andrew L. Byers

1 A - long the way of life are man - y foes That dai - ly
2 The bat - tle may be long and hard to win, And Sa - tan's
3 A mul - ti - tude of war - riors of the cross In ser - ried
4 With cour - age in my soul I'll do my part, For Je - sus

1 war a - gainst my soul; But con - stant vic - to - ry my
2 hosts may press me sore; But tho I may be tried I'm
3 ranks do brave - ly fight; They nev - er shall re - treat, nor
4 I will loy - al stand; So on the win - ning side tri -

1 Sav - ior gives to me As I press on to the goal.
2 on the win - ning side, I shall tri - umph ev - er - more.
3 ev - er know de - feat, They are win - ning for the right.
4 um - phant I a - bide With the faith - ful ho - ly band.

LOYALTY AND COURAGE

On the win-ning side, I'm on the win-ning side,
On the win-ning side,

I'm on the win-ning side with Je - sus; Tho hot may be the fray,
On the win-ning side with Je - sus;

My soul can bold-ly say, I'm on the win-ning side with Je - sus.

LOYALTY AND COURAGE

685

I'm Going On

"I have fought the good fight, I have finished the race, I have kept the faith."
—II Timothy 4:7

Based on II Timothy 4:5-8
Charles W. Naylor

I'M GOING ON
Andrew L. Byers

1 I mean to go right on Un - til the crown is won;
2 Should op - po - si - tion come, Should foes ob - struct my way,
3 I see a shin - ing crown A - wait - ing o - ver there,
4 Then for - ward let us go, Our hearts with love a - flame,

1 I mean to fight the fight of faith Till life on earth is done.
2 Should per - se - cu - tion's fires be lit As in the an - cient day;
3 I see a man - sion all pre - pared And decked with beau - ties rare:
4 Our snow - y ban - ner borne a - loft, In - scribed with Je - sus' name.

1 I'll nev - er - more turn back, De - feat I shall not know,
2 With Je - sus by my side, His peace with - in my soul,
3 Shall that which in - ter - venes De - prive me of my right?
4 The hosts of e - vil flee, And heav - en's o - pen gates

LOYALTY AND COURAGE

1 For God will give me vic - to - ry If on - ward I shall go.
2 No mat - ter if the bat - tle's hot, I mean to win the goal.
3 Nay, on I'll go un - til I reach That cit - y of de - light.
4 In - vite me now to has - ten where E - ter - nal glo - ry waits.

I'm go - ing on, I'm go - ing on, Un -
go - ing on, go - ing on, go - ing on, go - ing on,

to the fi - nal tri - umph I'm go - ing on; go - ing on.
go - ing, go - ing on; go - ing on.

go - ing, go - ing on;

LOYALTY AND COURAGE

686 My Heart Is Fixed on Jesus

"Let us fix our eyes on Jesus, the author and perfecter of our faith . . . "
—Hebrews 12:2a

Lavinia R. Brauff

FIXED ON JESUS
William J. Ramsay

1 My heart is fixed on Je - sus, the Sun of all my tho't;
2 My heart is fixed on Je - sus, with - out Him life is vain;
3 My heart is fixed on Je - sus, since I to Him be - long;

1 What won-drous work of grace His love with - in my soul has wro't!
2 His prom - ise is thru all my days to com-fort and sus - tain.
3 For ev - 'ry day He gives me hope, for ev 'ry night a song.

1 He found me poor and help - less, by ev - 'ry sin op - pressed,
2 I love to hear Him whis - per, "Be not a -fraid, 'tis I!"
3 Thru tri - al and deep wa - ter His prom-is - es are sweet,

1 And died that I might be re-deemed and have e - ter - nal rest.
2 As o'er the storm - y sea I sail be - neath a cloud-ed sky.
3 And, shel-tered 'neath His wings of love, I find a safe re - treat.

LOYALTY AND COURAGE

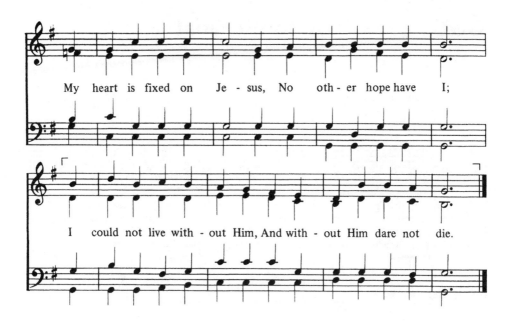

My heart is fixed on Je - sus, No oth - er hope have I;

I could not live with - out Him, And with - out Him dare not die.

Strength in Weakness 687

LEADER: And He said unto me, "My grace is sufficient for thee: for My strength is made perfect in weakness."

PEOPLE: *He said... "I am with you; that is all you need. My power shows up best in weak people."*

LEADER: Most gladly will I glory in my infirmities that the power of Christ may rest upon me.

PEOPLE: *Now I am glad to boast about how weak I am; I am glad to be a living demonstration of Christ's power, instead of showing off my own power and abilities.*

LEADER: For when I am weak, then I am strong.

PEOPLE: *For when I am weak, then I am strong—the less I have, the more I depend on Him!*

ALL: *Yes. God's power shows up best in weak people. So I boast of my weakness, for because of it others are able to know for sure that the power and glory they see in me has got to be the power of God—and if that power can be present in one such as I, it surely is available to them as well!*

—Gloria Gaither

688

On to the Goal

"I press on toward the goal to win the prize for which God has called me heavenward in Christ Jesus."—Philippians 3:14

Charles W. Naylor

ON TO THE GOAL
Andrew L. Byers

1 Turn-ing thy face from all the past, On to the goal keep press-ing;
2 Nev-er mind what the oth-ers do, On to the goal keep press-ing;
3 For-ward and up-ward, faint-ing not, On to the goal keep press-ing;
4 Je-sus a crown holds out to thee, On to the goal keep press-ing;

1 All of the weights from off thee cast, On to the goal keep press-ing.
2 They can-not run the race for you, On to the goal keep press-ing.
3 Bear-ing what-ev-er falls thy lot, On to the goal keep press-ing.
4 Heav-en-ly glo-ry thine shall be, On to the goal keep press-ing.

1 See in the dis-tance there a-rise Glo-ri-ous man-sions in the skies,
2 Wheth-er they run or turn a-side, Wheth-er in sin they still a-bide,
3 Trust in the Lord for strength to-day, "He is my help-er," bold-ly say;
4 Hap-pi-ness that no tongue can tell, Ev-er to prais-es shall im-pel;

LOYALTY AND COURAGE

1 Wait-ing for thee— a won-drous prize— On to the goal keep press - ing.
2 Fix - ing thine eyes on Him who died, On to the goal keep press - ing.
3 An - gels will guard thee on thy way, On to the goal keep press - ing.
4 Safe in His pres - ence thou shalt dwell, On to the goal keep press - ing.

On, on, on to the goal! Je - sus will add His bless - ing:
On to the goal, will add His bless - ing:

On, on, on to the goal! On to the goal keep press - ing.
On to the goal,

LOYALTY AND COURAGE

689 Onward, Christian Soldiers

*"But thanks be to God, who always leads us in triumphal procession in Christ
and through us spreads everywhere the fragrance of the knowledge of him."*
—II Corinthians 2:14

6.5.6.5.D.wR.
ST. GERTRUDE

Sabine Baring-Gould

Arthur S. Sullivan

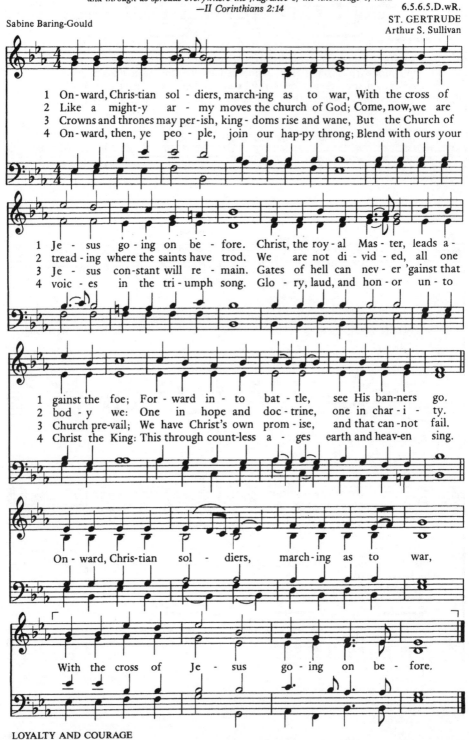

1 On-ward, Chris-tian sol - diers, march-ing as to war, With the cross of
2 Like a might-y ar - my moves the church of God; Come, now, we are
3 Crowns and thrones may per-ish, king - doms rise and wane, But the Church of
4 On-ward, then, ye peo - ple, join our hap-py throng; Blend with ours your

1 Je - sus go - ing on be - fore. Christ, the roy - al Mas - ter, leads a-
2 tread - ing where the saints have trod. We are not di - vid - ed, all one
3 Je - sus con-stant will re - main. Gates of hell can nev - er 'gainst that
4 voic - es in the tri - umph song. Glo - ry, laud, and hon - or un - to

1 gainst the foe; For - ward in - to bat - tle, see His ban-ners go.
2 bod - y we: One in hope and doc - trine, one in char - i - ty.
3 Church pre-vail; We have Christ's own prom - ise, and that can-not fail.
4 Christ the King: This through count-less a - ges earth and heav-en sing.

On - ward, Chris-tian sol - diers, march-ing as to war,

With the cross of Je - sus go - ing on be - fore.

LOYALTY AND COURAGE

When My King Shall Call for Me

690

"So he called ten of his servants and gave them ten minas. 'Put this money to work,' he said, 'until I come back.'" —Luke 19:13

Lizzie DeArmond

WHEN MY KING SHALL CALL
Andrew L. Byers

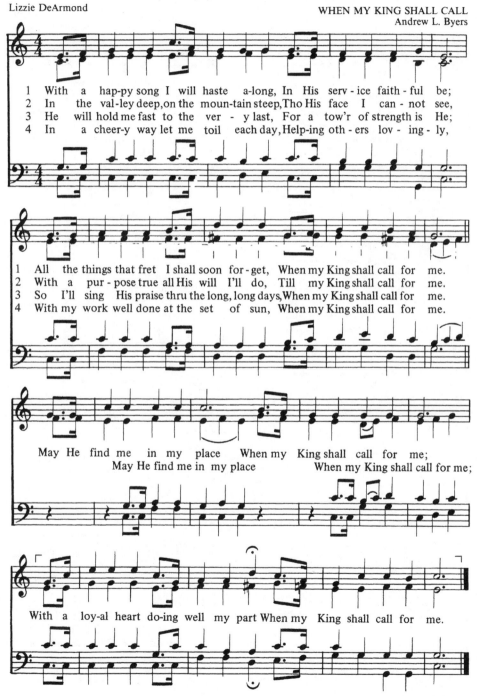

1 With a hap-py song I will haste a-long, In His serv-ice faith-ful be;
2 In the val-ley deep, on the moun-tain steep, Tho His face I can-not see,
3 He will hold me fast to the ver-y last, For a tow'r of strength is He;
4 In a cheer-y way let me toil each day, Help-ing oth-ers lov-ing-ly,

1 All the things that fret I shall soon for-get, When my King shall call for me.
2 With a pur-pose true all His will I'll do, Till my King shall call for me.
3 So I'll sing His praise thru the long, long days, When my King shall call for me.
4 With my work well done at the set of sun, When my King shall call for me.

May He find me in my place When my King shall call for me;
May He find me in my place When my King shall call for me;

With a loy-al heart do-ing well my part When my King shall call for me.

LOYALTY AND COURAGE

691
Who Will Suffer with the Savior?

"Resist him, standing firm in the faith, because you know that your brothers throughout the world are undergoing the same kind of sufferings."—I Peter 5:9

Daniel S. Warner

SUFFER WITH THE SAVIOR
Ludolph Schroeder

1 Who will suf-fer with the Sav-ior, Take the lit-tle that re-mains
2 Who will of-fer soul and bod-y On the al-tar of our God?
3 O for con-se-crat-ed serv-ice 'Mid the din of Ba-bel strife!
4 Soon the con-flict will be o-ver, Crowns a-wait the firm and pure;

1 Of the cup of trib-u-la-tion Je-sus drank in dy-ing pains?
2 Leav-ing self and world-ly mam-mon, Take the path that Je-sus trod?
3 Who will dare the truth to her-ald At the per-il of this life?
4 For-ward, then, we work and suf-fer, Faith-ful to the end en-dure.

Lord, we fel - low-ship Thy pas - sion, Glad - ly
Lord, we fel-low-ship Thy pas - sion,

suf-fer shame and loss; With Thy bless - ing pain is
Glad-ly suf-fer loss (shame and loss;) With Thy bless-ing pain is

LOYALTY AND COURAGE

plea - sure, We will glo - ry in Thy cross. (in Thy cross.)

O Jesus, I Have Promised   692

"We want each of you to show this same diligence to the very end, in order to make your hope sure."—Hebrews 6:11

John E. Bode

7.6.7.6.D.
ANGEL'S STORY
Arthur H. Mann

1 O Je - sus, I have prom-ised To serve Thee to the end; Be Thou for-ev - er
2 O let me feel Thee near me, The world is ev-er near; I see the sights that
3 O Je - sus, Thou hast promised To all who fol-low Thee That where Thou art in

1 near me, My Mas - ter and my Friend; I shall not fear the bat-tle, If Thou art
2 daz - zle, The tempt-ing sounds I hear; My foes are ev - er near me, A-round me
3 glo - ry There shall Thy ser-vant be; And, Je - sus, I have prom-ised To serve Thee

1 by my side, Nor wan - der from the path-way If Thou wilt be my Guide.
2 and with - in; But, Je - sus, draw Thou near-er, And shield my soul from sin.
3 to the end; O give me grace to fol - low My Mas - ter and my Friend.

LOYALTY AND COURAGE

693

Be Still, My Soul

"Be still and know that I am God; I will be exalted among the nations, I will be exalted in the earth."—Psalm 46:10

Based on Psalm 46:10
Catharina A. D. von Schlegel
Tr. Jane Laurie Borthwick

10.10.10.10.10.10.
FINLANDIA
Jean Sibelius

1 Be still, my soul! the Lord is on thy side;
2 Be still, my soul! thy God doth un - der - take
3 Be still, my soul! the hour is has - t'ning on

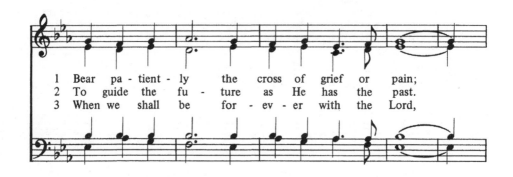

1 Bear pa - tient - ly the cross of grief or pain;
2 To guide the fu - ture as He has the past.
3 When we shall be for - ev - er with the Lord,

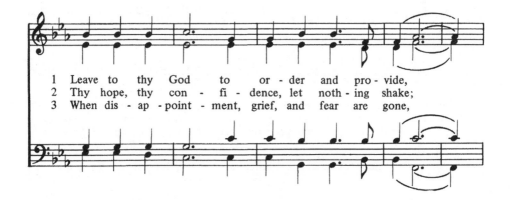

1 Leave to thy God to or - der and pro - vide,
2 Thy hope, thy con - fi - dence, let noth - ing shake;
3 When dis - ap - point - ment, grief, and fear are gone,

1 In ev-'ry change God faith-ful will re-main.
2 All now mys-te-rious shall be bright at last.
3 Sor-row for-got, love's pur-est joys re-stored.

1 Be still, my soul! thy best, thy heav'n-ly Friend
2 Be still, my soul! the waves and winds still know
3 Be still, my soul! when change and tears are past,

1 Through thorn-y ways leads to a joy-ful end.
2 His voice who ruled them while He dwelt be-low.
3 All safe and bless-ed we shall meet at last. A-men.

694 Keep Me, My Lord

"Yet I am not ashamed, because I know whom I have believed, and am convinced that he is able to guard what I have entrusted to him for that day."
—II Timothy 1:12b

Barney E. Warren

KEEP ME MY LORD
Barney E. Warren

1 Keep me in touch with Thee, My bless-ed Lord;
2 Lord, with Thy gen-tle-ness I would be great;
3 Con-quer my ev-'ry foe While here I stay;
4 O let Thy watch-ful eye Be o-ver me;

1 Thine shall the glo-ry be, Mine the re-ward (the great re-ward);
2 Blest with Thy ho-li-ness, Be this my state (my bless-ed state);
3 On to the end I'll go, Let me not stray (from Thee a-way);
4 Hear Thou my hum-ble cry, Com-ing to Thee (com-ing to thee);

1 Cov-er my soul with grace, In that most ho-ly place;
2 To Thee I all re-sign, O let Thy will be mine;
3 Down in-to noth-ing-ness, Hid in Thy right-eous-ness,
4 Guide Thou my steps a-right, Be Thou my song at night,

1 Till I shall see Thy face Keep me, my Lord.
2 In Thy great love di-vine Keep me, my Lord.
3 Firm in Thy faith-ful-ness Keep me, my Lord.
4 My theme and heart's de-light; Keep me, my Lord. A-men.

LOYALTY AND COURAGE

Press the Battle On

695

"No, in all these things we are more than conquerors through him who loved us."—Romans 8:37

Charles W. Naylor
Barney E. Warren

PRESS THE BATTLE ON
Barney E. Warren

1 For-ward, for-ward is the bat-tle cry, On-ward, on-ward to our
2 For-ward, for-ward, nev-er faint or fear— Christ, our cap-tain, is for-
3 For-ward, for-ward, put the foe to flight, We are bat-tling for the
4 For-ward, for-ward, there's a crown be-fore, See it shin-ing on that

1 home on high; We will con-quer for the Lord or die. The
2 ev-er near; Be cou-ra-geous, full of hope and cheer. With
3 truth and right; We shall tri-umph in Je-ho-vah's might, Then
4 heav'n-ly shore; We shall wear it when the con-flict's o'er— The

1 foe's re-treat-ing, press the bat-tle on.
2 full as-sur-ance press the bat-tle on.
3 do not fal-ter, press the bat-tle on.
4 prize is wait-ing, press the bat-tle on.

Strength-ened by the might-y pow'r of heav-en, We shall con-quer, we shall con-quer; Till the

rag-ing foe a-far is driv-en, Press the bat-tle on.

LOYALTY AND COURAGE

696 Should the Harvest Never Come

"We live by faith, not by sight."—II Corinthians 5:7

Gloria Gaither

HARVEST
William J. Gaither

1 Should the har-vest nev-er come, I still will praise You;
2 Should the har-vest nev-er come, I will not doubt You;

1 Should I not tie the sheaves with my own hand,
2 With joy I'll do the work that You have giv-en me.

1 I still will praise You for the prom-ise of the
2 The seeds I plant are from the fruit of some-one's

1 sow - ing; And though I should nev-er see it,
2 la - bor— So I know there'll be a har - vest

LOYALTY AND COURAGE

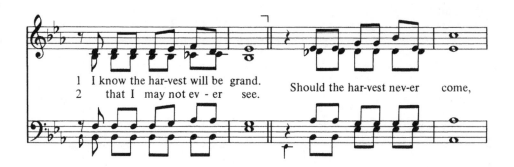

1 I know the har-vest will be grand.
2 that I may not ev - er see. Should the har-vest nev-er come,

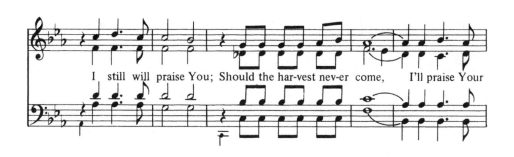

I still will praise You; Should the har-vest nev-er come, I'll praise Your

name. You are my God, the Lord and Mas - ter of the har - vest;

And should I nev-er see the har - vest, I will praise You just the same.

LOYALTY AND COURAGE

697 Lord, We Bring to You Our Children

"Impress them on your children. Talk about them when you sit at home and when you walk along the road, when you lie down and when you get up."
—Deuteronomy 6:7

Frank Von Christierson

8.7.8.7.
GALILEE
William H. Jude

1 Lord, we bring to You our chil - dren On this fes - tive, ho - ly day. Grant to them Your ben - e - dic - tion; Grant to us Your help, we pray.

2 Now may we in hon - est wor - ship, In this glad and sac - red hour, Give our - selves in true com - mit - ment To Your ser - vice and Your pow'r.

3 To the task of Chris - tian nur - ture: Teach-ing, train - ing, lead - ing still In the way of Christ - like liv - ing Till life's pur - pose we ful - fill.

4 Bless the chil - dren! Bless the par - ents! May they grow in Christ our Lord: Joined in faith and lov - ing ser - vice, In His Spir - it and His Word. A-men.

698 Within the Shelter of Our Walls

"But if serving the Lord seems undesirable to you, then choose for yourselves this day whom you will serve, whether the gods your forefathers served beyond the River, or the gods of the Amorites, in whose land you are living. But as for me and my household, we will serve the Lord."—Joshua 24:15

Elinor Lennen

C.M.
REST
Frederick C. Maker

1 With - in the shel - ter of our walls, Be pres - ent, Lord, to guide.

2 Trans-form our spir - its as we learn Thy lov - ing dis - ci - pline.

3 Make dai - ly bread a sac - ra - ment Which You, O Lord, might share.

MARRIAGE AND FAMILY LIFE

1 Where work is planned, where plea-sure calls, Where hearts keep ho - ly
2 When tasks are hard or du - ty stern, Give us the wis - dom
3 Give con - ver - sa - tion high in - tent; Our dai - ly strength for

1 fes - ti - vals, Find wel - come and a - bide.
2 to dis - cern Your com - rade-ship with - in.
3 You be spent With thought and lov - ing care. A-men.

A Prayer for Parents and Children **699**

LEADER:	Jesus welcomed children, healed them, helped them and listened to them in a time when children were probably ignored. He is still the best friend a child will ever have.
ALL CHILDREN:	*Lord Jesus, be with us through the days of our growing up. Sometimes we may forget you, but please, don't ever forget us. Help us to live in such a way that we please You. Forgive us when we do wrong. Help us to respect our parents and to do all that we can to make home a happy place. Be with those of us who have special problems and strong temptations, so that we may learn to trust You through hard times.*
ALL PARENTS:	*Lord Jesus, we assume again the awesome responsibility of being parents. We need Your creativity, Your power, Your stamina, Your insight if we are to treat our sons and daughters lovingly and justly. Help us to stay clear of favoritism; to see the gifts that are latent in the child who challenges us the most. In our loving may we reflect Your love so that our sons and daughters may see You in us. Amen.*

—Bryan Jeffery Leech

700 A Christian Home

"And how from infancy you have known the holy Scriptures, which are able to make you wise for salvation through faith in Christ Jesus."—II Timothy 3:15

Barbara B. Hart

11.10.11.10.11.10.
FINLANDIA
Jean Sibelius

1 O give us homes built firm up-on the Sav-ior,
2 O give us homes with god-ly fa-thers, moth-ers,
3 O Lord, our God, our homes are Thine for-ev-er!

1 Where Christ is Head and Coun-sel-or and Guide;
2 Who al-ways place their hope and trust in Him:
3 We trust to Thee their prob-lems, toil, and care;

1 Where ev-'ry child is taught His love and fa-vor
2 Whose ten-der pa-tience tur-moil nev-er both-ers,
3 Their bonds of love no en-e-my can sev-er,

1 And gives their heart to Christ, the cru-ci-fied:
2 Whose calm and cour-age trou-ble can-not dim;
3 If Thou art al-ways Lord and Mas-ter there:

MARRIAGE AND FAMILY LIFE

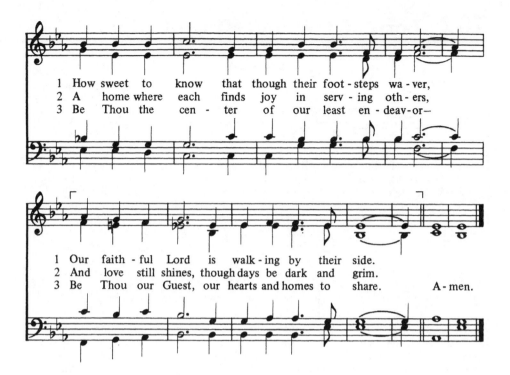

1 How sweet to know that though their foot-steps wa-ver,
2 A home where each finds joy in serv-ing oth-ers,
3 Be Thou the cen - ter of our least en - deav-or—

1 Our faith - ful Lord is walk-ing by their side.
2 And love still shines, though days be dark and grim.
3 Be Thou our Guest, our hearts and homes to share. A-men.

A Celebration for Family **701**
People

LEADER: God has called us to live within the privilege of family life. He has gifted us with mothers, fathers, sisters, brothers, aunts and uncles, and grandparents, and beyond this with friends who become equally precious to us.

PEOPLE: *PRAISE GOD FOR THE GIFT OF FAMILY LIFE!*

LEADER: Lord,

    We thank You for older folk who link us with the past and who enrich us with their experience.

    We thank You for the newborn so rich in potential greatness and goodness.

    We thank You for the gifts we see emerging in our children.

    We thank You for the excitement of living with those who are on the brink of adulthood, even though this is sometimes a time of struggle for all of us.

PEOPLE: *PRAISE GOD FOR THE GIFT OF FAMILY LIFE!*

LEADER: Eternal Father of us all,

    Enter our homes,

  not as the occupant of a guest room,

  but as the senior member of each household,

  that we may live out Your love in the most ordinary parts of life.

  Keep us human as You make us holy. Amen.

PEOPLE: *PRAISE GOD FOR THE GIFT OF FAMILY LIFE!*
        IT IS ALL YOUR DOING, LORD. IT IS WONDERFUL IN OUR EYES.

—Bryan Jeffery Leech

MARRIAGE AND FAMILY LIFE

702 Lord of Life and King of Glory

"Impress them on your children. Talk about them when you sit at home and when you walk along the road, when you lie down and when you get up."
—Deuteronomy 6:7

Christian Burke

8.7.8.7.8.7.
SICILIAN MARINERS
Sicilian Melody

1 Lord of life and King of glo - ry, Who didst deign a
2 Grant us, then, pure hearts and pa - tient, That in all we
3 When our grow - ing sons and daugh - ters Look on life with
4 May we keep our ho - ly call - ing Stain - less in its

1 child to be, Cra - dled on a moth - er's bo - som,
2 do or say Lit - tle ones our deeds may cop - y
3 ea - ger eyes, Grant us then a deep - er in - sight
4 fair re - nown, That, when all the work is o - ver

1 Throned up - on a moth - er's knee: For the chil - dren
2 And be nev - er led a - stray; Lit - tle feet our
3 And new powers of sac - ri - fice: Hope to trust them,
4 And we lay the bur - den down, Then the chil - dren

1 Thou hast giv - en We must an - swer un - to Thee.
2 steps may fol - low In a safe and nar - row way.
3 faith to guide them, Love that noth - ing good de - nies.
4 Thou hast giv - en Still may be our joy and crown. A-men.

Words used by permission of The Mother's Union, U.K.

MARRIAGE AND FAMILY LIFE

Happy the Home When God Is There 703

"But if serving the Lord seems undesirable to you, then choose for yourselves this day whom you will serve, whether the gods your forefathers served beyond the River, or the gods of the Amorites, in whose land you are living. But as for me and my household, we will serve the Lord."—Joshua 24:15

Henry Ware, Jr.
Bryan Jeffery Leech, alt.

C.M.
ST. AGNES
John B. Dykes

1 Hap-py the home when God is there And love fills ev-ery-one,
2 Hap-py the home where God's strong love Is start-ing to ap-pear,
3 Hap-py the home where prayer is heard And praise is ev-ery-where,
4 Lord, let us in our homes a-gree This bless-ed peace to gain;

1 When with u-nit-ed work and prayer The Mas-ter's will is done.
2 Where all the chil-dren hear His fame And par-ents hold Him dear.
3 Where par-ents love the sa-cred Word And its true wis-dom share.
4 U-nite our hearts in love to Thee, And love to all will reign. A-men.

Home and Family 704

In a day when our ears are bombarded by beckoning voices and our world is polluted with sound, Lord, let us hear You.

In a land dissected and muddled by mazes of roads and never-ending highways, Lord, help us find Your way.

In a world of easy promises, empty guarantees and quick-claim insurance policies, give us the security of Your hand, Lord Jesus.

At a time when we are confused by conflicting authorities that would tell us how to manage our marriages, our finances and our children, O Lord Jesus, show us Your way.

As we walk the tightropes of parenthood in these explosive days, training our little ones to live in a world for which there are no precedents, Lord, we need just You.

In all things, Gentle Shepherd, help us find the way.

—Gloria Gaither
From Gentle Shepherd

MARRIAGE AND FAMILY LIFE

705 When Love Is Found

"The greatest of these is love."—I Corinthians 13:13b

Brian Wren

O WALY WALY
Traditional English Melody

1 When love is found and hope comes home, Sing and be
2 When love has flow'red in trust and care, Build both each
3 When love is tried as loved-ones change, Hold still to
4 When love is torn and trust be - trayed, Pray strength to
5 Praise God for love, praise God for life, In age or

1 glad that two are one. When love ex - plodes and fills the
2 day that love may dare To reach be - yond home's warmth and
3 hope though all seems strange, Till ease re - turns and love grows
4 love till tor - ments fade, Till lov - ers keep no score of
5 youth, in hus - band, wife. Lift up your hearts; Let love be

1 sky, Praise God and share our Mak - er's joy.
2 light, To serve and strive for truth and right.
3 wise Through lis - t'ning ears and o - pened eyes.
4 wrong But hear through pain love's Eas - ter song.
5 fed Through death and life in bro - ken bread.

MARRIAGE AND FAMILY LIFE

Wonder of Wonders

706

" . . . They are the children God has graciously given your servant."
—Genesis 33:5c

Brian Wren

10.9.10.9.
BUNESSAN
Gaelic melody

1 Won - der of won - ders, life is be - gin - ning,
2 Now with re - joic - ing make cel - e - bra - tion:
3 Lord of cre - a - tion, dy - ing and liv - ing,

1 Frag - ile as blos - som, strong as the earth.
2 Joy full of prom - ise, laugh-ter through tears.
3 Fa - ther and Moth - er, Part - ner and Friend,

1 Shaped in a per - son, love has new mean - ing;
2 Nam - ing and bless - ing bring ded - i - ca - tion,
3 Lov - er of chil - dren, lift all our lov - ing

1 Par - ents and peo - ple sing at their birth.
2 Hum - ble in pur - pose o - ver the years.
3 In - to Your king - dom, world with - out end.

MARRIAGE AND FAMILY LIFE

707

Welcoming a Child

THE CHILD'S PARENTS: *Lord, You have trusted us with one of Your priceless treasures, a human child. You have allowed us to share with You in the miracle of creation and now that miracle has become flesh—and we hold it in our arms. We are excited and full of joy! But we are also fearful. O Lord, we are imperfect parents in such an imperfect world. Speak to us. Assure us of Your nearness—now, as we wait with this child, speak to us.*

LEADER: Unless you are converted and become as little children, you shall not enter into the kingdom of heaven. Whosoever shall humble himself as this little child, the same is the greatest in the kingdom of heaven. And whoever shall receive one such little child in My name receives Me.[1]

CHOIR: *Train up a child in the way he should go: and when he is old, he will not depart from it.[2] I am the Way, the Truth, and the Life.[3]*

LEADER: And all thy children shall be taught of the Lord, and great shall be the peace of your children.[4]

CHOIR: *Cast all your cares upon Him for He cares for you.*

PEOPLE: *Trust in the Lord with all your heart, and lean not to your own understanding. In all your ways acknowledge Him, and He shall direct your paths.[5]*

PRAYER BY LAYMAN: Lord, we have here in our church family a new child, a new person, a new soul. The responsibility for this little person is too much for any two parents alone. They need the loving support of the fellowship of believers as they train and guide and nurture little *[name]*. We give ourselves today, Lord, to the task. We accept the responsibility of helping to bring *[name]* to maturity in You. We will uphold him *[her]* with our love, teach him *[her]* the word of God, encourage him *[her]* when he *[she]* fails, and we will be careful not to bruise this tender bud by harsh words, quick judgments, and cruel criticism. For truly, Father, this is our child, and we want to protect and teach him *[her]* and to bring him *[her]* to the moment when he *[she]* will choose for himself *[herself]* to know You as Savior and Lord of his *[her]* life. Amen.

—Gloria Gaither

1. Matthew 18:3–5   2. Proverbs 22:6   3. John 14:6   4. Isaiah 54:13   5. Proverbs 3:5 (KJV)

MARRIAGE AND FAMILY LIFE

In the Circle of Each Home 708

"Fathers, do not exasperate your children; instead, bring them up in the training and instruction of the Lord."—Ephesians 6:4

7.6.7.6.7.7.7.7.

BEL AIR

Bryan Jeffery Leech

Bryan Jeffery Leech

1 In the cir-cle of each home, Lord, Your love is need-ed;
2 In the cir-cle of each home, Be our strong foun-da-tion;
3 In the cir-cle of each home, Lord, Your love is want-ed
4 In the cir-cle of each home, Is af-fec-tion grow-ing?

1 For that fra-gile cir-cle bends When You are un-heed-ed.
2 Lord, we need Your wis-dom there In each sit-u-a-tion.
3 So that we'll not take Your grace And our life for grant-ed.
4 Are there fruits of char-ac-ter From a care-ful sow-ing?

1 For that hu-man cir-cle breaks With our pro-longed de-fi-ance,
2 If we have Your sur-er pace, We'll march as to a drum-mer.
3 Should our chil-dren fail to see The proofs of what we've taught them,
4 Do we praise the good we see, And par-don oth-ers' sin-ning?

1 And we stand like win-ter trees Made bare by self re-li-ance.
2 Then our lives will fruit-ful be, Like trees we see in sum-mer.
3 Then we'll lack au-thor-i-ty, And fade like trees in au-tumn.
4 Are our branch-es blos-som-filled Like trees at spring's be-gin-ning?

MARRIAGE AND FAMILY LIFE

709 *Our God Is One Lord*

Hear, O Israel: The Lord our God, the Lord is one. Love the Lord our God with all your heart and with all your soul and with all your strength. These commandments that I give you today are to be upon your hearts. Impress them on your children. Talk about them when you sit at home and when you walk along the road, when you lie down and when you get up. Tie them as symbols on your hands and bind them on your foreheads. Write them on the doorframes of your houses and on your gates.

—Deuteronomy 6:4–9 (NIV)

710 Take Our Love, Lord

"And now abide faith, hope, love, these three; but the greatest of these is love."
—I Corinthians 13:13

Derric Johnson

TAKE OUR LOVE
Derric Johnson

Take our love, Lord, make it Your love; Take our life, Lord, make it Your life. Take our home, Lord, make it Your home; Take it all, Lord, make it Yours.

MARRIAGE AND FAMILY LIFE

Faith of Our Mothers

711

*"Dear friends, although I was very eager to write to you about the salvation we
share, I felt I had to write and urge you to contend for the faith that was once
for all entrusted to the saints."—Jude 3*

A. B. Patton

8.8.8.8.8.8.
ST. CATHERINE
Henry F. Hemy
Alt. by James G. Walton

1 Faith of our moth - ers, liv - ing still In cra - dle
2 Faith of our moth - ers, lov - ing faith, Fount of our

1 song and bed - time prayer; In nur-s'ry lore and fire - side love,
2 child-hood's trust and grace, O may thy con - se - cra - tion prove

1 Thy pres-ence still per - vades the air: Faith of our moth - ers,
2 Source of a fin - er, no - bler race: Faith of our moth - ers,

1 liv - ing faith, We will be true to thee till death.
2 lov - ing faith, We will be true to thee till death.

712 She Will Be Called Blessed

"Her children arise and call her blessed; her husband also, and he praises her."
—Proverbs 31:28

Based on Proverbs 31:10-31
Elizabeth de Gravelles

13.12.13.12.
IRENE
Joseph Barlowe

She will be called bless-ed By her sons and her daugh-ters;
Pre-cious to the Fa-ther Are those who seek His ways.
She will be called bless-ed, Held a-bove ev-'ry oth-er;
Bless-ed is the moth-er Who turns to God in praise.

713 Faith of Our Fathers

"Dear friends, although I was very eager to write to you about the salvation we share, I felt I had to write and urge you to contend for the faith that was once for all entrusted to the saints."—Jude 3

Frederick W. Faber

8.8.8.8.8.8.
ST. CATHERINE
Henri F. Hemy
Adapted by James G. Walton

1 Faith of our fa-thers, liv-ing still In spite of dun-geon,
2 Faith of our fa-thers, we will strive to win all na-tions
3 Faith of our fa-thers, we will love Both friend and foe in

MARRIAGE AND FAMILY LIFE

1 fire, and sword, O how our hearts beat high with joy
2 un - to Thee, And through the truth that comes from God
3 all our strife, And preach thee too as love knows how,

1 When-e'er we hear that glo - rious word! Faith of our fa - thers,
2 The world shall then in - deed be free. Faith of our fa - thers,
3 By kind - ly words and vir - tuous life. Faith of our fa - thers,

1 ho - ly faith, We will be true to thee 'til death.
2 ho - ly faith, We will be true to thee 'til death.
3 ho - ly faith, We will be true to thee 'til death. A - men.

Children — 714

O Father, remember little children whose unfolding lives turn for warmth
and light toward all those around them as flowers turn toward the sun.

*The only God they know is the God they see in us; the only Jesus they
know is the one reflected by our actions. Forbid it Lord, that we should
misrepresent Him and lead one child astray.*

We are thankful for the thrill and privilege of watching children develop,
not only in stature, but in understanding and appreciation of all that is
good.

*We are thankful for the simple and great lessons they teach us. We are
thankful for their candid look, their frankness, their simplicity.*

We pray that in the realm of seeking and knowing You, that You will
make us more like children. Help us to understand that to be childlike in
faith is not a sign of weakness, but rather an indication of growth.

*In the name of Him who set a little child in their midst to teach some of
the great lessons of life, we pray. Amen.*

—Marvin J. and Madelyn Hartman
from *He Restoreth My Soul*

MARRIAGE AND FAMILY LIFE

715 *Prayer for the Human Family*

LEADER: O God, who has made of one blood all people on earth, we acknowledge the bond of family which is Your intention for us.

PEOPLE: *Too often, O Lord, we have ignored that bond. We have gone placidly along our own paths, unaware of the pain and happiness, the sorrow and joy of our sisters and brothers. Awaken us, O God, sensitize our hearts and our minds to each other.*

LEADER: May we no longer be content to go our own way, caring only for ourselves and the needs of our own families.

PEOPLE: *Sometimes, Lord, we have even looked with distrust and disdain upon our brothers and sisters, for they did not look like us. Their skin was a different color; their language was different. We did not recognize them as our brothers and sisters.*

LEADER: But now, Lord, we praise You for black skin, for warm brown, for white, for creamy yellow and burnished red. We praise You for the differentness of each other.

PEOPLE: *Thank You for blond hair, and red, for brown and black; for silver and gray. Some hair is straight and some is curly; some is kinky and some is wavy.*

LEADER: What a magnificent array of color surrounds us! Thank You, Lord. It's all Your handiwork, and it's all beautiful.

PEOPLE: *Although we are many, we are yet one—one race . . . the human race. We are one body, the church, sons and daughters of the one God.*

LEADER: We celebrate our oneness, O God. They who have seen the light can no longer walk in darkness. We can no longer live for ourselves, oblivious of our sisters and brothers. We assume responsibility for each other.

ALL: *It is good to give thanks to the Lord, to sing praises to Thy name, O Most High:*
to declare Thy steadfast love in the morning, and Thy faithfulness by night,
to the music of the lute and the harp, to the melody of the lyre.
For Thou, O Lord, has made me glad by Thy work; at the works of Thy hands I sing for joy.

—Psalm 92:1-4 (RSV)

—Kay Shively

God of Our Fathers

716

" . . . from everlasting to everlasting you are God."—Psalm 90:2c

10.10.10.10.
NATIONAL HYMN
George W. Warren

Daniel C. Roberts

Trumpets before
each stanza

1 God of our fa - thers,* whose al - might - y hand
2 Thy love di - vine hath led us in the past,
3 From war's a - larms, from dead - ly pes - ti - lence,
4 Re - fresh Thy peo - ple on their toil - some way,

1 Leads forth in beau - ty all the star - ry band
2 In this free land by Thee our lot is cast;
3 Be Thy strong arm our ev - er sure de - fense;
4 Lead us from night to nev - er end - ing day;

1 Of shin - ing worlds in splen - dor through the skies,
2 Be Thou our rul - er, guard - ian, guide, and stay,
3 Thy true re - li - gion in our hearts in - crease,
4 Fill all our lives with love and grace di - vine,

1 Our grate - ful songs be - fore Thy throne a - rise.
2 Thy word our law, Thy paths our cho - sen way.
3 Thy boun - teous good - ness nour - ish us in peace.
4 And glo - ry, laud, and praise be ev - er Thine! A - men.

*optional text: "God of the ages"

CITIZENSHIP IN THE WORLD

717 America, the Beautiful

"Show proper respect to everyone . . . honor the king."—I Peter 2:17a,c

Katherine Lee Bates

C.M.D.
MATERNA
Samuel A. Ward
Descant by Fred Bock

1 O beau - ti - ful for spa-cious skies, For am - ber waves of grain,
2 O beau - ti - ful for pil - grim feet, Whose stern, im-pas-sioned stress
3 O beau - ti - ful for he - roes proved In lib - er - at - ing strife,
4 O beau - ti - ful for pa - triot dream That sees be - yond the years

1 For pur - ple moun-tain maj - es - ties A - bove the fruit - ed plain!
2 A thor-ough-fare for free-dom beat A - cross the wil - der - ness!
3 Who more than self their coun-try loved, And mer - cy more than life!
4 Thine al - a - bas - ter cit - ies gleam, Un-dimmed by hu - man tears!

Descant for first and last stanzas

1,4 A - mer - i - ca! A - mer - i - ca! God shed His grace on thee,

1 A - mer - i - ca! A - mer - i - ca! God shed His grace on thee,
2 A - mer - i - ca! A - mer - i - ca! God mend thine ev - ery flaw,
3 A - mer - i - ca! A - mer - i - ca! May God thy gold re - fine,
4 A - mer - i - ca! A - mer - i - ca! God shed His grace on thee,

CITIZENSHIP IN THE WORLD

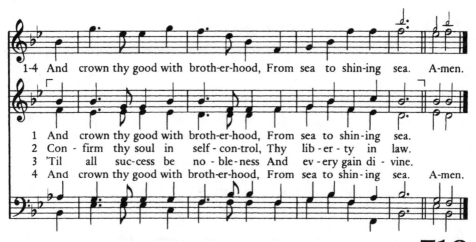

1-4 And crown thy good with broth-er-hood, From sea to shin-ing sea. A-men.

1 And crown thy good with broth-er-hood, From sea to shin-ing sea.
2 Con - firm thy soul in self-con-trol, Thy lib-er-ty in law.
3 'Til all suc-cess be no-ble-ness And ev-ery gain di - vine.
4 And crown thy good with broth-er-hood, From sea to shin-ing sea. A-men.

My Country, 'Tis of Thee   **718**

"Blessed is the nation whose God is the Lord."—Psalm 33:12a

6.6.4.6.6.6.4.

Samuel F. Smith

AMERICA
Henry Carey

1 My coun - try, 'tis of thee, Sweet land of lib - er - ty,
2 My na - tive coun - try, thee, Land of the no - ble, free,
3 Let mu - sic swell the breeze, And ring from all the trees
4 Our fa - thers' God, to Thee, Au - thor of lib - er - ty,

1 Of thee I sing: Land where my fa - thers died, Land of the
2 Thy name I love. I love thy rocks and rills, Thy woods and
3 Sweet free-dom's song. Let mor - tal tongues a - wake; Let all that
4 To Thee we sing: Long may our land be bright With free-dom's

1 Pil - grims' pride. From ev - ery moun-tain-side Let free-dom ring!
2 tem - pled hills; My heart with rap - ture thrills Like that a - bove.
3 breathe par-take; Let rocks their si - lence break, The sound pro - long.
4 ho - ly light; Pro - tect us by Thy might, Great God, our King!

CITIZENSHIP IN THE WORLD

719 O Canada!

"Blessed is the nation whose God is the Lord."—Psalm 33:12a

Robert Stanley Weir, stanza 1
Albert C. Watson, stanza 2

O CANADA
Melody By Calixa Lavalié
Arr. Frederick C. Silvester

1 O Can - a - da! our home and na - tive land! True pa - triot
2 Al - might - y Love, by Thy mys - ter - ious pow'r, In wis - dom

1 love in all thy sons com - mand. With glow - ing hearts we
2 guide, with faith and free - dom dow'r; Be ours a na - tion

1 see thee rise The true north strong and free. From far and wide, O
2 ev - er - more That no op - pres - sion blights, Where jus - tice rules from

1 Can - a - da, We stand on guard for thee. God keep our land
2 shore to shore, From lakes to north - ern lights. May love a - lone

1 glo - rious and free, O Can - a - da, we stand on guard for
2 for wrong a - tone; Lord of the lands, make Can - a - da Thine

CITIZENSHIP IN THE WORLD

1 thee. O Can - a - da, we stand on guard for thee.
2 own! Lord of the lands, make Can - a - da Thine own.

From Hearts Around the World, O Lord

720

"To shine on those living in darkness and in the shadow of death, to guide our feet into the path of peace."—Luke 1:79

L.M.

Elizabeth Patton Moss

TALLIS' CANON
Thomas Tallis

1 From hearts a - round the world, O Lord, Through cen - tu - ries of
2 Though war and hate have been our lot, The dream, the hope, of
3 Lord, use Thy church to point the way; May we Thy clear com-

1 blind dis - cord, There is one prayer which does not cease;
2 peace die not. Let noth - ing move our hearts from Thee,
3 mands o - bey. Be rec - on - ciled, for - give and bless;

1 The peo - ple yearn and grope for peace.
2 A - part from whom no peace can be.
3 May peace pro - ceed from right - eous - ness. A - men.

CITIZENSHIP IN THE WORLD

721 This Is My Song, O God of All the Nations

"Your kingdom come, your will be done on earth as it is in heaven."
—Matthew 6:10

Lloyd Stone
Georgia Harkness, stanza 3

11.10.11.10.11.10.
FINLANDIA
Jean Sibelius

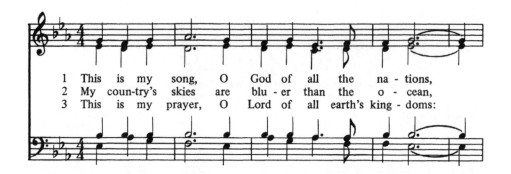

1 This is my song, O God of all the na - tions,
2 My coun-try's skies are blu - er than the o - cean,
3 This is my prayer, O Lord of all earth's king - doms:

1 A song of peace for lands a - far and mine.
2 And sun - light beams on clo - ver - leaf and pine.
3 Thy king - dom come on earth, Thy will be done.

1 This is my home, the coun - try where my heart is,
2 But oth - er lands have sun - light too, and clo - ver,
3 Let Christ be lift - ed up till all shall serve Him,

CITIZENSHIP IN THE WORLD

1 Here are my hopes, my dreams, my ho - ly shrine;
2 And skies are ev - 'ry - where as blue as mine.
3 And hearts u - nit - ed learn to live as one.

1 But oth - er hearts in oth - er lands are beat-ing
2 O hear my song, Thou God of all the na - tions,
3 O hear my prayer, Thou God of all the na - tions.

1 With hopes and dreams as true and high as mine.
2 A song of peace for their land and for mine.
3 My - self I give Thee; let Thy will be done.   A-men.

CITIZENSHIP IN THE WORLD

722 Peace in Our Time, O Lord

"Peace and mercy to all who follow this rule . . . "—Galatians 6:16a

John Oxenham

S.M.D.
DIADEMATA
George J. Elvey

1 Peace in our time, O Lord, To all the peo - ples, peace!
2 Too long mis-trust and fear Have held our souls in thrall;
3 O shall we nev - er learn The truth all time has taught,

1 Peace sure - ly based up - on Thy will And built in right-eous - ness.
2 Sweep through the earth, keen breath of heav'n, And sound a no - bler call!
3 That with - out God as ar - chi - tect Our build-ing comes to naught?

1 Thy pow'r a - lone can break The fet - ters that en - chain
2 Come, as thou didst of old, In love so great that we
3 O liv - ing Christ, who still Dost all our bur - dens share,

1 The sore - ly-strick-en soul of life, And make it live a - gain.
2 Shall cast a - side all oth - er gods And turn a - gain to Thee.
3 Come now and dwell with - in the hearts Of peo - ple ev - 'ry-where! A-men.

Words used by permission of Ms. Theodora Dunkerley.

CITIZENSHIP IN THE WORLD

O That Will Be Glory for Me 723

"I consider that our present sufferings are not worthy comparing with the glory that will be revealed in us."—Romans 8:18

10.10.10.10.wR.
GLORY SONG
Charles H. Gabriel

Charles H. Gabriel

1 When all my la - bors and tri - als are o'er, And I am safe on that
2 When by the gift of His in - fi - nite grace, I am ac - cord - ed in
3 Friends will be there I have loved long a - go; Joy like a riv - er a -

1 beau - ti - ful shore, Just to be near the dear Lord I a - dore
2 heav - en a place, Just to be there and to look on His face
3 round me will flow; Yet, just a smile from my Sav - ior, I know,

1 Will through the a - ges be glo - ry for me. O that will be
2 Will through the a - ges be glo - ry for me. O that will
3 Will through the a - ges be glo - ry for me. O

glo - ry for me, Glo - ry for me, glo - ry for me; When by His
be glo - ry for me, Glo - ry for me, glo - ry for me;

grace I shall look on His face, That will be glo - ry, be glo - ry for me.

CITIZENSHIP IN HEAVEN

724

We'll Understand It Better
By and By

*"Now we see but a poor reflection; then we shall see face to face. Now I know
in part; then I shall know fully, even as I am fully known."*
—I Corinthians 13:12

Charles A. Tindley

BY AND BY
Charles A. Tindley

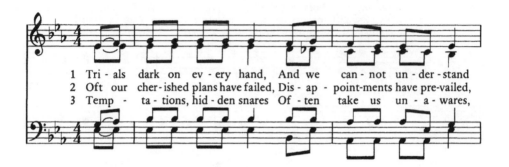

1 Tri - als dark on ev - ery hand, And we can - not un - der - stand
2 Oft our cher - ished plans have failed, Dis - ap - point-ments have pre-vailed,
3 Temp - ta - tions, hid - den snares Of - ten take us un - a - wares,

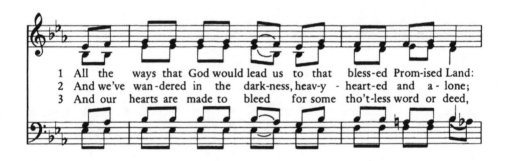

1 All the ways that God would lead us to that bless-ed Prom-ised Land:
2 And we've wan-dered in the dark-ness, heav-y - heart-ed and a - lone;
3 And our hearts are made to bleed for some tho't-less word or deed,

1 But He'll guide us with His eye, And we'll fol-low till we die; We will
2 But we're trust-ing in the Lord, And, ac - cord-ing to His Word, We will
3 And we won-der why the test When we try to do our best, But we'll

CITIZENSHIP IN HEAVEN

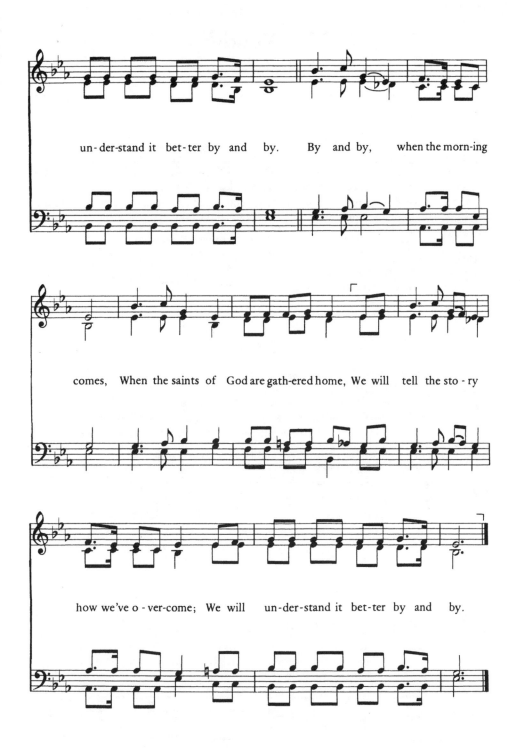

un-der-stand it bet-ter by and by. By and by, when the morn-ing comes, When the saints of God are gath-ered home, We will tell the sto-ry how we've o-ver-come; We will un-der-stand it bet-ter by and by.

CITIZENSHIP IN HEAVEN

725

When the Roll Is Called
Up Yonder

"For the Lord himself will come down from heaven . . . with the trumpet call of
God . . . "—I Thessalonians 4:16a

James M. Black

TRUMPET
James M. Black

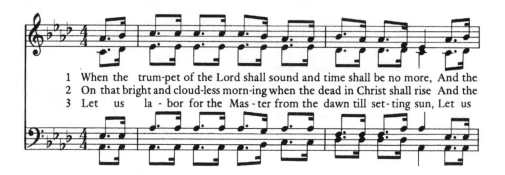

1 When the trum-pet of the Lord shall sound and time shall be no more, And the
2 On that bright and cloud-less morn-ing when the dead in Christ shall rise And the
3 Let us la - bor for the Mas -ter from the dawn till set-ting sun, Let us

1 morn-ing breaks e-ter-nal, bright and fair; When the saved of earth shall gath-er
2 glo - ry of His res - ur -rec - tion share; When His cho-sen ones shall gath-er
3 talk of all His won-drous love and care; Then when all of life is o-ver

1 o - ver on the oth - er shore, And the roll is called up yon - der,
2 to their home be-yond the skies, And the roll is called up yon - der,
3 and our work on earth is done, And the roll is called up yon - der,

CITIZENSHIP IN HEAVEN

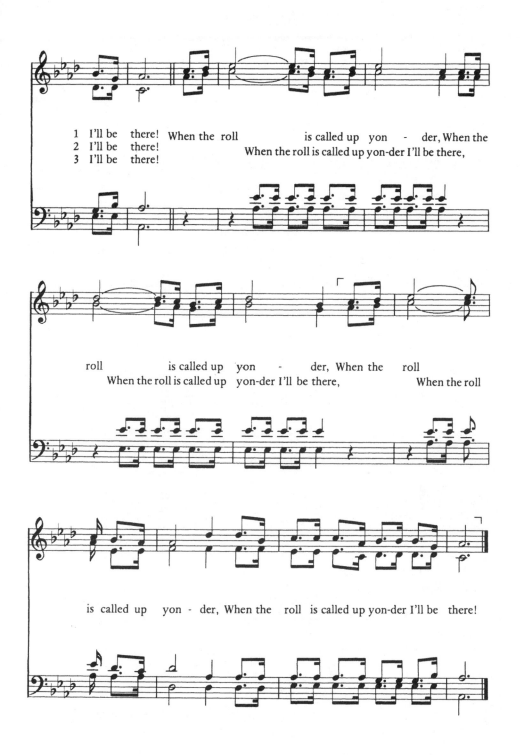

1 I'll be there! When the roll is called up yon - der, When the
2 I'll be there!
3 I'll be there! When the roll is called up yon-der I'll be there,

roll is called up yon - der, When the roll
When the roll is called up yon-der I'll be there, When the roll

is called up yon - der, When the roll is called up yon-der I'll be there!

CITIZENSHIP IN HEAVEN

726

Beautiful

"I saw the Holy City, the new Jerusalem, coming down out of heaven from God, prepared as a bride beautifully dressed for her husband."—Revelation 21:2

Barney E. Warren

BEAUTIFUL ROBES
Barney E. Warren

1 Beau - ti - ful robes so white, Beau - ti - ful land of light, Beau - ti - ful
2 Beau - ti - ful thought to me: We shall for - ev - er be Yours in e -
3 Beau - ti - ful things on high, O - ver in yon - der sky, Soon I shall

1 home so bright, Where there shall come no night; Beau - ti - ful crown I'll wear,
2 ter - ni - ty, When from this world we're free; Free from its toil and care,
3 leave this shore, Count - ing my trea - sures o'er; Where we shall nev - er die,

1 Shin-ing with stars o'er there, Yon-der in man-sions fair, Gath-er us there.
2 Heav-en-ly joys to share, Let me cross o - ver there—This is my prayer.
3 Car - ry me by and by, Nev-er to sor-row more, Heav-en-ly store.

CITIZENSHIP IN HEAVEN

CITIZENSHIP IN HEAVEN

727 We Have a Hope

"I write these to you who believe in the name of the Son of God so that you may know that you have eternal life."—I John 5:13

William G. Schell

WE HAVE A HOPE
William G. Schell

1 Have we an - y hope with-in us of a life be - yond the grave,
2 Bless - ed hope we have with-in us is an an - chor to the soul,
3 Since we've walked the straight and nar-row way, our path has ev - er shone
4 Life will end in joy - ful sing-ing, "I have fought a faith-ful fight."

1 In the fair and ver - nal lands? Do we know that, when our
2 It is both stead - fast and sure; It is found-ed on the
3 Bright-er, bright - er day by day; Hope with - in our hearts as -
4 Then we'll lay our ar - mor down; And our spir - its, freed from

1 earth-ly house by death shall be dis-solved, We've a house not made with hands?
2 prom-is - es of Fa - ther's writ-ten word, And 'twill ev - er-more en - dure.
3 sures us it is bet - ter far-ther on, It is bright-er all the way.
4 earth-ly ties, shall take their hap - py flight To pos-sess a star - ry crown.

CITIZENSHIP IN HEAVEN

We have a hope with-in our souls, Bright-er than the
per-fect day: God has giv-en us His Spir-it, and we
want the world to hear it; All our doubts are passed a-way.

CITIZENSHIP IN HEAVEN

728 I'll Fly Away

"We are confident, I say, and would prefer to be away from the body and at home with the Lord."—II Corinthians 5:8

Albert E. Brumley

9.4.9.4.wR.
I'LL FLY AWAY
Albert E. Brumley

1 Some glad morn-ing when this life is o'er, I'll fly a-way;
2 When the shad-ows of this life have gone, fly a-way, fly a-way;
3 Just a few more wea-ry days and then,

1 To a home on God's ce-les-tial shore, I'll fly a-way.
2 Like a bird from pris-on bars has flown, fly a-way, fly a-way.
3 To a land where joys shall nev-er end,

I'll fly a-way, O glo-ry, I'll fly a-way;
fly a-way, fly a-way, in the morn-ing;

When I die, hal-le-lu-jah, by and by, I'll fly a-way.
fly a-way, fly a-way.

CITIZENSHIP IN HEAVEN

When We All Get to Heaven 729

"And if I go and prepare a place for you, I will come back and take you to be with me . . . "—John 14:3a

8.7.8.7.wR.
HEAVEN

Eliza E. Hewitt

Emily D. Wilson

1 Sing the won-drous love of Je - sus, Sing His mer - cy and His grace;
2 While we walk the pil - grim path-way Clouds will o - ver - spread the sky;
3 Let us then be true and faith - ful, Trust-ing, serv-ing ev - ery day;
4 On - ward to the prize be - fore us! Soon His beau - ty we'll be-hold;

1 In the man - sions bright and bless-ed He'll pre - pare for us a place.
2 But when trav - eling days are o - ver Not a shad - ow, not a sigh.
3 Just one glimpse of Him in glo - ry Will the toils of life re - pay.
4 Soon the pearl - y gates will o - pen— We shall tread the streets of gold.

When we all get to heav - en, What a day of re-joic - ing that will

be! When we all see Je - sus, We'll sing and shout the vic-to - ry!

CITIZENSHIP IN HEAVEN

730

Until Then

"Be patient then, brothers, until the Lord's coming."—James 5:7a

UNTIL THEN
Stuart Hamblen

Stuart Hamblen

1 My heart can sing when I pause to re-mem-ber
2 The things of earth will dim and lose their val-ue
3 This wea-ry world with all its toil and strug-gle

1 A heart-ache here is but a step-ping stone
2 If we re-call they're bor-rowed for a while;
3 May take its toll of mis-er-y and strife;

1 A-long a trail that's wind-ing al-ways up-ward,
2 And things of earth that cause the heart to trem-ble,
3 The soul of man is like a wait-ing fal-con;

1 This trou-bled world is not my fi-nal home.
2 Re-mem-bered there will on-ly bring a smile.
3 When it's re-leased, it's des-tined for the skies.

CITIZENSHIP IN HEAVEN

But un-til then my heart will go on sing-ing,

Un-til then with joy I'll car-ry on—

Un-til the day my eyes be-hold the cit-y,

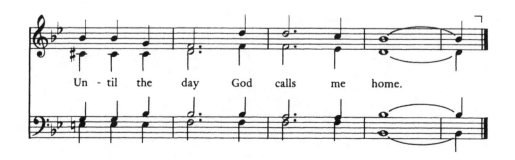

Un-til the day God calls me home.

CITIZENSHIP IN HEAVEN

731   Shall We Gather at the River?

*"Then the angel showed me the river of water of life, as clear as crystal,
flowing from the throne of God and of the Lamb."—Revelation 22:1*

Robert Lowry

THRONE OF GOD
Robert Lowry

1 Shall we gath - er at the riv - er, Where bright an-gel - feet have trod;
2 On the bos - om of the riv - er, Where the Sav-ior-King we own,
3 Ere we reach the shin-ing riv - er, Lay we ev-'ry bur-den down;
4 Soon we'll reach the shin-ing riv - er, Soon our pil-grim-age will cease;

1 With its crys - tal tide for - ev - er Flow-ing by the throne of God?
2 We shall meet and sor-row nev - er 'Neath the glo - ry of the throne.
3 Grace our spir - its will de - liv - er And pro - vide a robe and crown.
4 Soon our hap - py hearts will quiv - er With the mel - o - dy of peace.

Yes, we'll gath-er at the riv - er, The beau - ti - ful, the beau - ti - ful riv - er,

Gath - er with the saints at the riv - er That flows by the throne of God.

CITIZENSHIP IN HEAVEN

In the Sweet By and By

732

"Your eyes will see the king in his beauty and view a land that stretches afar."
—Isaiah 33:17

9.9.9.9.wR.

Sanford F. Bennett

SWEET BY AND BY
Joseph P. Webster

1 There's a land that is fair - er than day, And by faith we can
2 We shall sing on that beau - ti - ful shore The me - lo - di - ous
3 To our boun - ti - ful Fa - ther a - bove We will of - fer our

1 see it a - far; For the Fa - ther waits o - ver the way, To pre-
2 songs of the blest, And our spir - its shall sor - row no more, Not a
3 trib - ute of praise, For the glo - ri - ous gift of His love And the

1 pare us a dwell - ing place there. In the sweet by and
2 sigh for the bless - ing of rest. In the sweet
3 bless - ings that hal - low our days.

by, We shall meet on that beau - ti - ful shore. In the
by and by, by and by.

sweet by and by, We shall meet on that beau-ti-ful shore.
In the sweet by and by,

CITIZENSHIP IN HEAVEN

733 Sin Can Never Enter There

"Therefore, just as sin entered the world through one man, and death through sin, and in this way death came to all men, because all sinned—"
—Romans 5:12

Charles W. Naylor

SIN CAN NEVER ENTER THERE
Barney E. Warren

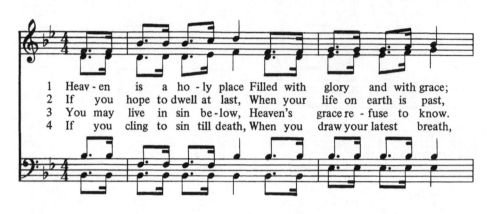

1 Heav - en is a ho - ly place Filled with glory and with grace;
2 If you hope to dwell at last, When your life on earth is past,
3 You may live in sin be - low, Heaven's grace re - fuse to know.
4 If you cling to sin till death, When you draw your latest breath,

1 Sin can nev - er en - ter there: All with - in its gates are pure,
2 In that home so bright and fair, You must here be cleansed from sin,
3 But you can - not en - ter there; It will stop you at the door,
4 You will sink in dark de - spair To the re - gions of the lost,

1 From de - file - ment kept se - cure, Sin can nev - er en - ter there.
2 Have the life of Christ with - in, Sin can nev - er en - ter there.
3 Bar you out for - ev - er - more, Sin can nev - er en - ter there.
4 Thus to prove at aw - ful cost, Sin can nev - er en - ter there.

CITIZENSHIP IN HEAVEN

Sin can nev - er en - ter there, Sin can
Sin can nev - er en - ter, nev - er en - ter there, Sin can

nev - er en - ter there; So if at the judgment bar
nev - er en - ter, nev - er en - ter there;

Sin - ful spots your soul shall mar, You can nev - er en - ter there.

God Be in My Head

734

God be in my head, and in my understanding;
God be in my eyes, and in my looking;
God be in my mouth, and in my speaking;
God be in my heart, and in my thinking;
God be at my end, and in my departing.

—Traditional

Index of Indexes

INDEXES

The 🎵 *logo under the item numbers indicate heritage songs and writings.*

Throughout **Worship The Lord**, brackets (⌐ ¬) have been placed to serve
as suggested introductions for the accompanist. When the introduction
encompasses separate sections of the hymn, two sets of brackets have
been used.

The Editors

---

*The Publisher has made every attempt to locate copyright own-
ers. Any omission or error will be corrected in future printings
when valid information is offered by the claimants.*

*The Publisher is grateful to the owners of the many copyrighted
selections who have graciously permitted us to use their property
in this hymnal. If you wish to make further copies, transparen-
cies, or use these selections on recordings, cassettes, videotapes,
or any other use, permission must be sought from the copyright
owner, not the publisher of this hymnal.*

Alphabetical Index of Authors, Composers, Contributors, and Sources of Hymns

Smith, Leonard W. (1942-   )   225
Smith, Michael W. (1957-   )   54, 76, 353
Smith, Oswald J. (1890-   )   270
Smith, Samuel F. (1808-1895)   718
Smith, Walter Chalmers (1824-1908)   34
Southern Harmony   237
Spafford, Horatio G. (1828-1888)   612
Spiritual   411
Spiritual, Traditional   411
St. Francis of Assisi (1182-1226)   542
Stainer, John (1840-1901)   146, 172
Stallings, John (1938-   )   643
Stanphill, Ira F. (1914-   )   406
Stassen, Linda   101
Stead, Louisa M. R. (1850-1917)   647
Stebbins, George C. (1846-1945)   241, 395, 405, 469, 482
Stockton, John H. (1813-1877)   191, 386
Stone, Lloyd (1912-   )   721
Stone, Samuel J. (1839-1900)   282, 286
Stralsund Gesangbuch (1665)   1
Suffield, Kittie Louise (1884-1972)   565
Sullivan, Arthur S. (1842-1900)   295, 689
Sumner, John B. (1838-1918)   585
Swedish Folk Melody   662
Sweney, John R. (1837-1899)   364, 491, 619
Sykes, Bessie (1905-   )   125
Sykes, Seth (1892-1950)   125

Taff, Russ (1953-   )   324
Taff, Tori (1956-   )   324
Talley, Kirk (1958-   )   64
Tallis, Thomas (1505-1585)   720
Tate, Nahum (1652-1715)   154
Tattersall's Psalmody (1794)   606
Taylor, Mrs. Walter G. (1932-   )   199
Teasley, D. Otis (1876-1942)   50, 80, 82, 102, 217, 239, 281, 354, 384, 417, 615, 639
Teschner, Melchior (1584-1635)   188
Theodulph of Orleans (c.760-821)   188
Thompson, Will L. (1847-1909)   240, 404
Threlfall, Jennette (1821-1880)   187
Thring, Godfrey (1823-1903)   215
Thrupp, Dorothy (1779-1847)   660
Thum, Pamela Starr   97
Tindley, Charles A. (1851-1933)   644, 665, 724
Tomer, William G. (1833-1896)   610
Toplady, Augustus M. (1740-1778)   630
Tourjee, Lizzie S. (1858-1913)   107
Towner, Daniel B. (1850-1919)   128, 525, 573
Townsend, Frances (1906-   )   106
Traditional   12, 57, 78, 122, 181, 223, 339, 452
Traditional Spiritual   264
Traditional, 2nd century   10
Trueblood, David Elton (1900-   )   250
Tucker, Leon (19TH CENTURY)   546
Tullar, Grant C. (1869-1950)   526

Vader, Randy (1950-   )   64
Vail, Silas J. (1818-1884)   455
Van de Venter, Judson W. (1855-1939)   403
Von Brethorst, Leona   7
Von Christierson, Frank (1900-   )   556, 697
von Weber, Carl M. (1786-1826)   499

Wade, John F. (1711-1786)   184

Walford, William W. (1772-1850)   343
Walter, Howard A. (1883-1918)   511
Walton, James G. (1821-1905)   711, 713
Ward, Samuel A. (1847-1903)   717
Ware, Henry, Jr. (1794-1843)   703
Waring, Anna L. (1823-1910)   672
Warner, Anna B. (1820-1915)   232
Warner, Daniel S. (1842-1895)   269, 285, 330, 348, 435, 461, 485, 520, 580, 593, 599, 614, 618, 649, 661, 674, 691
Warren, Barney E. (1867-1951)   2, 46, 330, 397, 399, 425, 435, 481, 485, 492, 496, 522, 528, 567, 568, 574, 593, 597, 599, 601, 614, 616, 618, 620, 631, 649, 651, 674, 694, 695, 726, 733
Warren, George W. (1828-1902)   716
Warson, Albert C.   719
Waters, Chris (1951-   )   166
Watts, Isaac (1674-1748)   22, 53, 89, 133, 150, 190, 201, 623, 646, 676
Webb, George J. (1803-1887)   307, 683
Webster, George O. (1866-1942)   355
Webster, Joseph P. (1819-1875)   732
Weeden, Winfield S. (1847-1908)   403
Weigle, C. F. (1871-1966)   584
Weir, Robert Stanley (1856-1926)   719
Welsh Folk Tune   381
Welsh Melody   34
Welsh Melody, Traditional   136, 140
Wesley, Charles (1707-1788)   52, 77, 90, 153, 162, 203, 204, 233, 234, 252, 510
Wesley, Samuel S. (1810-1876)   282, 329, 507, 654
Westendorf, Omer (1918-   )   381
Whitfield, Frederick (1829-1904)   457
Whittier, John Greenleaf (1807-1892)   477
Whittle, Daniel W. (1840-1901)   310, 424, 433
Wilkinson, Kate B. (1859-1928)   493
Williams' New Universal Psalmodist   284
Williams, Aaron (1731-1776)   301, 356
Williams, Clara T. (1858-1937)   586
Williams, Peter (1722-1896)   655
Williams, Ralph Vaughan (1872-1958)   33, 116, 431, 549
Williams, Robert (1781-1821)   204
Williams, Thomas (1869-1944)   219
Williams, William (1717-1791)   655
Willians, C. C. (19TH CENTURY)   394
Willis, Richard S. (1819-1900)   182
Wilson, Emily D. (1865-1942)   729
Wimber, John   277
Winkworth, Catherine (1827-1878)   1, 111
Wolcott, Samuel (1813-1886)   305
Wolfe, Aaron R. (1821-1902)   380
Wolfe, Lanny (1942-   )   259
Wood, James H. (1921-   )   468
Wordsworth, Christopher (1770-1872)   206
Work, John W. (1871-1925)   176
Wren, Brian (1918-   )   219, 703, 706
Wyeth, John (1770-1858)   18, 238, 300, 445

Yates, John H. (1837-1900)   678
Ylvisaker, John (1937-   )   370
Young, John F. (1820-1885)   167

Zelley, H. J. (20TH CENTURY)   627
Ziegler, Edward K.   143
Zion's Hymns   382

Index of Copyright Owners

Alphabetical Index of Tunes

page 761

Metrical Index of Tunes

Index of Keys

page 770

page 772

Index of Scriptures Appearing with Hymn Titles

page 777

Index of Scripture Based Worship Resources

Alphabetical Index of Worship Resources

Scripture quotations identified (NEB) are from The New English Bible. Copyright © the Delegates of the Oxford University Press and the Syndics of the Cambridge University Press, 1961, 1970. Reprinted by permission.

Scripture quotations identified (NIV) are taken from *The Holy Bible, New International Version.* Copyright © 1973, 1978, 1984 by The International Bible Society. Used by permission of Zondervan Bible Publishers.

Scripture quotations identified (NKJV) are from The New King James Version Copyright © 1979, 1980, 1982, Thomas Nelson, Inc., Publishers.

Scripture quotations identified (TJB) are from THE JERUSALEM BIBLE, Copyright 1966 by Darton, Longman, & Todd, Ltd. and Doubleday & Company, Inc. Reprinted by permission of the publisher.

Scripture quotations identified (TLB) are taken from *The Living Bible.* Copyright 1971 by Tyndale House Publishers. Used By Permission.

Scripture quotations identified (RSV) are from The Revised Standard Version of the Bible. Copyright 1946, 1952, 1971 by the Division of Christian Education of the National Council of the Church of Christ in the U.S.A. and are used by permission. All Rights Reserved.

Scripture quotations identified (NASB) are from The New American Standard bible. Copyright by the Lockman Foundation 1977.

Scripture quotations identified (GNB) are from the *Good News Bible* and the Bible in Today's English Version. Copyright © American Bible Society 1966, 1971, 1976.

Alphabetical Index of Heritage Hymns and Worship Resources

Topical Index of Hymns and Worship Resources

page 788

page 792

Alphabetical Index of Titles

page 795